How *Vine Leaves Literary Journal* began...

In 2010, when Jessica Bell, Australian award-winning author, designer, and singer/songwriter, kept getting rejections from literary magazines claiming that her work wasn't finished, she realized that there was a gap in the literary magazine market.

"Someone needs to cater to writers like me who believe that 'unfinished' work is actually an art form all of its own," she said to her long-time friend and critique partner, author/screenwriter Dawn Ius. Dawn agreed, and together they founded *Vine Leaves Literary Journal* in late 2011, to offer the vignette, a forgotten literary form, the exposure and credit it deserved.

When submissions opened, they realized immediately that they had made the right decision because they received response after response along the lines of, "Wow, thank you! Now I know what it is that I write!"

In 2011, Jessica couldn't find one single article online that explained how to write a vignette. Now ... there are hundreds. Jessica and Dawn like to think they had a hand in that.

Founders

Jessica Bell & Dawn Ius

Publisher

Jessica Bell

Editors

Jessica Bell
Theresa Milstein
Lindsay Adkins
Melissa Slayton
Alana King
Andrew Merton
Paul Alan Fahey
John McCaffrey

Designers

Amie McCracken & Jessica Bell

Letter from the Editor

We live in a world which focuses too much on the finished product rather than enjoying the process that gets you there.

Too many of us, in this day and age of admiring success and fame a little too much, miss out on the moments in life which make life what it is—worth living. I believe the vignette forces you to take a look at these moments. It forces you to slow down, to distract your focus from the future to the present, to admire the beauty in the world around us, even when on the surface, it may seem ugly.

The vignette gives a voice to a world that passes us by because we're too focussed on the world that is not yet in our reach.

I think we need this.

I think everyone needs to take a moment every day, to look at what is right in front of them, to put their existence into perspective.

And I believe that reading a vignette can facilitate that.

So ... what are you waiting for? Read on ... for the last time ... with Vine Leaves.

Jessica Bell

Vine Leaves Literary Journal: A Collection of Vignettes From Across the Globe
ISBN: 978-1-925417-63-0

Cover photograph, 'Evanescence' © Francesca Grazioli
Cover design by Jessica Bell
Internal design by Amie McCracken & Jessica Bell

National Library of Australia Cataloguing-in-Publication entry
Title: Vine leaves literary journal : a collection of vignettes
from across the globe / edited by Jessica Bell.
ISBN: 9781925417630 (hardback)
Subjects: English literary.
Short stories.
Poetry.
Anthologies.
Vignettes.

Vine Leaves Literary Journal

a collection of vignettes from across the globe

compiled & edited by jessica bell

Vine Leaves Press
Melbourne, Victoria, Australia

Table of Contents

"A poem is like a wine glass in which you can hold
up a little bit of reality and taste it."
GWEN HARWOOD

Reverse the Moon
by Ashlie McDiarmid

The light is borrowed, turned to silver,
etched hard and cold. An ancient link
to the feminine. There used to be a silent purr
I could only feel when I opened the dark doors
of my hands. Female means magic of small comforts.
The smell of cinnamon, tiny flames drawing out the skeleton
of my space. Laid down the Moon is reversed, small gifts
of twisted shapes distort my confidence, my need to push back.
Somehow, I must flip that silver coin, save my empty cathedral
while I still believe in salvation.

Let Loose
by C. Wade Bentley

After a while we just lost touch with each other,
he said, and I pictured her lifting off, tethered
to the planet, briefly, like a Mylar balloon,
and then loosed aloft, catching fire in the sun
until lost over the horizon, only to be found
some giddy days later by schoolchildren in Oaxaca,
just a pool of quicksilver now, the kids shouting
astronauta! astronauta! certain they had found
remnants of a galactic traveller, a new explorer
still learning gravity, still figuring how to fall.

Bloom
by Jessica Gawinski

Near a Station of the Metro
(after Ezra Pound)
by Gregory Piko

Holding maps and money for a day at Versailles. Watching mimes whose wonder and delight reflect in our eyes. Looking down and around. Maps, but no money. Perhaps my notes floated like petals to the ground.

white faces win applause from the crowd
coins fall   without   any sound

August Morning
by Kelsey Dean

Sunlight, spattered across the futon like paint; my chest a canvas. Your lips are resting in the curve of a sleepy smile. *Good morning*, I say, and your breath is warm when you kiss my shoulder in reply. Golden dust motes hang lazily in the air around us, as sluggish as the humidity unrolling along our spines. Cicadas thrum over the splutter of a faraway lawnmower. This wrinkled cotton sheet is your chrysalis, and my hair sprawls across it like the silky contents of a split-open milkweed pod.

gasoline and lilacs
the heavy scent
of summer

Being Seen
by Jalil Buechel

A window of light was speaking
from her eyes

telling me a little story
her son wrote about
a horse and a rabbit who became friends.

She was translating from Japanese
and paused…
struggling slightly
to find a word plucked from the ocean
between our countries.

Silent I listened
a hollow tree in the forest you can tell all your secrets to.

I dove where our roots touched
a place where living words
each have a life themselves.

She told her story
a shy, lonely girl
an only child invisible to her mother.
Her sudden courage to leave Japan
strong woven into her long black hair.
Holding herself suddenly straight
she paused
feeling my full attention
then laughed
Released
A crane over water gliding to the next reflection of itself.

She stopped and smiled me a thanks
for being seen.

Insert Art Here
by Trisha Farnan

September 7
by Lisha Ruan

the dust snaking like crosses
       a red path in summer

the loyal code of birds
       quarters and timid butter
a devil mourning history
       tea in a café

the gods like blue weather
       a bench in a quiet spot

the studios sinking like edges
       a distant object
throats and paper planes
       insects and timid keys

an egg mourning a plate
       meaningless numbers
a town hiding an outlaw
       funerals on distant rocks

asides and quiet singers
       the faded maps

Pacific Paradise
by Faisal Warsani

Khaki Puppies
by Mori Glaser

On desert sand waiting
for the siren to call
seconds to life or death
khaki puppies poise for action
piled in the shade of an armoured tank.

Meatloaf Sing-Say-Do
by Alaine Dibenedetto

Love, I would do anything, go anywhere
for you, like every single love song says, even Meatloaf's.
Ain't no mountain. Ain't no ocean. No wind, no
rain. This is what we sang, painted, wrote poems and stories
swearing to. Nothing
we wouldn't try, try, try. Nothing
we wouldn't do to be together. But nothing,
or nobody, ever warned us about crossing that Mason-Dixon
line. No cautionary tale or verse.
No long distance refrain
sung by Diana Ross or any other band. Not even Meatloaf.

We lied. Lied right up until we house-hunted in Santa Fe'
during that summer snow. We never saw
a single house. Never even looked at one, stucco,
or otherwise. So many
reasons to stay stuck. But here we are again
about to begin again, or end again,
again; over turning our vacation—
relationship into something permanent. This very last time,
one last try climbing mountains high enough,
oceans wide enough, lovemaking perfect enough, true
love words, words, words with that damned north-south line
looming dead ahead. I would
do anything, Love. Would you? Will we
do anything, everything, and not say, but I won't do that?

Ice in August
by Joanne Jackson Yelenik

"They were so cold to me."
Now, it is you who are ice and
I am sitting before an entrance committee;
you not caring if I hurt.
Why do you shoot your arrows at me?
Free your lava steaming blood,
melt the icicles shimmering
in your navy blue eyes.

Wind Chimes
by Jalil Buechel

The plane with my daughter on it
took off today for Costa Rica.
She left her bicycle, books
a purse with a brightly stitched bird she bought
in Guatemala.
Odds and ends of life's stages.

We hugged at the airport
Her smile reminding me of the video I took of her
dancing ballet at 5,
playing the harp at 10,
spending the summer in Guatemala at 17,
getting married at 19
getting divorced at 22.

Her Spanish is her warrior element
she speaks it perfectly.
It is attached to her wings.

She left her job in customer service
at a cooperative market
of organic vegetables and full of
Diversity.
Which only reminded her of the world
She missed—the everything of everywhere else.

A citizen of the world
luggage full of books
clothes and adornments of heart.
Which she will give to indigenous people
But no room for
wind chimes,
which she gives to us.

The wind chimes hang outside our kitchen window.
When the wind blows from
changeable weather or jet engines
passing overhead
they sing her song
Muy amable
Muy amable

Dollin
by Gleah
Powers

Imagine, the Fly by Noreen Lace

A life, in 24, rose-coloured hours.
Born at 7am, in love by 9, devastated by 10,
Or did it even last that long?
Falling again with the afternoon sun,
Gone too fast for any of us.
For some, 24 hours is far too short a life
to actually waste on love, they fuck their hours away.
Maybe that's the fly's life,
and maybe there's a secret to that life.
If I was a fly, I'd waste those precious hours, as I have,
on love, and on those who didn't love me back.
Sometimes, a fly doesn't last all those hours.
Sometimes, you're hit by a truck, or a flyswatter.
Sometimes, you welcome that.
Because, sometimes, 24 hours can seem like an eternity.

War So Beautiful
by Chad W. Lutz

This morning I watched
A tiny hummingbird fight
the wind and rain;
two things so beautiful,
so innocent, like a baby fighting
a flower, in conflict over nothing,
engaged in the same wars as the homeless
woman v. hunger or the dying man v. isolation.

A spider fell from the ceiling
onto a crowded table during
class this morning and no one
noticed but me until,
fifteen minutes later,
a girl shrieked and
spread its guts on the
composite wood surface.

An orange tabby cat saw a man running up a hill
This morning, and when it got too close,
The cat crossed to the other side of the road,
And avoided the man altogether.
No one noticed but the tabby.

Apparition
by Chad W. Lutz

Ghost is a word for something that's there but isn't.
Like a flash of light you can still see floating in little
Reds or greens behind closed eyes long after the bulb
Has dimmed and the filaments darkened.

I still get traces of you floating around my periphery;
Amorphous blobs of the ways you used to make me feel.
We lived in a place you said would never be your safe bet,
But you make no moves to leave.

Now I'm going to be a trace, an onion-skin outline,
A dab of darkness and flicker of white light
Here and gone in the blink of an eye.
I'm moving to California, where people stay rooted

In what they love even if they're homeless,
Like the misplaced in Denver, the hopeless in D.C.,
And the wide-eyed wanderers that flock the Northwest:
People who shed their paranormal surroundings

In search of remedies for the spectres that haunt
Their pasts at any cost, at any price, because
Sleeping on the ground is sometimes better than
Spending another moment with someone who
Refuses to acknowledge you're there.

Bush Windmill
by Trevor O'Sullivan

Emergence in Green

by Dick Evans

Until Tomorrow

Vigil

Vision in the Desert

Urban Woman
by Diana Whiley

On Filing A Missing Person Report
by Claire Scott

I had been on hold for four hours & forty-seven minutes
when finally an annoyed clerk picked up
clearly I was disturbing his scrutiny of an OkCupid profile
a most promising woman who likes sushi & sex
in no particular order provided there is plenty of both
I said I wanted to report a missing person
who is more & more missing by the minute
each minute you didn't pick up the phone
(may you choke on teriyaki rolls)
he asked when the person went missing
I could hear him typing a note to the woman
with a flurry of keystrokes & kisses
       looking for fun & free to meet you
       at Kabuto's say eight o'clock
I said hard to tell exactly, maybe as early as last May
or even the May before
he paused typing, losing his train of thought
adrift somewhere between sushi & sex
then said he needed a detailed description
& returned to typing his message
(may you get salmonella from elderly shrimp)
which one?
the man who ran six miles each morning
stretching taut muscles after
wrote articles for *Quanta Magazine*
explaining leptons & quarks
chaos & complexity
held me when he crawled into
bed long past midnight
diagrams dancing through dreams
or the man sitting across the room
slumped in a chair
slopping tea on his shirt
staring into space
books unopened
on the floor

Clearing Out
by Jean Gill

If Eric had not built the walk-in wardrobe, the rail would not have been high enough. It was sure to be strong enough though, as his DIY skills could be trusted completely. And of course the stool was neatly in place to enable her to reach the rail. Angela inspected each item of clothing in turn, starting with the crammed corner she never visited. Eric had asked her to clear out. She ran her fingers along the fabric of her life. A maternity dress, smocked and floral, that she'd kept, just in case. No chance of that now. Her graduation gown, still starched and smelling impossibly of pipe smoke and her tutor's study, a whiff of academic ambitions. Her wedding dress, a froth of lace.

She gave each item due consideration, made her judgement and moved on. She had always found it difficult to choose what to wear. She knew what she didn't want. Not black, not denim, not sexy. Well into the everyday section, she found what she was looking for. If she shut her eyes, she could still find it by following the faint trace of creosote from the time she painted the garden fence. There were even brown splashes on the blue quilting, in the shape of smiles. Her gardening coat had been battered by a million raindrops, scratched by a trillion thorns, kept her company for decades in moments of solitary peace. She took it from the hanger, slipped into its frayed lining, felt completely at home.

Then she found a scarf, tied it over the rail and noosed it round her neck as she stood on the stool, the one Eric had placed there for her convenience. When he found her, he would approve of the blue scarf—it matched her coat.

Breathing
by A.J. Varden

You cause your family pain each time you breathe. Inoutinout. They see your face and think of her, inoutinout. Brown hair, green eyes; you're the same, you and she. Only difference is, you're alive. Right? You cross 8th Street and take the bus. You don't drive anymore. No one revoked your license so you threw it in the lake, imagined it tumbling, gliding as it sank, your pinkish face pressed against the silt, buried by your guilt. Or did you forget that, too?

Did you let it stream off your shoulders like brackish water?

Did you watch your family shrivel up,

did you see them mourn with accusation,

did you feel lonely and alive?

You're a consolation and a curse. You sit across from a man and think of telling him this, but he streams Netflix on his phone and doesn't see you. You've seen this episode. You watch it through his glasses, familiar images backward and distorted, and you wonder if she would have talked to him. She could have drawn him out, made him smile, even. She could have spoken with a voice that was sanded, cut smooth, and pretty.

"She dies at the end," you say. Your voice is cracked and ugly.

He glares in your direction and it occurs to you someone might not want a warning.

Inoutinout.

The bus stops and you get off. You spin stories in your head. Maybe they aren't as bad. Maybe they're worse. Girl Number One, Monica you call her, gets into the car of Girl Number Two, who you name Natalie. Their lack of connection crackles through the empty space with the final throws of a dying spark.

Natalie lights a cigarette and Monica rolls her window down, coughing ostentatiously, "Still killing yourself, I see."

"Almost constantly."

"Did you call mum on her birthday?" A pause, "On the thirteenth?"

Exhalation, "No."

"Busy?"

"Sure."

Silence. Inoutinout. Your feet slap onto Government. You know how the story goes. Or how it doesn't.

"I understand," Monica confesses. "Why make an effort for someone who wouldn't do the same for you?"

Natalie smiles to herself as they pass the lake; it spreads out beneath them, separated by a thirty-foot drop and thin metal railing. They drive uninterrupted.

That might have been nice.

Instead, her words raked against the burning coals of your existential guilt. "Honestly, you couldn't do one selfless thing if it killed you."

You turned to her, hurt. Your eyes left the road, only a second, to search the face of your sister. Hard, impassive lines met your scrutiny as the car went off course, just like your life. She reached for the wheel, desperate, but you had already hit the metal railing. Cars flood fast, but she never saw a drop.

You emerged from the lake, panting because you couldn't save her, because you survived.

Your feet come to a halt as you stare out at the placid lake.

Guilt fills your lungs as you breathe,

inoutinout.

The Key to a Cosmos
by Alex Garcia Topete

"I want to steal you away."

His words made her shiver with a bolt of the forbidden, the harder T's of his accent reverberating in her ear as the warmth of his breath lingered upon her skin after his whisper.

Had he really said that?

His hand landed where her back lost its name, pushing aside her hesitation. His eyes met hers, glistening with sincerity, and sending them both into an abyss of intimacy even amidst the noise of the party ambience and the haze hinted by empty glasses.

They would not come out of that abyss without scars and a story. Their story.

Is this really happening?

He let his other hand wander until it found hers, and held it with the strength and purpose talked about in love songs. More than a caress, it was a plea, an argument, a bargaining, a whole conversation folded into that single gesture. Through their hands they said to each other what not even God or the Devil should listen.

They drank some more, as if trying to drown any words that may ruin their moment, or blur the vision of the world around them. Without looking, they had stumbled upon the privacy found only in a crowd. People surrounded them, but they were together in their solitude. Music and banter filled the air, but they shared a passionate silence. The whole world kept turning, but their moment stood still.

What if this never ended?

He broke their peace and made a move, his move—he gave her his key. He first showed it to her, with his eyes full of hope as the backdrop, he took her hand gently, put the room key on her palm with the weight of a wish and a promise, and wrapped both his hands around hers.

His hands. Her hands. Touching. Their hands did all the talking they could handle.

His was a proposition that had but one desirable answer—one that she yearned to give.

Everybody's watching … But … That's not … What if . . .?

She knew what to answer, yet she knew how she responded mattered just as much. It mattered to the world, that human wilderness beyond the two of them. It mattered to the world, so it mattered to her. He just waited and craved for her answer, patient, anxious, wishful.

They walked together away from the crowd, leaving behind a trail of whispers, caresses, and doubts. Each step brought them closer to a collision of destinies, as they ventured into the mood lighting of a starry night.

Now … The key …

A thousand steps and two flirtatious eternities later, the key opened for them a small universe of their own to explore, towering a hundred feet above the ground. Their hands, always their hands, explained to each other their personal languages without uttering a word. They existed by their touch—they made each other exist, gave meaning to the cosmic dust of their bodies, making themselves burn celestially bright.

Time stopped. No tomorrow. No yesterday. No end. They were a singularity of touch, of thought, of feeling, of freedom, of chance, of choice, of nows that made them be and not be at once. And just as fast, their universe collapsed and they were back to herself and himself. Back to the world.

What now …?

In came the morrow, bringing along the language of a new day. Destinies had collided and entangled like some galaxies do, yet her reality and his dream had not. He would fly away, a comet tail of fantasies behind him, and she would come back to earth, abandoning the abyss and taking with them this story. Their story.

A Million Years
by Christopher Owen Nelson

Infusion
by Roy Dorman

A summer breeze separates itself from the evening winds and enters a bedroom window with the intention of bringing renewal to the two people lying sleeping as far from each other as the bed will allow.

Phat
by Nancy Devine

If all human fat in the world
were distributed equally among its inhabitants,
what would we look like?
Pandemic of perfection?
Flat stomachs formerly concave or convex?
Heavenly hips,
nothing distended upended untended pretended?

Da Vinci's man on every street corner not proud
or ashamed about being naked;
it's just like a cough,
not one promising disease,
merely what one does before one speaks
to make sure the voice is clear?

(I think I'd still want to lie with you.
No. I know I would. We might
look practically the same as we do now.
Ready. Hoping to clutch some version of light.)

This fat along my flanks that grooves and
bulldozes in this life with me I got.
This yellow dappled sap,
tufts of too-much stuff droopy on my form.
I curse it running to nowhere
on a treadmill where I almost arrive
like a newbie debutante.

Some woman in a desperate country
needs some manna now strung tight
from my bone-collared sky.
If I could, would I share?

So what do I have that's like fat
or money or time or breath of
pulse or electricity
that carries taste in equal parts to all. Maybe this.
…this thin rendering is it.

The Lesson
by Madeline Sharples

"Worry a little bit every day and in a lifetime you will lose a couple of years. If something is wrong, fix it if you can. But train yourself not to worry. Worry never fixes anything." Mary Hemingway

If only on that day in July
when she was a chubby tan nine-year old
lazing away the summer
swimming in Lake Michigan,
reading a book curled up
on the red plaid club chair
in her brother's room,
or helping her mom
with her new baby sister,
her favourite uncle,
the handsomest guy she knew,
who said he wanted to marry her
when she grew up and lost her baby fat,
hadn't gotten a migraine headache
and decided to go home to California
one day ahead of schedule.

If only her dad hadn't come home early that day
and stood at the doorway sweating rings
under his arms and telling her mom
in that low clipped voice of his,
"Give me the baby."

If only her mom, hadn't cried out,
"What's the matter?"
as she sat down, squeezing her skirt,
her hands opening and closing
over the flowered print
as it travelled
up and down her thighs.

If only her dad hadn't said,
Phil—that was her uncle's name—
was in a plane crash
in the Burbank mountains,

and was only recognizable
by the ring he always wore
on his pinky finger.

If only her mother hadn't said,
as she ran down the hall to her room,
with her daughter close behind,
"I didn't have time to worry,
that's why it happened,
I was too busy with the baby to worry."

Then she wouldn't have learned
that the way to prevent bad things
from happening is worry
all day and all night, no matter what,
even if a baby has just been born.

Small Change
by Roy Dorman

After purchasing her favourite bistro from its former owner, she decides the only change she'll make for now is to turn the battered cardboard sign on the front door from CLOSED to OPEN.

Choose to Forget
by Alyssa Cooper

So Sad
by Roy Dorman

Raggedy Anne lost an arm in the fire, and her only dress is charred around that now empty sleeve. But the loss of her best friend, Isabelle, hurts her more.

Crescent
by Kim Peter Kovac

The crescent moon slices Orion's arm and the night sky screams. #screamingnightsky

Journal Entry
by Grant Clauser

After the morning shift
I went to Dod's house
and found him knees down
in the back yard,
his dad screaming,
picking up handfuls of dog shit
and throwing it at him,
Dod taking it like a door
takes slamming, swinging shut
without comment,
a crack starting in the frame.

We tried to hide the loss with laughter, giggling hysterically through tears as we stole our last uncertain touch and caress. But when his eyes met mine, locked on like a search light, the sinful sound died in our throats. The sole participants in a grotesque comedy, we each took a solemn step back; away from each other, and toward something terrifyingly unknown. We took stock of the moments that we would carry with us, and more importantly, the moments we would conveniently choose to forget.

Ceremony without Tea
by David Anthony Sam

The cup is empty
filled with secrets
steeped in wrath and mourning

sipped quietly
into silent lips
twisted by bitter words

The hand that holds the cup
turns it on its saucer
as if reversing time

Each time the cup is raised
from its chipped plate
it savours its secrets

An empty cup tastes
what is left behind
in the silence of a poet's voice

Oysters
by Laura Eppinger

The night we met you mentioned
them twice; two separate anecdotes. By now
you've told and you've told digging around
tired personal legends like maybe this time
you'll find that pearl. But not with me, I'm no
help still you tell and you tell, tell me once
you were on a beach with your ex, her
mother, champagne, the sinewy being
fought as it slid down your throat but you choked
it down, what luxury. The part you seem to relish
most is that everyone you'd ever met (along with me,
though you didn't know me yet) was living in squalor after
a storm with the innocuous name Sandy. We swallowed
cold soup, no power for a week but you, you on that
French beach. Then your second story, just a barroom offhand
growl *It's the same reflex*, you assure me, *after sucking
a guy off*. That knowing look, oh yes you've pushed
that mucus down and yes dammit I can see that
oysters, to you, must be pig-headed affluence or illicit
sex. God forbid you walk with me along
the Chesapeake, past shack after shack, old family land,
the tradition, the toil—God forbid! You leave palpably
uninterested.

Sea Chops
by Deborah Guzzi

The islands rise and fall with ferry motion
upon a speckled platter of sea. Wave's crest
dollops of rice-white among the strands
of nori unanchored by Pacific storms.

Beppu's *Ryokan* with its *onsen** calls. The vessel:
hum-jiggles each passenger within the ginormous
floating fun house soothes caterwauling infants,
and raises pink roe on cheeks topside.

Scraps curled from the paper chits of losing players
scurry across the deck of artificial grass. Gamblers
downstairs feed pachinko machines which flash neon,
strobe crimson, and sound zingers.

In the cafeteria chop-sticked okasans scoop
loops of ramen into the maws of peckish toddlers.
After hours at sea, the loudspeaker announces our arrival.
Sleepers tumble from futons and redress their feet.
Footsore myself, I smile.

Soon, I can pickle the deep-bone pain of travel
in the sulphur waters of Beppu's hot springs.
Soon, I will be one with earth and the sky above
me. At high noon, the Sunflower docks.

*Ryokan onsen: hot spring resort

Woman of the Stars
by A.D. Ross

"A straight line
can readily be drawn
among each of the two series of points
corresponding to maxima and minima,
thus showing that there is a simple relation
between the brightness of the variables and their periods."
—Henrietta Swan Leavitt[1]

Dark browed and tight lipped as she discerns
through the Harvard observatory, peering over photographic plates,
neck curved over the data, looking like her feathered namesake.

Late under weak light,
learning the luminosity of Cepheid
variable stars, pulsating radially.

Those important, distant indicators, measuring
distance between an odd earth and each faint galaxy.

Her death did not stop
Hubble from finding through her data
the growth and spread, galaxies like champagne bubbles,
an effervescent expansion of our known universe.

---

[1] Leavitt, Henrietta Swan and Edward C. Pickering. "Periods of 25 Variable Stars in the Small Magellanic Cloud." *Harvard College Observatory*. Circular 173. 1912. Provided by the NASA Astrophysics Data System.

The Final Problem
by Jessica Gawinski

Sidewalk Composition
by Erica Travers

We walk down the street
passing words and a tightly
rolled joint back and forth

as the autumn leaves crunch under
our feet like the long overdue
death rattle of summer.

You stop to admire houses:
an accidental sidewalk composition;
and who but you would have the words

to capture the beautiful discord of one red door
among drab brown shuttered houses
built to contain only photocopied dreams?

arts and crafts style, 4br, 2½ bath, nice yard
by C. Wade Bentley

Over here is where the drunk guy was singing
through his drunk-walk playlist before he threw
up on the forsythia. As you come up the steps
to the front door, I draw your attention to the chip
in the second step where seven-year-old Brooke
biffed it on her scooter, taking out her newly—
minted two front teeth. This very dining room
table is the historical site where three minutes
forty-nine seconds went by without a word
after Jake introduced Liam, the love of his life.
Total gut of the kitchen in 2014. Soft-close
drawers, under-cabinet LED. Every holiday
before that we sat around the old island
on wooden stools, and they made sugar cookies
while I complained about the mess. Before
the new blue granite, obviously. On the landing
up to the bedrooms is where my wife Sarah
swore she saw her own apparition three months
before she died and hoped that maybe if she never
wore the dark green, tea-length dress the ghost
was wearing she would never die. Not to worry,
though, she hasn't been back. The pencilled
height-lines on the bathroom door are easily
painted over. Here, in the master bedroom,
if you are lying awake at night, you can hear
the beams and the load-bearing walls flexing,
adjusting the load, like Atlas, maybe, a subtle
shiver of doubt, now and then, vis à vis the weight
of the world. Original white-pine panelling.

The Orphaned Shore
by David Anthony Sam

The long white beach
rehearses for storms
by slowly giving itself
back to solemn waves.

It is its own art reshaped
by what itself is shaped,
by what cannot be seen
but strives within water.

She is a lost voice now
travelled in thought to
light that rises in the jagged
east gazing for divinity.

I pray the voice of sand
by palming crystals
in my hands until they
sing the distant dead.

Steam Rises
by Charles Leggett

a coffee mug

Steam rises as ceramic peregrines
Face each other like two continents.

Black background seeps between the long, beaked jaws,
Orange to pineapply yellow to dim lime.

Their heads, a dusky blue housing an iris
Of deep mauve. Each shows a wing—outstretched

And nearly meeting (gesture, not attempt)—
Pineapple lapsing into Braeburn red,

The lime for outline. In turquoise green
Signed, *"1993 J. Sweetwater."*

The longer that I look, the less the steam.

Oceans Oceans
by Cooper Hepburn

i know, i know you're living tired
like scratched up black and white photos
on old fragile paper from 1908
and i know i do it too sometimes
curling up twisted sheets
or breathing in shallow tide
washed out on bad weather days
but there's ocean
its bottomless inside your ancient heart
waves crashing and love and waves and crashing
and i told you i am buoyant and writhing

Palace of Infinity
by Daniel DeLeón

In the Palace of Infinity
There dance
Two lonely souls

And neither soul
Is lonely
Anymore.

Sunset Beach
by Faisal Warsani

The Unguarded Moment
by Adam Byatt

Start with a wide-angle shot of the inside of the convention centre. Track the swarming throng of people. Listen to the thrum of conversation; a diegetic, subsonic hum.

Narrow the focus. Tighten the frame. Slowly differentiate the cosplayers from the onlookers: Disney princesses, doctors of all regenerations, cartoon, anime and manga characters, TV and movie roles represented in hats, dresses, capes, coats, and homemade weapons.

Find a focal point.

A woman dressed as Belle in a yellow ball gown. Zoom in and make her the centre in a broad full-shot.

Capture the *mise-en-scene*. Belle holds court in the centre of an intersection between stalls, twirls slowly for casual photographers with cameras disguised as phones, accented by flashes from professionals. The poses are practised and deliberate, an authentic representation of the cartoon.

This bright, yellow sunflower draws little sunbeams. Some are coaxed from behind mum or dad's legs with her winning smile and welcoming gesture while parents fumble for their phone to take a quick snap. Others ask if they can go over to the princess and lead the way. And then there are the ones who rush headlong into an embrace. Belle kneels to their height, eye-to-eye, for the briefest of moments to become the centre of the child's universe; the cartoon mythology made flesh. A chance to believe in the three-dimensional representation of their imagination.

From the left-hand corner of the frame, a young man dressed as Gaston walks by. He spies Belle, puts his chest out and assumes the character. The congregated audience applauds the serendipity. Belle withdraws, shy and coy, hiding behind her gloved hands as Gaston approaches. Together, they pose. The crowd winks their approval in the faux-snap of a mechanical lens on a digital phone. Gaston nonchalantly salutes Belle then the crowd and slips away to the right of frame.

Narrow the focus further. The frame fills with pops of yellow as Belle twirls for a young girl. Capture the imitated shuffley-stamp of little feet. The smile of ecstatic joy. Belle laughs as she bends down and reaches into the small purse she carries and gifts a sticker. The little girl carries away this simple joy with her.

But there is a glimpse of something else? Stop. Something different? Maroon Converse Chuck Taylor's hidden beneath the netting of the hoop skirt. An intangible subtext. One thousand words in a simple glance.

Into this scene another cosplayer, a woman of a similar age, dressed as Harley Quinn, approaches, leaving the orbit of her companion to join Belle's.

"Can I please have a photo with you?"

"Certainly."

Her companion raises a camera. The lens snaps. A winking eye, a knowing glance, captures the subtext of the scene.

"Thank you." *I see you. Do you see the real me, too?*

"Thank you." *I see you.*

For the briefest of moments, the masque is revealed because adults playing dress-ups understand the metaphor is also literal.

Harley Quinn returns to her companion in character before it disappears with a drop of the shoulders.

Belle's looking for anyone she's missed. Pan the camera from left to right to follow her scanning of the crowd. She searches for the unspoken conversations of the people who wait to engage with her: the little girls whose eyes sparkle and the enthusiastic smiles of the fathers and mothers who accompany them, to the young people and middle-aged people in costume who understand the power the disguised dialogue provides.

A momentarily stillness. The noise of hundreds of excited voices, a ruptured static, and then—

"Hello, Belle."

Cut away to a group of concubines from Mulan, cooing from behind fluttering fans.

Belle breaks from the crowd to join her friends. Track the party through the crowd as it heads to a quieter spot for hugs and air kisses. In costume but no longer in character.

Hear the sound effect of a text message pinging.

Belle pulls a phone from her purse.

Cut to an extreme close up. A text message from Belle's daughter about her autistic brother.

Joey's crapped himself again. On purpose.

Put him in the shower. Washing's on. When can I expect you home?

Fade to black.

Salt
by AM Morton

It's always the salt. You feel the floury bap in your mouth, hear the crunch of your teeth coming down on the bacon, the touch of the liquid egg on your lips, but the first sensation is that sharp but seductive tang—the taste of salt. And when you've finished the egg and bacon roll, salt stays on your tongue along with regret that you might not ever eat another breakfast.

It's 8 am in winter on the North German plain. The dark mass of the frosted trees stretches out in front of me. Did Roman soldiers feel that same internal quiet, that personal isolation before they too went into battle here in German forests?

A shout. Movement behind me. A message pad thrust at me. He's young, a baby really. Seventeen? But he's so eager to do his duty. I read the message and sigh. Five kilometres away to the east. I can almost sniff them.

A senior man, his short grizzled hair the sign of a veteran, approaches. He stands by me and stares out at the forest. He offers me his mug of tea. I shake my head. I'm still relishing the salt taste even though it's nearly dispersed. We look at our watches, then stare again into the distance. The birds have stopped singing.

A young woman approaches, her uniform too bright and clean to have seen any action. She's gripping the strap of the rifle slung on her shoulder. It's time. The senior man extends his hand to me. I grasp it, proud to have served with him. The baby soldier and young woman watch us gravely. We are the last stand. A plane flies low over us. It's not one of ours. Fear in the others' faces and in mine too.

None of us runs.

Salt. Those beside me are the salt of the earth. And we will salt the earth ourselves very soon.

Magpie
by Carrie Mumford

After I find the condom wrapper lodged in the vacuum head I sit on the carpet beside the bed for a long time.

I watch the magpie in the backyard diving at the pool of water that has gathered on the uneven patio stones, its sleek blue-black wings glinting in the sun. I watch the neighbour's curl-covered head bob above the fence as she waters her hanging lilies. I watch until the sun makes its way around to the side deck, and then I stand, put away the vacuum, move the laundry to the dryer and go down into the kitchen.

Buried in the very back of the vegetable drawer I find what I'm looking for: a just-about-to-go-bad potato.

I take out the bamboo cutting board and one of the fancy Japanese knives his mum gave us for Christmas. I slice the potato into four, then twelve, letting the rank slime slide across my fingers. I put the slices on the freshly Windexed stove and climb up beside them, careful to keep my bare toes out of the burner wells.

One by one I drop the slices behind the stove, spreading them for maximum effect.

I go upstairs and pack my bag—undies, toothbrush, flip-flops, T-shirt, tank top—and I leave. A week later, when I come back, I have to pull out the stove and clean up the potatoes. They are no longer slimy, only dried-up bits that don't have the decency to emit any of the horrible, fishy odour I'd planned on.

As I step on the pedal and toss the potatoes into the open garbage can I think: *I should put shrimp in the vents*, and then I remind myself that I'm here to stay this time, that he had said "never again" and "I love only you" and "I'll get help."

I stand in front of the kitchen window, looking out over the lawn that needs mowing, arms crossed over my chest, holding everything in. The magpie is back, on the fence this time, its beady eyes boring into mine. *At least he used a condom*, I whisper to the magpie.

A Lesson in Pain
by Alexis Henderson

Her insides went rotten when he touched her. Heart trilling, staccato, against her sternum as if to the time of a drunken jazz band. In that moment she imagined him strung from his thumbs or bundled up like a baby, bound by blankets, and squealing like a piglet. In the end it made no difference.

Reckoning Vermont
by Jonathan Riccio

Leaving one writers' conference for the next, I drove past a notary public attached to a bait shop, an unlocked bed and breakfast, not a proprietor in sight, garbage embroidered around the spokes of a bicyclist merging gully into road. I printed my boarding pass, propellers sweetened the escalator's drone. Always the agoraphobe and never the air show, heart rate shoeless as if destination could stall a relapse fore-sewn. "Tell me about your job screening surveillance at the Laundromat," I said to my seat-mate as restroom ammonia flitted among tomato juice in a row no larger than a liquor cabinet. I reflected on my fears: people, flying, the coals between voyeur and interloper walked—

biography,
the first agoraphobe in space,
rocket fuel with each breath.

Fathering is not an option...
by Jonathan Riccio

... and 18 is knowing between sterile and flayed. Twenty years on, my friends are gay or PhD and I'll have a playpen on pastrami, staring at my parents' estate (what it's called in front of the insurance man), its fish-scale driveway offset by sprinklers timed to the meridian of their Atlantis, and I who've eschewed the half-lives of lawn ornaments, relating to my mother at an age where she checks for cysts, how, during her hospitalization, she refused to eat without my father so he visited in granola increments. For her I teeter between agoraphobe and aesthete, love I edit into a quasar's gladiola.

Shopping for cornmeal,
fatherhood's opposite
feeds itself.

Spokes/Synthesis
by Jonathan Riccio

There are some advantages, cameoing as a heartthrob for the gay shut-in set: "Knowing Roseanne dabbled in agoraphobia makes it more palatable," Spokesmonarch says, careful to pronounce four- and six-syllable words correctly, the conscience in his earpiece telling him to namedrop Kim Basinger, another one-time-a-phobe, holder of the Oscar for the way her eye shadow brought out that police car's daiquiri blue. Spokesmonarch fields a question: "As a current homocanvasexual, do you feel an affinity toward . . ."

"... feel it like a Lifetime movie crammed into a two-daddy Christmas." The umbilical in his earpiece sighs. Next question: "Do you mortify or compel?" "Depends if you're talking about leaving the closet or coming out of the house." Asked of his life, all the time—something he keeps in mind en route to the open-air parade obliged to manufacture one confession per float,

earpiece stressing:
"Diction before reign."
The rest is unbecoming.

Disappointment
by Kendra Liedle

Hers is coloured in anger and highlighted in sorrow. She stands alone, lost in the sadness of being let down by someone she cared deeply about.

That someone, is at this very party. With *someone* else.

Immersed in this image, Aileen doesn't notice the man who has his eye on her. He scans her face and admires her beauty, undetected.

Two minutes from now, when she finally turns her head away from impossibility, Aileen will see him walking toward her.

The man who will ask her dance.

The man who will become her husband.

And there will be romance. *Italicized.*

Saturday Afternoon
by Jim Gustafson

When we went to the museum you stood still
looking at a painting of an off-orange peach.
It was well done. The fuzz obvious, almost
shaking in the light.

The time you gave to it was more than any peach deserves.
You were, I thought, thinking about something
other than fruit. You were, I thought, thinking
about rotting, how fresh does not last long.
If not picked and tasted, things turn mushy colours.
How if taken down and bitten the juice runs
the chin sticky. Sometimes we must wash
our hands and face clean and find fresh fruit.

This is what I was thinking, when you turned,
moved in and kissed me on the cheek. Your breath
tasting of peaches. You took my hand,
and pulled me on to the next painting,
a landscape. Its bottom brushed close with grass,
fading to a horizon line moving beyond its frame.

Finger-Painting
by Donna-Claire

Someone must have made me,
while they were finger-painting away their
white-wine-red-wine fuelled
white-hot-red-hot rage.

Made me gummed up and muddy,
from streaking four colours,
mixed with the dirt settled
in the grooves of their prints.

Picture it:

Their shredded fingernails
gutting the palette, orchestrating
a session of heavy petting,
with an eight-and-a-half-by-eleven inch
white piece of canvas:
stolen from the office supply closet
I think about hanging myself in.

Monet to Monet
by Richard Weaver

Claude M. had come to visit
his dying friend and painter
with a syncopated last name.
He was dressed for the times,
nappily so, and entered the room
with the air of a man who has dined
well, smoked afterwards, and had
walked the odd few blocks
to the hospital where Edouard lay
in bed, stricken. Claude, a gentle—
man and an artist, removed his
hat upon entry, glanced leftward
towards his friend. Their eyes
met, recognition occurred,
the moment captured by each
in memory, a sign Claude took
of welcome, and so proceeded
bedward. Noting the light,
and shadow, the composition
of a stilling life, but still a life.
Hat in hand, a quick nod urged
him closer. At the bed's foot
he settled his hat or so thought
when his friend and dying painter
screamed his final scream:
"Take care. You'll hurt by foot."

The Cosmos by Nory Marc Steiger

Returning to the 5th floor
by Jude Goodwin

The 5th floor
in the cancer clinic is where they put you
when they know your time has come
and you'll not be leaving
alive. They don't tell
your family this. People
come in, all smiles.
They bring snacks and pretty
scarves for your bald head
and worry when they see
things like breathing tubes
and morphine drips.
Everyone chats
about Christmas—
who will host the feast
this year, will the baby
arrive before or after
Santa. They don't bother
with flowers, you're coming home
tomorrow, or Sunday,
or so they think. Someone
will bring out a camera
and everyone crowds around you
like any other goofy family
photo shoot but later, when you've actually died,
the picture is stuffed in a book
that no one wants to open.
Because in the photo they can see
that you are dying.
Now that they know
about the 5th floor,
they wonder about other floors,
in other buildings,
and they wonder what they haven't been told
or can't see because of Christmas:
the twinkling and the scent of fir—
what will be lost, unrecognized,
because of the most
wonderful time of the year.

Blush
by Diana Whiley

The Golden Atlas
After Fernando Vincente
by Amanda Chiado

First, your mother draws your upturned face, which
takes up the whole of Asia. They are so excited;
they have to have a glass of Chianti to silence their
nerves. They hand the pencil back and forth in fair
share. Under your father's stroke, you throw your
head back and your cheeks are fat in Japan, neck
a desolate Siberia, and your eyes are well-suited
in the Pacific where sailboats can catch the gusts
of sun-struck-blue, swirling round your pupils.
Your thick hair is drawn tossed and curled upon
the Himalayas; the richness of your tendrils' reach
makes your parents' hands tingle with anticipation
to hold you. They will kiss you endlessly in the
Mediterranean of your neck, Africa resting its heartbeat music on your shoulders. Your body cannot fit
on the map. Your parents aren't artists; proportions
of heart-space are learned through time, through
embrace. Besides the map was a hand-me-down,
your grandfather was drawn there too, the ink since
folded and unfolded into history. When they felt
they had captured a trueness that would carry you
throughout your life; out into the grand world—
They pinned the great map of you over the kitchen
table and sat back to admire you, but the map was
upside down and your parents laughed loudly into
the night because they knew then, that your smile
would be sweeter than that of a dozen gods, singing
the fate of the golden atlas.

Comes a Revolution (bored at the bookstore)
by Chris Tannlund

In Russia, they jail their poets—Ten years
busting Siberian ice for even
the most futile charge on any gulag of the heart.
Then there's you, roaming free

in Capitalist Pig America, whipping
out your Gold Card to purchase: *Poet's
Market:1800 Places to Sell Your Poetry!* The clerk
is rolling his eyes as he hands you the pen. He's picturing

you washing dishes, taping game shows, playing
bridge with housewives in wall-flower dresses—Then you
sneaking off to the garden, sipping iced tea and writing
poems about flowers—*lilacs, chrysanthemum ...*

struggling for a rhyme and finding
only *anthems*, battle hymns, war songs. His clearly
fantasy-prone brain births a Moscow apartment, and you
have donned a black beret, a tulip-shaped

scar on one cheek like a third eye. Your dirty garden
apron has sprouted bandoleers. He sees you
gathering dissidents like daisies for a summer
centrepiece, a bouquet of angry poets, blooming

all around him like red, red roses. He takes
a cautious backward step—He's feeling
around beneath the counter—*"Oh,
Christ! Where's the alarm!"* He'll

alert the authorities. He knows your kind, sees
right through your shrinking violet veneer—You'll
cut down his children
with words sharper than pruning shears, plant

your marigold mines in the dark and loamy
soil of his bleeding heart, outside—agitate
his peace-lily mind with your incendiary
poems like snap dragons exploding in his face.

Apex
by James Donohoe

The apex of a kiss
Is when one starts wondering
Where all this is going

While the other one is still
Drowning in bliss.

Set of Five Face Fragments by Susan Stamm Evans

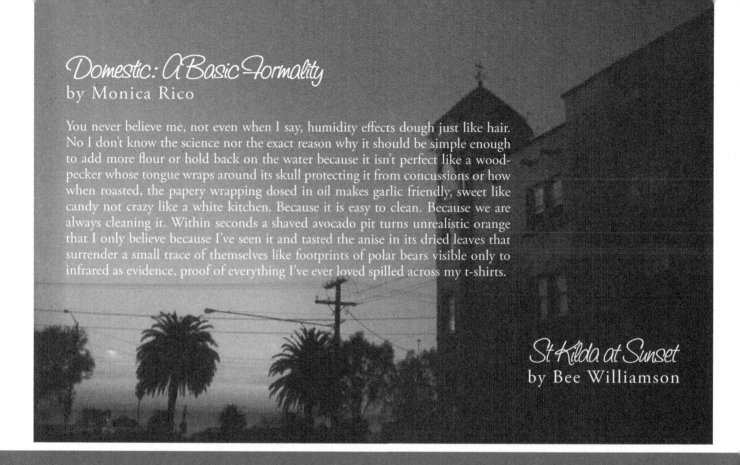

Domestic: A Basic Formality
by Monica Rico

You never believe me, not even when I say, humidity effects dough just like hair. No I don't know the science nor the exact reason why it should be simple enough to add more flour or hold back on the water because it isn't perfect like a wood-pecker whose tongue wraps around its skull protecting it from concussions or how when roasted, the papery wrapping dosed in oil makes garlic friendly, sweet like candy not crazy like a white kitchen. Because it is easy to clean. Because we are always cleaning it. Within seconds a shaved avocado pit turns unrealistic orange that I only believe because I've seen it and tasted the anise in its dried leaves that surrender a small trace of themselves like footprints of polar bears visible only to infrared as evidence, proof of everything I've ever loved spilled across my t-shirts.

St Kilda at Sunset
by Bee Williamson

Royal Feast *Boulder City, Nevada* by Steve Prusky

At this oasis desert park, just inside the far edge of man's domain, the Mountain Big Horns trust implicitly.

The Rams, their curled horns rippled crowns of sovereignty, nobly descend the rock-strewn wash to file up on the black asphalt cul-de-sac below. The procession parades resplendent in their molted summer coats stained desert beige. Their padded hooves tap our house-lined pavement like battle-weary, yet still alert cavalry. Just past the rise off Patti Lane, early morning sprinklers dust off chaste July heat, greening the festal meadow prior to their royal feast. They'll graze 'till noon, aloof as sovereign guests on foreign soil; honored royalty immune to threat or harm.

These monarchs pasture on the north lawn no man's land, a cautious distance from the park accouterments we claim. From our barrack tennis courts we ever present sentries of the swings and slides are kin to 'at the ready' palace guards at attention when they arrive. On our watch no coyot' packs creep up in surprise, no famished mountain lion lurks too close, no hunter's bullet strikes its mark, no thirst or famine occurs. The tree-lined boundary of this verdant desert realm sanctifies these kings, we lowly commoners, and serfs.

By noon, high mountain Sirens wail enticing songs in company with symphonies of blustery Mojave Desert winds. Lyrics from the charming nymphs beguile our noble lords to familiar, cooler craggy heights; their nocturnal empire sleepless vigilance, cunning predators, moonless night.

Ebony Fleece
by Vakseen

Absorption
by Christina Dalcher

The woman with the Burberry raincoat and the matching umbrella enters the park at the east gate, passes the old man who lives on the patch of damp ground, the one who was there this morning and yesterday and three months ago, and she thinks *why did they take the benches out of the park*? because if the old man had a bench he'd at least be out of the wet, but with the weather turning and the days shrinking he'll be dead by Christmas if he doesn't dry up, and first thing tomorrow, she'll call the city, just as soon as she gets into work, but when she thinks about work and Stephen, Mr. New Vice President who asked her out to a drink before he knew her name, she realizes she hates her fucking job and would rather be cleaning toilets at the Y than work under Stephen, who reminds her way too much of her ex-husband, a half-man-half-child who came onto her at the coffee shop on the next block, and then she decides she'll buy the old man on the sodden grass a steaming cup of coffee, maybe tea—tea is better—tea's good for the system, especially if it's green and hasn't been brewed burnt by too-hot water, and speaking of hot water, she really must call the plumber about the taps in the bath on the first floor because something's definitely wrong and she knows the woman who sold her the house was holding back about the mould that's probably growing behind the shelves, and man, when she discovers *that*, Miss Non-Disclosure is going to get an earful, and now she's leaving the park at the west gate and she can't remember what she was thinking about when she entered it.

A Light Day at the Office
by Cooper Lysek Gomez

I walk around the back side of the theatre and scale the wall. Then I enter through a broken window and step onto a large balcony. I scan the area: one hostile on the right, two on the left. I've brought my .223-caliber, scoped rifle with silencer, a suppressed 9mm and, my personal favourite, Shinobi throwing knives I picked up at a museum a couple months ago.

I throw a knife into the back of the hostile on the right, taking him down instantly. I sneak to the other side of the balcony and kill the other two guards. Two shots each. *This is going to be a quick hit*, I think to myself. I gaze across the auditorium, searching for a blond guy in a brown suit. My eyes fall upon the mark. Hard to miss. He's on the stage directly below me. I mount my rifle on the railing and begin to level my eye with the scope.

When 'I Love You' Were the Wrong Words
by Charley Karchin

Marie told him that she loved him, but that was only when he was twisted uncomfortably in her sheets with his face between her legs, trying to find a breath that wasn't dampened by skin or hair.

He made the mistake of saying the same words to her over dinner at her place after six months. They were seated on her tan suede couch, with plates of Chinese food that he ordered and paid for. Her dark hair was up in a bun because it was too long for her to not slurp up with her noodles and her eyes never travelled to his face from her plate of food.

It was when she was chewing more than a mouthful of lo mein when he said she was beautiful and that her eyes made him fall in love with her more and more every day. She coughed and a bit of noodle hit him in the cheek. He let it slowly peel away from his skin and fall to his lap.

When she composed herself and swallowed the noodles. She blinked her big hazel eyes at him, clear and wide with bewilderment.

"Why would you say that?"

He said he didn't know.

"I think you should go."

He set his plate down, half-eaten, on the coffee table and left the remaining food at her apartment. When he tried to call her the next day to apologize, he got a recording of an automated female saying the number was unavailable before disconnecting the call.

Misused
by Dresden de Vera

"It's a strange phenomena," I told her, "People who date out of comfort."

"You mean phenomenon?" she asked, "Just the one event, right? Because 'phenomena' is plural."

Once, I tried sharing how I grew up with cystic acne. I pointed to how the legions would spread from my chin to my temple.

"Lesions," she told me, "A legion is a militant group. Usually, overwhelming in number."

I replied, "But that's exactly what I

mean."

She nodded. "Yes, but it's still wrong."

Another time, I confided my wish to be more clairvoyant, then she stopped me to say that the word in that form is supernatural. To be clairvoyant is to be prophetic, to have biblical powers. To want clairvoyance, though, is perfectly acceptable. So instead, I should start saying that I want clairvoyance.

"Sometimes," she said, "I think you use words that you only kind of know. You probably shouldn't do that. Clarity is key."

On another lazy Saturday, we lounged on her bed. I whispered, "I'm never so mellow than when we're lying together."

"Lying," she said, "The word you want, is lying."

Ex/Current
by Eliza McGowen

I thought it was a good plan to go hide-away in the mountains, at least for a little while. I was trying to molt you like a bad sunburn, rubbing you off against the branches and rocks along alpine trails. The mountains were large and over-bearing and they quickly occupied all my time.

But this was good because they were not you. They were not from Tennessee; they did not major in finance; they did not try to dress me in the mornings, taking extra time on tightening my belt. But then mountains didn't have ex-girl-friends in Arizona. Or was it current girl-friends in Arizona?

Yet your sticky accent still stuck to the nooks and crannies of my car and there was nothing I could do about that. I forced myself awake early to hike. I trip as I tire and my scraped knees burn red

just like your beard when the sun touched upon it. The frost turning to dew turning to mist is the steam of your coffee.

How are you here, too? How are you the mountains?

Grocery List
by Elizabeth Bruce

One dollar. Off frozen string beans. That'll work. Fifty cents off peanut butter; we can do chunky, the kids'll eat it even if he won't. Seventy-five cents off mac and cheese—I know it's crap but it's cheap and filling. Oh look, I have three of those. Woo-hoo! OK, let me check the sales. I could take the H2 down to the Safeway if they're not on sale at Giant. Oh wait, bus fare. Shit, have to add that in. Fuck. Oh well, I can walk, got my cart. Good for me anyway, work off some of that big butt he's always fussing about. Yeah, you used to like it, buster, cushion the ride, you said. Oh well, screw that anyway, you're never home. Just as well. Good riddance I say, Jesus, what a grouch. Take the damn job, why don't you. It ain't fuckin' beneath you. Going hungry is beneath all of us, most especially Robbie who's only three for Christ's sake. How the hell is he supposed to under-stand your ridiculous pride? Oh, there's an opening in the kitchen at his school, did I tell you? Put in for it yesterday, will hear on Monday. Got my sister praying for me, I don't care how much you hate that. Shit, it can't hurt for heaven's sake, it's only words and she loves to do that. OK, so that's $3.75 in coupons plus whatever the sales save. Make it an even $5. This week's economy goal! Not bad. Well done, mom. You rock. Yeah, that's right. I rock. Save a nickel, save a dime, save a goddamn dollar one day at a time.

Sweat
by Elizabeth Bruce

One dollar.

The old woman pressed the worn bill between her hands. She raised it to her cheek beneath the eyes that no longer saw. Rumpled, she thought, an old bill. Old like we became. She found its corners, one dog-eared, another torn, and touched them to her lips. A bene-diction.

It smelled faintly of sweat, whose sweat, she wondered, is it mine? Lord, I have shed some sweat in my time. Or his, bending his back against the torments of the sun, sweat darkening the small of his back, under his arms, across his neck. Man sweat, husky and rough and somehow sweet. Sweet, like the whispers they had made together, even there near the end before he passed, before his spent body curled up one last time into itself, before he had called her to him and given her the dollar.

"My last dollar, sugar," he had said, gathering his last words like the posies he used to pick for her, "First, last, and every dollar in between," he whispered. "They are all for you, they were all for you, my love."

The old woman felt for the corners of the old bill and folded it over into itself, as his old body had done, and tucked it into the old pocket above her heart.

Trees
1168
1160
1125
1148
1078
by Sue Jenkins

Trees
1076
1011
1037
1021
1013

by Sue Jenkins

The Rhododendron
by Kate Soules

And there the rhododendron drifts in the breeze and drops
her pink pearled tears in the hazed afternoon.

For a while two girls climbed out of the window at nap time—
abandoning what was needed to pick the blue flower,

to curl with the cat underneath the sycamore by the road
and sing the alphabet in winding circles.

And there in her rocking chair by the road
she cuddled a kitten and sang in hushed lullabies

rocking in the grace of the moment
when innocence was still bottled in the glass jar on her shelf.

Morphing Archer
by Kim Peter Kovac

The sign of the archer guides the girl on fire through the hunger
games, which have morphed from fiction to fact. #reallydead

The Weaver of Bruges
by Laura Morelli

Agnès fingers the small silk envelope where she
has collected the fibres of her lover's garments.

Across her straw mattress, she lays out what is
left of the foreign blue-eyed boy: a woollen vest
and soiled breeches, the simple clothing of a
travelling dyer's son. Then there is the crimson
swath of silk that he presented to her as a token.
Agnès trails it under her nose one last time,
inhaling the boy's scent.

She closes her eyes and hears the boy's beautiful
voice singing of ships and silk in her ear.

20 rue Laferrière, Angoulême
by Lee Nash

Ever looking for signs,
I choose the bridal blend tea,
the heart-shaped infuser,
and, despite its bitter aftertaste,
the home-made quince jam.
Our fingers entwine beneath
white linen. Upstairs,
a cold and empty room,
freshly laundered sheets
neatly folded under.
The landlady wants to talk—
antiques, love—he strokes
her walnut sideboard sensually,
his lips pronouncing
foreign words with easy grace.
An overnight bag is still in the hall;
his desert scarf veils the back
of a chair. Despite her incentive
and the promise
of a continental breakfast,
I can't go through with it,
won't wake up tomorrow morning
underneath her salt and pepper tiles.
To take tea with a stranger
is one thing, to be shut into
a chamber, as Solon advised,
is quite another.

Interface
by Susan Stamm Evans

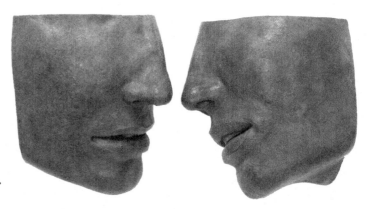

Daydream
by Dick Evans

Italian Luxury
by Faisal Warsani

Crossing the Lake with Natalie
by Grant Clauser

Don't think the waves as things
that crash but things you ride.
The water's not as tough as you.
Just lift your paddle high
and stroke hard. Pulling
against wind, the weather boats
were made to break through.
Water is everything behind you
and ahead there's sun and me,
old dad at starboard looking
out for stumps or something
like a branch floating past,
something we missed
the first time out.

Heartfelt
by S.M. Mack

The dark of night, yet
The silver porch light is on
And I know I'm home.

Katama Bay
by Kate Soules

In Oregon we would set fire to the sand—
anything to stay one moment more beneath the sky
        by the dark sea and soaring Douglas trees.
        We clutched the moon as if there would never be another.

Stolen from where such things thrive and now
sunken in the East and these cold, dark bay waters,

I find myself catching the same pregnant blue crab
over and over again, an acquaintance I can't bring home.

Small Wars
by Alyssa Cooper

He never meant to lie to me; of that much, I am sure.
He just never knew the truth. He was as uncertain as
I was, in such desperately different ways. Thrashing
in vain against hell and high water, I found I couldn't
press forth with all the resistance of his ambivalence
pushing back. In a moment of sanity I would never be
able to take back, I rose my sails with shaking arms,
and I plotted the course that would carry me away
from him, off to the shores of a far and distant land.
He was too small a war to be fighting so hard.

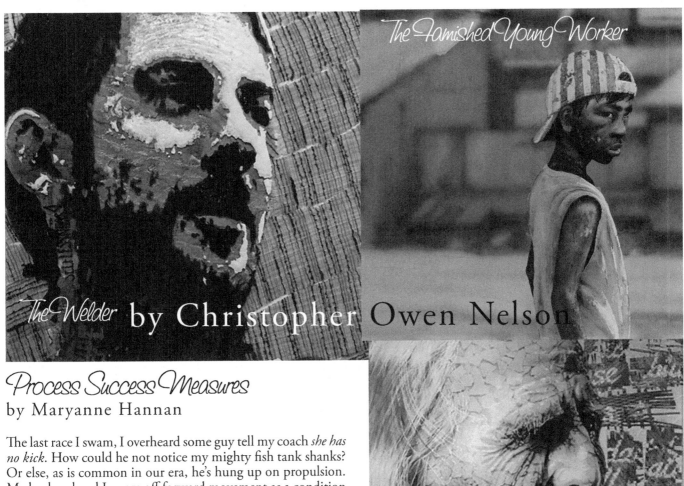

The Famished Young Worker

The Welder by Christopher Owen Nelson

Tornado

Process Success Measures
by Maryanne Hannan

The last race I swam, I overheard some guy tell my coach *she has no kick*. How could he not notice my mighty fish tank shanks? Or else, as is common in our era, he's hung up on propulsion. My husband and I swore off forward movement as a condition of our relationship long ago. But we're still committed to the *one hand knows what the other hand is doing* program. Every Saturday morning he re-screws all the light bulbs in the house. I, defying physics, whip soymilk soufflés. With hands like ours, who needs a kick?

Cremation
by Nicholas Finch

I wear Father's summer suit. I keep a smoke in the mouth, finger the matchbox in his pocket. Mother doesn't know where the suit went. Stick-matches are bones at my fingertips, the box a casket. The mouth-end of the smoke flakes like skin. I swallow the paper-skin and never smoke.

The Wasp's Nest
by Elizabeth Lovatt

I want to tell you about the time I lost my childhood.

We were down in the woods, near the bottom of the hill where the fern was at its thickest. It was Sarah, Joe, my brother and me. I don't remember if one of us spotted it before it fell. All I know is Joe and my brother were high up in the tree, our favourite for climbing, and I was helping Sarah, too short to do it on her own, reach up to grasp the first branch.

It hit the floor with an ugly thump and the air exploded into life. Sarah screamed and tried to run. One flew straight into her ear and started stinging from inside. My brother grabbed her by the arm and looked up at me.

And I felt it then, the sudden crushing weight of it. There was no-one else. With my little finger I reached into her ear and scooped it out.

It stung me too but I didn't say a word.

In the Polar Bear Suite
by Brad Garber

I could lie here, all day
listening to the pillows
with the air off the lake
like lips tasting my neck.
The bear was a juvenile
its danger not fully formed
and your body upon me
bobbed like a seal's head.

Howl and Feel
by Anna Graziosi

I become aware of the teeth in my
mouth, pressing against my lips.

Thorns erupt and my smile turns deadly and wicked.

As I bark out
at you and scream,
I cut my own lips open.

Don't Strip Me of My Stripes

Don't Hurt Me for My Horns

by Katerina Pravdivaia

i

more than they ever had before
they began to suspect that their fingernails
shrank with the daylight their hair
curled uncurled curled to follow
the magma deep beneath their feet their feet
fell exactly where a specific raindrop
fell in the year without a summer their
eyebrows mimicked perfectly the spaces
in between the grass stalks selected
for this purpose and this purpose alone.

ii

yes, it's just like that, only lower down
in the pecking order of rhythm and meter.
it is discordant. the sound will make you
uneasy to the degree that you are not
conscious of listening to it. you won't
understand the cadence, you won't feel
an underlying pattern, or you will
and it won't be the one that's really there.
you will dismiss it. it will continue.

iii

we spent the weekend throwing paper darts
at your brother's model trains, passing the bottle
between us like a handshake, and you
with your envelopes and your wreck of a haircut
tracing over and over again the letters P R O O F
and telling the circumstantial evidence joke
like I haven't heard you say it a hundred
damn times. how can anybody say
we ought or ought not to go, to stay, to find
some unambiguously superior third path forward
sitting there like a gift for the one who rummages behind the couch cushions?

by Margarita Tenser

Sunday

When the storm arrived we were not prepared.
The windows had been left open, the door ajar;
you had left your laundry playing carefree in the garden,
the soft cotton of your sheets dancing with the moon.
In the deluge there was the lost figure of a man.
His dark eyes had known all of you, the petals on your back;
his voice seemed to stick in his nose or behind his front teeth,
but he was gentle in his way and kept your secrets loyally.
I drove for hours. I arrived at the seashore and listened.
The conversation was hushed, the waves distrustful of the shore;
I had wanted to find myself open, knowledgeable, beautiful,
but I stood for hours and heard only the gales.

Monday
(In The Downstairs Bedroom
I Remember What I Had Forgotten)

I bent down naked on all
four of my limbs and lapped
at the moon that lay quivering
in the lake spilled from my glass;
I held my arms up above my head
and spun myself around and around,
my feet tied to the wise old radiator.
For a long time, the coherence of the carpet
was lost on me; Several weeks later the carpet
appeared to have the same pattern as the palm of
my hand: the imprint of twigs on the sand, the sketch
a line in a slow arc of descent, reaching out into nowhere
for a circle; I arranged thirty plain white sheets of paper, knelt,
looked closely at the carpet and spent a month calculating the co-ordinates.

by O Mayeux

Tuesday

I know those ears. Years ago,
a kind of depthless snow

fell all around and I
held my cheek close

to a small, warm cup.
I felt a kind of lobeless

join, a curve to the face
as if there was a hurry

to speak rationally
about that month.

Transient Song
by James Donohoe

The park pond choked with dandelion puff,
The throng of dawn-soaked subway-takers clumped,
Massing up and down grimy concrete steps,
Splatter through rain pools: flat gray chunks of wet.

The throng of dawn: soaked subway-takers clumped
With mortar in motion, trickle and sun
Splatter through rain pools, flat gray chunks of wet;
Light-poles shed looming shadows, each bedecked

With mortar in motion, trickle and sun;
A man-hole exhales—a sulky breeze rubs
Light—poles shed looming shadows, each bedecked
In wiry sinews, black, an inky mess;

A man-hole exhales—a sulky breeze rubs—
A scum-toothed man dissects a dumpster's guts;
In wiry sinews, black, an inky mess
He untunes wordless songs; his mutt-dog sits.

A scum-toothed man dissects a dumpster's guts,
"There's treasure here," he says, "Sellable stuff."
He untunes wordless songs; his mutt-dog sits.
"You just gots to know where to look, is it."

"There's treasure here," he says. Sellable stuff
Appendages the throng, while he looks up.
"You just gots to know." Where to look? Is it
The overdose of taxis disturbing

Appendages? The throng? While he looks up,
On soggy food fragments fat pigeons glut
The overdose of taxis disturbing
The shallow pot-holes in the intersections;

On soggy food fragments fat pigeons glut
In the under-belly beauty that loves
The shallow pot-holes in the intersections,
How each engenders a disconnection;

In the under-belly beauty that loves
Massing up and down grimy concrete steps,
How each engenders a disconnection:
The park pond choked with dandelion puff.

Pas de Deux
by Joanne Jackson Yelenik

You are the one I can't replace.
Your face, I can't erase.
Your voice fits my ear;
your words to me are clear.
I speak from my soul
without design, plan or goal.
I feel I rest within your grace,
unbound by time, unleashed in space.
You are the one I have sought,
a treasure found, not bought.
Whatever comes, don't fret for me;
you are the dream I dreamed I'd see.

Poolside Grafitti
by Gleah Powers

Layers of
Eminence
by Vakseen

Spanakopita
by Andrea Farber De Zubiria

You can buy the filo dough almost anywhere now, but I still like to get it from the refrigerator at the back of Ani's Armenian Bakery. I can get the feta and big blocks of butter there too. Ani's is on a busy corner, a few blocks from my house. Shopping there makes me feel like I live in a "real" neighbourhood, even though most of the other businesses around here are fast food restaurants or big box stores with "Maxx" in their names.

At Ani's the mother is always in the kitchen in an apron with a white cap over her dyed red hair. Her daughter is usually at the register. She's around 30 with long dark hair and thick eyeliner that sweeps out and curls up at the corner of her eyes, like Cleopatra in the old movies. She looks too exotic to work in this small store full of plastic tubs of humus and packages of baklava and string cheese all day. I don't know her name, but the last time I was there, she asked me what I did for a living. When she heard that I work in a medical clinic, she told me about all these aches and pains she has and how she always worries that she might have cancer. When she tells me that three doctors have told her that there's nothing wrong with her, but that she still worries about cancer all the time, I cautiously offer "being depressed can make you hurt." She stares me down with her cat eyes and says defensively, "I was a psychology major; I know all about that." Now I feel awkward, so I just say that I hope she feels better soon and leave with my groceries.

At home I chop onions, wash spinach from our garden, and pour olive oil in a pan, watching it spread as it warms. The onions sizzle when I drop them in. I sauté the spinach, crumble feta in a bowl, add egg. While the butter melts and slides around in the pan, I unroll paper thin sheets of the machine-made filo dough, slicing each in thirds with a pizza cutter, keeping the rest covered so it won't dry out. I brush them with butter and layer them, spooning cheese and spinach onto the end. I form the dough into triangles, something like a flag folding ceremony. Now more butter and repeat until there's an entire pan-full ready to brown in the oven, ten minutes per side. People have probably been making some version of this for centuries and it's one of the few good dishes that I can make from memory, but it wasn't passed down through my family. I'm not Armenian or Greek or Turkish (I'm Eastern European Jewish, New Englander transplanted to California) but I picture myself making this with my granddaughter in a few years (she is Colombian, Mexican, Portuguese, California-born).

The next time I think to go into Ani's, I hesitate. I should ask the daughter how she is feeling, but I don't really want to get into another sad conversation while I contemplate jars of imported spicy red pepper paste and sesame candy. But I go in, ask how she is and she says "fine" like she knows I'm just being polite—not looking for details. She's right. I want to have the friendly neighbourhood ethnic feel, a mom and pop experience, but without actual intimacy. I want the romantic idea of the family, the tribe, the community but without obligation. I want the savoury flavours of baked cheese and spinach without the hours of labour to make the dough that holds the spanakopita together.

When the Party Ends
by Annalisa Crawford

The kitchen's cold; everyone's gone home, or sprawled out across sofas and armchairs, in happy stupor. The house creaks and settles. It's just you, sitting at the table, surrounded by empty bottles and the remnants of alcohol at the bottom of glasses. You consider pouring the last of the vodka, but instead you walk to the kettle and switch it on.

It was a good year, the one just gone. It was your year, and you're apprehensive about what's to come. People don't always admit that, do they, that they're scared? They make resolutions, they plan; they look ahead and become motivated.

They're going to be skinnier and richer and more relaxed and stop eating chocolate and drinking alcohol. They'll quit their job, they'll definitely do that.

But here, in the chill deserted kitchen, you're uncertain how to proceed. You cling to the dying hours. Earlier, you wanted the hands of the clock to slow down, but instead they skipped along with arrogance.

And around you, everyone else was playful and joyous—they held their glasses high and toasted the next year. They teased your anxiety until you ended up sitting on the stairs alone. You heard them counting down the final seconds, and bony hands seized your chest.

Jess stuck her head out—"Come on, you're missing it!"—but she was dragged back into the room and forgot about you.

Two o'clock in the morning, now.

Nothing remarkable has happened yet. Outside, a firework or two is still being let off, an isolated purr into the air and a pitiful fizz. You stand by the window in case you can catch the embers falling.

The harsh overhead light makes the furniture and appliances look 3D, stuck on to the grey shadowed background—too sharp, it makes you blink to refocus. You turn the light off, allowing the kitchen to be illuminated by the digital clock on the oven and the encroaching bulb from the hall.

You yawn, exhausted, battling to remain in last year.

It's just another day, you tell yourself. Time ticked over from one minute to the next; just before midnight became just after—nothing really changed. There's comfort in the evenness of the hours and days and months.

The kettle boils, you jump. You pour water into the mug and watch the teabag swirl. You consider the dishes for a moment. You're still in your emerald green party dress; people don't do dishes when they're dressed up. You don't. You'll do them in the morning, the dependable Monday morning.

Rain
by Elyse Hauser

She woke up in his house and it was raining. The effervescent sunlight that had drawn iridescence from their mixed hair on the pillow in the mornings for weeks was replaced with a diffused gray stillness, broken by the once-familiar sound of rain against a glass window.

If the weather had never changed, they probably would have carried on indefinitely the way they had been all summer. The flitting feeling of sweat trickling as they wandered the streets together. Any thoughts of decision or foresight were subsumed beneath the heat bearing down from above, radiating from the pavement, making the simple pleasures of existing seem paramount above all else. Even sex was just something to do while waiting for the hottest part of the day to end. Sweat passed from one body to another in a sort of purification ritual from the winter romances they'd had before.

She turned to him. The intensity of sunlight had washed what little colour there was out of his eyes before, but now, in the rain, they were marbled like agates, almost green. A very soft roll of thunder sounded in the distance.

"Hey," he said.

The last few weeks had held debauchery. Long days of beer and whiskey and weed. She breathed in with some difficulty and then laughed hoarsely. "I'm all congested," she said. "I guess my body's done with me living this way."

"Do you want me to make you some tea?" he said.

"Yeah. That'd be nice."

She'd had some sort of plans, a friend to meet for brunch and some errands to run later, all forgotten by the time she'd pulled on a sweater printed with flowers and had the tea cup in her hands. She looked outside and watched the rain fall from uncertain clouds until she felt his hands reaching around her from behind. There was a sense of stillness in the air in spite of the rain, as though something liquid was congealing.

When she left his house, it was still raining. He walked her to her car and when she turned to him, she saw something new in his eyes: a very gentle kind of concern, almost like fear. There was a tension around his mouth. So she did something she'd never done before and kissed him there, in public, in broad daylight in the parking lot.

Driving back to her house, she stared at the rain-streaked windshield sightlessly, operating the car while her thoughts stayed on that look in his eyes. Things had changed with the weather and she could not pinpoint exactly how or why. She could not shake the feeling that she'd done something wrong.

Marcus Aurelius
by Alyssa Cooper

You are the dream that I have each night, the one that I struggle to remember in the early glow of morning, your face painted in the curtains as I open my eyes to diamonds of sunlight dancing in the lace. With the blurred details of a half remembered night time adventure, cast in soft focus by the heavy flavour of amber shots and the heat of smoke rushing down my throat, you are my memory of childhood, tarnished and ragged from the passage of time. But in the midst of that murkiness, in that great sea of churning grey, there are moments of clarity: your eyes staring down at me, from such great heights; your hands clutching mine, with your short, bitten fingernails; your tears, as cold as ice, falling baptismal through the childish tangle of my hair.

Magic Nights
by Diana Whiley

Tara
by Cameron Mount

Tara, we called her
when she wasn't standing at her podium.
We used to hang around the classroom
long after the bell
asking her increasingly inappropriate
questions, but never
quite crossing the line.

When she started working afterschool,
we read far more
into that than we should have.
I once brushed against her
the way a fifteen-year-old will
but neither of us mentioned it.

I saw her cut loose only one time
at a snowball dance
or something like that.
We saw her grinding against Russ,
who we called Mr. Wilson
when he wasn't on the sidelines
yelling out at us.

The next week I teased him,
and he'd winked,
but I didn't get it then.
I thought it was avoidance
or shame or fear that he'd lose
his tenure if it got out.

It's been twenty years now,
and I just read Bukowski's "The Puking Lady"
and that wink, I think about it,
about Tara, and about the way
I'd thought of her back then.
That wink told me everything
I needed to know
but didn't yet understand.

Sphinx
by D. W. Schmidt

Our fully-grown family of four rides along a suspect stretch of Main Street
        toward the nicer part of downtown with its Tap Room featuring
        local craft brews and pub grub.
It is the weekend after an unfortunate election, and the car's passengers take turns
        cursing the twittering President-elect.
Then.
The driver spots a man crossing a side street.
The man wears a battered backpack and walks hunched forward.
Upon his shoulders calmly stands a grey and white cat.
Dumbstruck but hungry, we continue on our way to lunch,
        leaving behind the answers.

Standing Stones
by Jalil Buechel

We walked the path to the treeless hill
and leaned our packs against the stones.
As so many had done before we gazed
we felt the ground give up its bones.

Around us rose the circular stand
tall wisdom robed in rocky ground.
We quickly wandered from reason's road
as we listened to the windblown sound.

Out of death came life, the air had changed
as if filtered through some ancient lands
Where people met and carried the stone
to mark where body and soul held hands.

We stayed and we played hide and seek
when a family of five came along
and hid behind the rockiest face
while the standing stones sang songs.

20th Anniversary of Germany's 30,000 Stumbling Blocks
by Gerard Sarnat

After *nazcommuncentralista* gulag massmind nonsense
all falls down and *più fascista* statued walls get blown up,
our demonumentalized hearts pound before deciding whether each
of our individual statures steps on or around enumerated cobblestone
flickers: I figured that pause in Berlin was the end of it, but then
when we pulled into our driveway in America where Jews
have never had life so good … every day I'm reminded.

Coco Chanel
by Richard Weaver

There are ways to die, and ways not to die.
Choices to be made. Always choices. Good ones.
Ones that will work with the light, or deny the dark
edges. Always control. Control what is yours.
Colours. Shapes. Sounds. Even the aroma of wind.
It is yours. Always. Never doubt that. Never
give that to others. Never relinquish
until that moment when you are sure, you know
with certainty that all is ready, and you as well.
"You see, this is how you die."

In the Community I'm of the Generation
by Patrick Blair

Creation with a "c" or do
you want it to be "k" can you
stop it once it gets to "z" or
is it ok to start with "A+"?

A lunar tick. The team is on it.
A solar flare. The generation of
doubt and prediction.

Melting ice. A mint tulip.

Call it "mint". Call it "tulip".

Discuss in a chat. Chat
in a foreign room.
Digital castration, for
the moment you had.
Send out fish to your friends.
Last longer than was meant.

Source a code as below:

As:
of material:soil:meat:as:
above:as: "e" equaling "f".

Down in order. Combust,
line, blue smoke.

Quitting time. Laugh in
your chairs.

Bring cash from machines.
Buy condoms. Leave no germs.
Tackle Monday.
As Sunday
is your rest.

Then I'm a fish, and
all my children are artists.

And I can't leave with that.
I can't swim around myself,
a tidal funeral:sharks:
equal:light: surrounding blue.

White as above as below, blue
as above as below; foreign; etched;
follow the leader; as against
the walls; as against one code.

Immersion
by Diana Whiley

Maybe the Plane that Landed in Rain Saved my Son's Life, or maybe it was the Dog
by Maria Teutsch

Thank-you for that rarity: the on-time arrival: a day's delay would have proved fatal.
Finally home, heavy sleep lugged me into that world without clocks.

I still don't know what woke me: no thunder bark, or siren racket,
just the click of a small dog's nails on hard wood.

Or why I lumbered out of bed
to carry my grown son up the stairs, slurring

and spilling apple juice everywhere
like a Roethke daddy-dance of horror.

Night's silent shadow voice hisses and laughs.
Or why I took a shower before the silver

hooks of morning ensnared his sleeping form.
Or why I wrapped myself in the mourning dove's shawl

and crept like mist into his room to see a puff of breath
shallow enough to ratchet a squall of tiny nails into my eyes.

How fast life knots piano wire around bolts.
Slip and spring back into a tight coil of phone line—

you pant then, you get told by the operator to calm your ass down,
and you save his life. At least up until now that is.

Now life's a trip wire buried in tall grass.
My body quarry for each day's dawn-scavenge.

A braid of sunlight swishing my back can soon double as a noose
Should he ever attempt again, and succeed.

I don't know what woke me that night: perhaps
god is a small dog with furry paws,

and prayer a ball thrown into a blackberry bramble-thicket

which she sometimes brings back,
all slobbered up, to drop at my feet.

Don't Treat Me Like a Trophy
by Katerina Pravdivaia

Headlamp
by Laura Eppinger

This is why I recoil, not
only the headlamp, the jerking
of hands, the sudden
intimacy of it all, not to be
coy, not to punish
you for saying, *Come on,*
you know I still love
that rotten mouth.
The question threads
my gum line, nerves
like a track of fluid inside
the lighter that got me
here. That question: Will
there ever be a curtain to
draw? Do I get to hide
behind a *Confidential?* Or
is that just another sacrifice
we make to stay
in a relationship? (I learned long
ago that claimed women never
have time alone. No space. No
thought no soul they own)
Or is this simply
what I get for heading straight
from the dentist to a lover's
bed? Yes, what I got, fillings,
numbness, the drill. A copay, and now
a flashlight to the face. *Show me,*
you say, *it's only me, open*
up.

A Celebration on the Way
by Dick Evans

Sarah Bernhardt
by Richard Weaver

They say that acting is a whore's career. Don't they wish! The small-membered
bastards. I say, it is what you make it. Whatever you are willing to make yourself.

Onstage. Offstage. Is there really a difference? I'm not telling. I'm dying.
This is my final role. Don't distract me. I've watched others die in life, in this

real world. Sure I took notes. Lots of mental notes. They don't run with tears.
But these rehearsals are killing me. How many times must I approach and open

the damn door? And me without a leg. Is there a password? A shibboleth? I'm not
really Jewish. So what's the point? And why a door and not a window, or a set of stairs?

As if dying wasn't confusing enough and overtime hell on those hoping for a bit-part.
It's not the light. It's not the divine dark that calls. I hear a director's voice yelling

complaining telling me "how slow my death Agony is." Damn critics!

Athens
by Erika Bach

Day #555 (Artist-In-Progress)
by Stephanie Yu

new york city can be so f* depressing. especially as an ARTIST-IN-PROG-RESS. no one too fancy, but someone at least necessary. especially when it's raining. especially when dirty slush forms on the ground after it snows and you trip and fall and there were no witnesses. though you were actually relieved people didn't see you eat shit, yet sadly not a soul was there to empathize with you in that intense shot of momentary pain.

and then come the times when you should meet up with friends, distant acquaintances, possible network gurus. but then you realize people won't get you to where you need to be. art is not a career. art is art. and then you get lazy from too much thought and then you find yourself stuck in your apartment wasting time in the virtual world futilely hoping that your friends would come to you, but they most likely ended up doing e-x-a-c-t-l-y what you did.

you feel on top of the world sometimes dreaming big getting big getting inspired feeling inspired. inspiration all around spurned on by discussions that seem significant. you have a good amount of time to waste and think. you try to make sense of the world based on your own limited observations that you feel are so incredibly valid. why does new york give you that kind of stupid non-sensical kind of pride. I suppose it's in the wind.

what is the fleeting desire to be famous, to have a following. is that the dream. and why is that the dream. it's hard to stick to what you love to do in the privacy of your own space, while not getting distracted by the masses.

Increase the fire inside so it burns out of your entire being and sets everyone else around you on fire. its exposure. and when you are exposed you want people to say they love you in your nakedness. that you are not ashamed to be seen. that you are worthy to be seen. and when they don't tell you this you notice small lines on your skin that begin to itch. and you realize they are merely wrinkles.

The abandoned car
by Kate LaDew

'The' because no other car exists now but yours
no other unanswered cell phone, no other empty apartment,
no other missing child or endangered girl
(because you will always be a girl to me)
nothing else exists but this feeling,
pushing fingers into my heart and letting the blood drain.
you are not here, and you are not here
and the possibilities of where you might be
and what might be happening to you
and the sound of your voice and the rise of your chest and the beating inside you—
you are not here.

and the world is never so vast as when you're looking for someone

Tollway (History of the Dogs, Part Two)
by Melissa K. Downes

That pretty beagle,
all white and life
and liver spots,
in tumbling play
of awkward paws
and intense youth,
dashes, focused joy
and freedom, across
the four-lane tollway.

In the rear-view,
I see the toss and imposs-
ible-to-survive acrobatics
of cars and puppy. I taste bile
and mourning for sixty miles.

Kalamunda Summer
by Kerry Wingood

Pyramids of yellow sand shift on the verge
And bake in the spiky heat
Boondie furnaces for tomorrow's fight
Stiff goanna leather cures against tar
A totem of my youth
Butterfly dust smears bug catcher windows
Death under fake green leaves
A pool pony sags in tepid water
One eye staring at the sun
My Ice Magic lost its crackle long ago
Coke can bongs litter the scrub over the road
Where oily thorn bushes grow
Leaves that pop and burn under glass
The bogans flank the wall by the shop
Drinking Southern Comfort from a coke bottle
Picking butts off the ground
Plastic cheese toasties, soup in a cup
In the cold concrete under croft
We sit on the monkey bars
Where boys can see up your skirt
Talking about nothing
The maths teacher leers
Crumbs in his beard, tinted glasses
He peers over them at my breasts
There's tea and biccies at the church hall
Stubby-fingered bigots pat each other's backs
And priests bask in the attention
From the safety of their cassocks

The Sounds of Silence
by Brigita Orel

The grass under my boots is trampled from my shuffling feet. Perhaps they will think I hesitated but I'm only taking in this last view.

Further up the road there's Dante's cave, the place where supposedly the poet was inspired to write *Inferno*. How peculiar that one can only visit the cave with special equipment but there's no special equipment needed to visit hell—it's open to us all.

The gorge below my feet feels bottomless, dark and cold, and I am as if suspended in thin air. The memories and thoughts invading my mind should be fleeting compared to the stillness that has filled this spot since prehistoric times. But they haunt me to the brink of insanity.

The hillsides blush pink with the breaking dawn; it's far too early for tourists. For a short moment I think I should feel sorry for ruining their trip. I imagine their shocked expressions, revulsion. I've gone through it all. The helplessness shattered me and maybe I could've been rebuilt if the silent draughts of the heart hadn't blown at the pieces and scattered them. Indeed, silence was worse than helplessness.

The stream below murmurs so continuously it becomes a new sort of silence. It's almost calming. I've thought a lot about silence since you've been gone but these days it sounds different than it used to. It meant repose and freedom from your cries and needs, now it's heavy and excruciating and loud in my mind.

A bough stuck between two rocks created a dam in the creek and a leaf snags. After a few moments, it flutters free and continues its journey. Will I snag?

The wings of the buzzard above reflect the tender, early-morning sunshine, the dark bird and the sun creating a majestic, almost Dantean image. Time doesn't heal, it just continues, irreverently.

The wind makes the trees on the hillsides murmur as if they're whispering encouragement to me. The stream chants its fluid song as it caresses the rocks and stones, cold and white, bone-like. The sounds swell and then all goes silent.

Renovation
by Brigita Orel

I stopped the car by the side of the road, turned off the ignition until all the lights on the dashboard went out. I watched the soft dark floating down over the valley. The bluish outline of my house in the hazy distance was a home that was not. A pretend family. A history of running away. It all added up to being me.

I felt cold, and the movement in my belly sent shivers down my arms. It had started with barely perceptible flutters which had grown into strong kicks. Everything started innocently enough, until it grew into something one couldn't control any longer.

I regretted coming home and discovering I was not who I had thought I was. I regretted not coming earlier. My mother was not my mother, my aunt was my mother. My father's drinking was my fault. Everything was my fault. I was the reason for my own undoing. If I hadn't been born ... But that was an easy answer to even the most difficult questions. An answer I wouldn't have needed to go searching for all over the world. I could have as well made it up.

There was no one left to demand answers from me, except myself. The only one left who mattered was the child's father but he might—would, most likely—leave tomorrow, maybe next week or month.

As my eyes refocused on the decaying house, I knew I couldn't keep digging at the foundations and expect the edifice to resist the disturbance and remain standing. The cracks may not be visible at first, but over time, stress fractures deepened, nano-fissures opened up, until, in the end, they formed a gaping mouth that swallowed it all.

By leaving I had caused more fractures and deepened old ones in us all. I could prod and dig at them still, or I could choose to inject them with cement and seal up the foundations. I could spread the damage or pretend that the parts of the building below surface didn't exist. None of it felt right, but that was part of it all. I could fix the shutters and doors of my old house, but I couldn't swap the walls that held the roof, not without levelling it with the ground first. Perhaps it wasn't so much about what the house could become. Perhaps it was about the house unbecoming everything it wasn't, de-cluttering, so it could finally be what it had been meant to be.

Unquenchable
by Carmen Kern

She steps over the loose board on the porch steps. Her feet are cracked at the heel, hard from running without shoes for more months than she could count. Jemma's hand-me-down dress hung low around her skinny arms, exposing the buds of breasts that would one day be pinched, sucked on and in the end, left to sag like the dress she wears. The pond is close. She walks soft across the grass-worn path and through a line of pine and elm. The water sweeps away the dust bowl swirling on her hem, she slips into its warmth smooth as a gator. It claims her. Tells her she belongs nowhere else but here in a land that hasn't been fed anything other than sorrow.

"Annie! Child, get yourself over here and help pack up this wagon!"

She hears the voice of her ma, muffled and distant as she floats near the surface.

The weeds wave around her, sliding across her hungry skin.

And she is hungry.

For something other than potato soup or black bread. She is ravenous for fresh water, cold and clear to ease her soul.

Annie pulls herself upright, standing on the green-slimed bottom of a vanishing life. Water drips off her hair, hitting the dirt in a line that trails behind her. She looks back to see where she has come from but the earth is already dry. She couldn't find her way back even if she wanted to.

Bourbon and Gingham
by Carmen Kern

Marlene has the radio on; Elvis sings smooth blues while she smokes one of her husband's cigarettes. She blows the smoke through the open window beside her. She isn't dressed yet, but soon she'll put on one of her polyester dresses with some kind of matching heels. She stretches her bare feet in front of her trying to remember what the feel of sand or dirt or cut grass feels like between her toes. She pushes the glowing end of the cigarette into the ashtray, careful to empty it in the sink. She wipes it clean before putting it back on the table beside his chair.

Upstairs, Marlene rolls large pink curlers in her hair before brushing mascara on her lashes and dabbing a hint of peach lipstick that brings out the slight tan on her face. Not enough sun to bring on the freckles she had when she met him but enough to take away the pale look that most of her PTA friends wore like a badge of honour. She puts on the white skirt with red polka dots, and a red blouse, something fun that might remind her that they used to dance together in the alley behind their house and drink bourbon out of the bottle.

Marlene checks all the rooms in the house, tucks in the end of a bed sheet, straightens the blue gingham tablecloth she made and sweeps away cigarette ashes that had drifted across the Formica countertop.

Five more minutes.

She pours the gin and chips off the ice, shaking them cold, so cold she sucks on her fingers to warm them. She pours the mixture into the polished glass hoping that tonight he will be tired from yelling on the trading floor while shifting and moving money around as if it all meant something. She chews on one of the ice chips from the shaker before dumping them.

Two minutes.

She had spent some time making prepared dinners from Albertson's look like she had made them herself. The casserole dish warms in the oven and the plastic containers are tucked away in the bottom of the garbage can by their garage. A car door slams in the driveway. She'll linger with her kiss, hand him the drink and ask about his day. And later, in bed, if he turns out his light without reaching between her legs, she will dream of walking on a dried up shoreline with her feet bare and bourbon steaming off her tongue.

Sharp Shoes
by David Pratt

"My grandfather died when he was ninety," he says. "He was a blacksmith. I grew up in Tweed. There weren't no roads then. In winter you'd just get out the horses and a cutter. The trains used to stop at the trail crossing to pick you up." I asked him whether they changed the horseshoes in winter. "Yes, they used sharp shoes, you see. But then they came out with these spikes you just screw into the shoe, and take them out again at the end of winter. And that hit the smiths pretty hard. When people first came over here, they didn't have to buy the land. You just drove stakes in. And if you figured you could work twice as hard as the next man, you staked twice as big an area. People would start with a one-furrow plough. Then they'd get a two-furrow plough, and two horses. Then they went to the disc plough and that was a three-furrow plough. Then they went to tractors. But then you had to have more cows for the milk to pay for the gasoline. 'Cause the horses, see, you could feed them through the winter from the straw stack."

Remnants
by Madeline Sharples

Flying Circle Dragons by Nory Marc Steiger

My father sold upholstery and drapery textiles.
He'd use his shears to cut tapestries,
antique satins, Jacquards, raw silks,
and sheer voiles to size.
He'd call what was left the remnants –
the remainders,
the throw-aways,
the leavings,
all the bits that went into the trash,
gone, forgotten,
making room for the next better piece of material
to come along.

I've been thinking about the remnants of my life,
the little pieces left behind long ago:
childhood girlfriends like Phyllis,
who walked to school with me in first grade.
holding hands, carrying little purses,
and walking on tiptoe,
pretending we were grown up enough to wear high heels,
my favourite uncle killed in a plane crash when I was nine,
leaving me forever longing to tell him goodbye;
getting rid of my baby fat when I was twelve,
falling in love with Eugene
with the gorgeous blue eyes in eighth grade,
who threw me over for a girl he met at camp,
the family house sold and swept clean of old books and toys –
even my first diary with a lock and key—gone,
and my family's move from the Midwest to California
without ever looking back.

Through the years more went by the wayside:
a house in Riverside CA with a view
of orange groves out the kitchen window,
a short work stint on a Pacific island
with my husband and our two little boys,
a job working on proposals
in the aerospace business,
teaching engineers how to write –
and more friends coming and going,

more getting ill and dying
now than ever before.

Also gone are my son Paul and his things:
his old plaid flannel shirts,
Levis with rips in the knees,
Doc Martens worn from his long walks
to escape his demons,
cuttings from his last buzz,
synthesizers,
recording devices,
computer,
records,
and books.
Yet I still have some remnants:
a poem he wrote soon before he died
a memory of how he looked his last night,
his piano now refinished,
and his room that I turned into my writing room
where he resides as my muse.
These are the remnants I don't throw in the trash.
These are the bits I save.

Loons
by Michael Campagnoli

Across the cove
a woman's scream
a peal of girlish laughter.
> *Loons*

First time,
a cry so loud it startled her;
the decibel force of it.
a pitch so high,
it took her breath away.

There, in the distance,
two threw back
their wet black heads, gave
> *answer and reply*
> *answer and reply*
> sad-sweet skirl of melody

Almost entwined, they slipped
beneath the water's edge. Silent.
Disappeared.

Loons

The black and white geometry.
The crisp and heaving glow
of beak and neck and eye.
The haunted-peculiar call:
> *euphoric horn*
> *cello of melancholy*
> *ephemeral and doomed*

Swimming. Their backs
like
white

spotted
endless

night sky.

Loons.

Managing Your Meta-Buzz
by Maryanne Hannan

My husband doesn't understand anything meta. If I say I don't eat sugar and then order pecan pie for dessert, my husband's surprised. *You've changed your mind?* he asks. Of course not. It's meta-talk for my meta-health. Delete the sweets, a delicate leaf from an artful scroll of meta-talk designed specifically for my needs. Not all husbands and healthcare providers understand, but some professionals are catching on. Yesterday, my beautician treated my hair with keratin. Said it was the cat's pyjamas. Uh-oh, my husband's allergic to cats. Better not be any feline dander in this. *Don't be ridiculous*, she said. She was right. And last night, I slept like a cat in a coma.

Arroyo
by Veronica Scharf Garcia

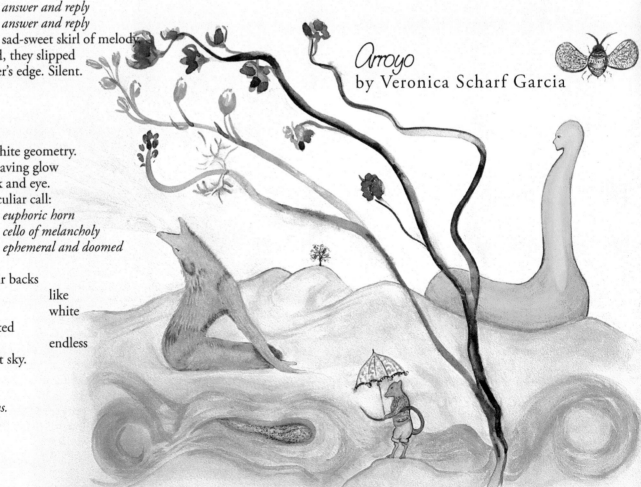

Shadows Succulent
by Bee Williamson

Martini, Bitters, Cocktail
by Brenda Yates

Martini: A British army rifle used in the 1800's. But remember, to get one's bitters was to get one's just deserves. Argue here over desserts, deserts, or desert as in to abandon, to make desolate, or go back even further to what originally meant uninhabited place; or a barren, even arid locale one might be exiled to as happened when Molotov (of bottle-bomb fame), fell out of favour, the way fashions of mixed drinks come and go.

Words
by Irene Blair Honeycutt

Italicized words are from Robert Hass, "Calm," in Human Wishes *(The Ecco Press, 1989)*

When Bob Hass reads from his manuscript at Squaw Valley, some of the pages drift to the floor and rest next to the lectern. He seems not to notice. Not to care. Then borrows someone's reading glasses. Says he knew one day this would happen. The glasses make things worse. He laughs and holds the Milosz book at arm's length in dim light. The words scattered on the floor become jealous. Especially the page he steps on now as he intones Seamus Heaney. The words crawl off the page, away from his feet. And when he shifts and recites from his heart his own poem, the words on the floor turn into *muskrats* and *black-eyed Susans* and *ponds. You can go into that meadow . . . . You can go there.* His reading ends. Amid applause, he reaches down, gathers the pages from the floor as if picking wild flowers, tries shuffling them into a bouquet. The words are stubborn as briars. He keeps calling them back as if calling to something in the *blue-gray distance.* The words obey. And the words that never were there on those pages are listening at the windows.

Rituals of Regret
by Alaine Dibenedetto

Cleaving The Map
by Kim Peter Kovac

An off-hand question about upcoming elections to the bubbly Indian children's book author elicits flashing rage about politics, simmering since the 1947 Partition, a time that even outsiders know was filled with disruption, destruction, and death. "Brit colonialists", she spits, "carved the country with cleavers, ignorant and arrogant: splitting Punjab and Bengal right through their spines". She notes that the wounds to families, cities, religions—and herself—still ooze bright and wet, splashing festered pain on the current campaign.

Slap the Fire
by A.D. Ross

Slap the fire,
because it's 2:00am somewhere.

Yes, she whacked it wet, right outta him,
flames licked firm fingertips.

Face hit hard with a slight, sullen crack.
And she'll do it again.

Because he slammed the blue door
on the soft, padded top of her open toe,

shut out of a dirty, sundown home
built on cigarette butts and empty coke cans.

And all those black blocks
he scattered to the floor

went crash with the slap of a flat, open hand.
The community forgives,

yet some blows will bend
the straight and sturdy back

of our own biology. Send back,
spit back that festering, green speech,

let it curl off the tongue like a sharp snake in your mouth.
After she's done

imagining, cracking
his sweet rib bone between talons and teeth,

they work to cement sense together again.
Changing city sidewalk with permanent shoe prints.

The coming day was a paste made of bottled, twilight tears
and the hot, thick blood they drew.

The Alley
by Benjamin Wheeler

I slipped my ear buds back into my ears and they gave a crackle as I shoved my hands into my pockets against the old, frayed cord. The thumping of Big Sean's "Dance Remix" was back to sonically isolate me from the world and prevent me from really feeling the cold. Using only my eyes to dissect my surroundings, I turned down the next alley.

Oh, fuck …

The bass flooding my ears kept me from really zeroing in on the smell, but without looking I knew the big, blue dumpster on my right held treasurers my eyes would never behold. Guess that is what I get for choosing the alley way behind the butcher. I blinked a few times, and pulled my gaze from the dumpster to the backs of the houses on the other side of the alley. The sea foam green tiled roof of the second house cleansed me as I took a second to go nose blind. As I was looking, a plump pigeon splattered haphazardly onto the ridge of the roof top. Its feathers were all ruffled, like it had narrowly escaped a shop keepers broom or an overzealous child in the park. I kept looking and it turned its iridescent head to flaunt the apple proudly stuck in its beak.

Lucky pigeon.

My feet had then decided it was time to walk again and so it was. As I set off, my pace slowed and Kendrick's "Bitch, Don't kill my vibe" joined in on this mobile concert. My head bobbed gaily side to side like it was suspended by some spring rather than my normally stiff neck. I scanned the alley way. Nothing to see it seemed, the wind cutting through my jacket didn't even seem to be hauling leaves away to oblivion. I was a few steps past the next dumpster when the shadows shifting caught my eye. I pivoted on my right heel to see my eyes weren't playing tricks on me, but rather a large black cat sat licking its paws. I stopped and stared, waiting for the cat to notice me. It's brilliant yellow eyes stayed locked on its paws as they passed steadily in front of its mouth like a grandfather clock arm.

Damn cat.

I turned, and in a huff headed down the alley. "Fergalicious" had just started and I skipped ahead and "Kanye's Spaceship's" opening bass line came in. I passed a tidy single car garage with a Mini Cooper packed neatly in besides cans of paint and tools evenly spaced on the shelves. I could see the next cross street, a few houses away now, and began to mentally flip a coin which way to go next. A lean young couple pushing a stroller walked on the sidewalk in front of me and when they had passed the fat pigeon was there picking at the apple. The black cat then swiftly trotted past me like a sudden gust of wind, headed directly for the pigeon's small patch of grass. The pigeon didn't seem to mind or notice the cat was picking up speed and locked dead on its next tasty meal. But as the cat reach the sidewalk it suddenly slowed and sat down across from the plump bird. The pigeon, or Bernard as he was now known to me, looked up with the nonchalance of an old friend seeing their daily lunch partner had arrived. Clarice, the cat, then softly meowed, followed by a brief coo-coo from Bernard. I reached the sidewalk and both Clarice and Bernard gave me cold, harsh looks like I had walked in on the meeting of a secret society. Clarice grabbing the apple and Bernard taking flight beyond the trees lining the streets, they were both gone.

Goodbye.

Egypt, 1954
by Carol Cooper

* The Corniche stretching all the way from the harbour to Montazah.
* A blue parasol fringed with pompoms.
* My mother in a voluminous scarf, and a swimming costume that would never get wet.
* Father studying *Al-Ahram*.
* Uncle Selim in his black and white lace-ups.
* My swimsuit with frills round the bottom, and straps that cut into my shoulders.
* A huge block of ice that only Abdou could lift.

It seemed unfair that one of our servants, usually Abdou because he was younger and stronger than toothless old Ibrahim, had to lug giant blocks of ice to the beach, break them up with a pick to keep our drinks cool, then look after us all day instead of enjoying himself. Displaying one gold tooth, he replied, "*Maalish.*" He said it a lot. It means never mind.

After Abdou put up deck chairs and the parasol, Father would install himself with an Arabic newspaper while Mother read *La Réforme Illustrée*, with special attention to the accounts of who had worn what dress at whose party.

I gazed at the sparkling blue sea. Across the waves in front of me lay countries like England, where many of my school-teachers were from.

"That's Yorkshire, where Miss Brownlee is from," I said with certainty.

"You're pointing straight at Cyprus," said Odile.

Being two years older than me, Odile knew everything. She was also a better swimmer, and boasted she could swim out to those rocks, if she wanted to, just as older boys did to show off. I hoped she wouldn't try. Even back then, I was afraid of losing her. Without her, I would fade like a newspaper in the sun. I knew I would.

My parents said things would change after 1952. They hadn't. Uncle Selim, who was not my real uncle, would often join us, sitting on a chair in white trousers, straw hat, and leather shoes. His glasses were dark so you couldn't tell where he was looking. Sometimes my aunts Adeline and Josephine, who were real aunts, would arrive, draped in matching scarves. I have no idea what they found to talk about with Mother, but they were never quiet. As the three of them rattled away for hours in their usual mix of French and Arabic, their hands provided an accompaniment to add emphasis or embellish descriptions. Rashida, the Lebanese *da-da* who looked after Odile and me, was rarely at the beach. She was too busy at home doing essential things like stuffing vine leaves and praying to St Anthony.

I built sandcastles which pleased me greatly. Too grownup for playing in the sand, Odile people-watched. "Look. There goes Fifi."

I looked up to see Fifi wiggling her hips as she strolled past by in another new swimsuit. Nobody could remember her real name but she was part Italian, part Egyptian. It was normal for everyone to be part something, just like us. Fifi was impossibly old, maybe about thirty, and she chewed gum and had a wide mouth

like the film stars at the Rialto. She made us laugh, but later at bath time Odile tried to perfect her wiggle.

During the afternoon I'd scan the sands for my cousin Victor. He was almost exactly my age and the last person I wanted to see at Sidi Bishr, or anywhere else.

Eventually the grownups would decide it was time to go home. I never wanted to leave the beach, but there were compensations in the form of *dora*.

Vendors punctuated the Corniche, yelling about their pretzels, nuts, and soft drinks. My favourite vendor cooked ears of corn on a makeshift charcoal grill, fanning the embers with a piece of cardboard. The *dora* was sweet and needed no seasoning. Too hot to touch when you first got hold of it, I used part of a leaf to hold the cob at each end.

Father drove us home in the big Taunus that was festooned with blue stones to keep us safe against the Evil Eye, and other drivers.

As the sun dipped lower, it painted building after building orange with its glow. A breeze came off the sea now. In vacant lots, a few boys in pyjamas flew kites.

At sunset, the sky turned every shade of pink, red, and purple. Why wouldn't it? This was Alexandria, where tomorrow was bound to be another fine day, more than suitable for shepherds. As the sun sank, there was a momentary green flash on the horizon. That was when you were supposed to make a wish, just before the sun set like a stone into the sea.

My wishes were:
To be more like Odile.

For my pen not to leak all over my uniform again.

Never to have lamb for lunch again.

Cousin Victor not to visit on Sunday.

Friday for George Lucas
by Cooper Lysek Gomez

George Lucas was lying on his couch thinking about his legacy when, suddenly, representatives from Disney came bursting through the door. George knew what had to be done: he morphed his body into that of the Incredible hulk and smashed through the wall and out into the street. He looked around a bit, then proceeded to the supermarket. There he took every food item off the shelves and carried it all to the car. Once he was finished eating, he grew wings and flew across the country to Steven Spielberg's house.

"Look at me," Lukas said.

"Why, George, you're huge!"

They talked until someone started banging on the door. It was the Disney representatives. George fought them off with his Hulk fists and ran off. He stopped at a gas station and filled himself up with diesel fuel. Once he was full, he started running on all fours down the road. The Disney representatives were still on his tail. They had been chasing him ever since he'd turned down their offer. They wanted to buy Star Wars but he wouldn't sell. So he kept running. Eventually, he pretended to be a cat and hissed at people he walked past. People were wondering what was so wrong with George Lucas, but no one could tell.

Love Hate
by Vakseen

October Maze
by Bruce Louis Dodson

How does the poet's song
forget itself in telling
lost
I cannot see myself
in mirrors of my making
as reflections swim a labyrinth of silk and carburetors
scent of gasoline and lipstick.
Become a weaver, someone told me
plait life into something tangible.
The shuttle passing though my hands is time
I cannot stop the passing of the hour
as captive of the loom I weave
from one side to another
staggering home.

Thumb
by Elizabeth Lovatt

My Granddad died when I was five. I do not remember
him much. I am told I would sit on his knee and try to
twist him thumb around, he would let me and pretend
it caused him pain to make me laugh. My mother says
my sense of humour comes from him.

If I sit and think, sometimes in the gaps of thought
I can feel my Granddad's knee hard beneath me; his
too large thumb grasped in my two small hands as
I try to bend it back. I can feel the resistance of his
thumb; determination and youth against strength and
age. Then that moment of triumph and amusement,
unfairly won but freely given.

I do not know if this is a true memory or something I
have created from the story my mother tells me. But
it is my only memory of him, and so I cling to it, with
something that feels like love.

For Gene
by D.W. Schmidt

A woman sits sideways on the edge of the dying man's bed.
She holds his hand and speaks to him, but I hear only pieces.
I lean forward in the only chair in the room,
        perhaps two feet from the end of the bed.

Neither the man nor the woman can see, as I do,
        out the door of the room, into the hall,
        where patients, determined to complete their "rehab,"
        inch into and out of my view, clawing forward, if need be,
        with one tip-toe, covered in a rubber-soled slipper,
        pulling a wheelchair weighted only with what is left
        of a living body.

Wheelchair Nudes: a group portrait of cancer survivors
by Alan Catlin

Sitting, totally exposed in their
wheelchairs, lower limbs useless
weights, appendages, limp, some
with feet bent at impossible-for-walking
angles, others like rubber with toes,
crotch hair wild, hips wide, real girth
for weight support of ample torsos,
full breasts, some sagging, others
supple, pert, ripe for squeezing,
a handful and more, faces hard,
arrogant, way-beyond resentment,
assertive, eyes hardened, silently
suggesting, "We are still women.
Sexual creatures, our nakedness is
all the proof you should need."

1 Eye 2 Eyes 3 Eyes
by Jessica Gawinski

How to Survive Mental and Physical Distress
by Maryanne Hannan

With all the self-described lonesomes I've met lately, I'm getting more into Gordon, the nickname I gave my screen saver guy. He must have been crouching on the ground in front of the Quebec City mural and sprung up the instant I tried to shoot the cute little dog there. Now his chock-a-block face pops out at me every minute and a half, whenever I daydream at my computer. Not even his mother has seen him this close and personal in years. *Hail, fellow, well-met!* I say when he appears, but he never loses his anxious look. Maybe he doesn't like his new name. *Embrace the process*, I plead with him, *we're together for a reason. Names don't matter.* Every day in the nursing home, I tell my mother-in-law *I'm not Betty*, when she calls me Betty. *Of course you're not.* Then, *I'm not Barbara*, when she calls me Barbara. When I say, *I've been married to your son for twenty-seven years*, she gets mad, demands to know why I never mentioned it before. I can wait; soon she'll squeeze my hand, touch lightly somewhere real.

My Last Eden
by Dick Altman

Northern New Mexico
1.
Ancient geometries of solitude,
turquoise and fire. Beguiling
as the ruby-winged tarantula wasp,
no less merciless.

You who cobbled the west of cloth
and clay, who bled to subdue the dirt.
You goad me to root.

2.
No garden of ease greens here. What
flowers, starves into stubble of survival.
Hardpan, thin water, dust-sodden winds
ennoble, humble the bloom.

Futility writes itself across shard
and glyph, mesa and canyon. I walk
the same path, work the same earth.

3.
Root crops falter and stunt, hands crack,
soil sleeps—a time of dying wakes.
Desert snow whispers its arrival. My body
numb as caliche[1] warms to its coming.

Mountains understand a slow death.
I look for signs mine will be worth
the wait.

——————————
1 *Caliche:* clay hardened soil

Dash of Mayhem
by Margo Davis

Again tonight I heard
pebbles tossed up by a worn tire
like persistent lapping on
the shore. Why must waves
haunt one so? The pull could be
the taut moon overhead or memory
hypnotic as that night I walked along
the beach with a man who wouldn't
speak if he now could. And yet
he and I once were intimate as
sea foam coaxing my toes.
A haunting sound, waves, rhythmic,
a pattern that today still lures
with its recurring urge. Friendship ends
and people pass and waves
wash over bungles and bounty.
Pebbles fly, and when nicked
we make of its toss what suits us.
One sharp click is another's
stone stuck in its rut.

Morning Glory
by S.M. Mack

It is too early for the night to end
But we are both awake, and soon
I will get up, and leave.

Together, we will break
My heart for the first time.

Not yet, though.

He thinks I am asleep.

Hanalei Bay
by Faisal Warsani

Unmoored
by Robyn Groth

The bay is scattered with boats, unmoored and
unmanned. *Are they sick?* I wonder and pull one
into shore. I climb in. *Warm*, I think, and the
seat softens me, *but not feverish*. The engine holds tight to the gunwale, and when I test it, it
hums iambs. The hull is solid and smooth. I find nothing wrong with the boat and release it.
The water flips over and over, gilded, like Bible pages. Gulls shout and eat. Sand crabs make
the beach treacherous, every inch another deep pit. The boats just sun and sun, then nod to the
moon. *So strange, those boats, without direction or owners.* The tide stretches farther up the shore,
and I dip my hands in it. The gulls settle in groups, beaks under wings. I tuck the sand crabs in
for the night, fill their pits back in with sand as I walk over them.

The Remex
by Michael Campagnoli

bones of sugar maples crossed
the road, underfoot
pale and paper thin
the tattered remnant
fallen slow, the last
to go, yellow leaves
and filtered glow
tunnel of gold. Light,
last light, before
the time of long shadows.

    running the Back Cove
    in mittens and hat,
    scarf trailing behind
    the blink of silver water
    straight ahead

"Anna," she thought she heard.
"Anna," someone called.

She turned, but
no one there.

Near the hunter's cabin
where the creek spills
to the water's edge,
she saw the loons were gone.

Parents just the week before
and now the chicks,
gone
Grown and flown.
All that remained was a

    single
    black
        flight feather
in the clearing near the shore.
      The remex
soft and weightless
lonely in the mirrored light

She knelt down
held it in her hands
a perfect thing
fragile and living

The wind began to stir
and blow and yet once more
there came,

"Anna, I'm waiting…"
    a hollow numbness
    a tightness in her chest
    certain, now, she heard
    the name.

"Anna," a male voice called,
    deep, rich baritone
        of melancholy.
"Anna," it called,

        "Come."

She rose slowly to her feet
brushed the feather close
to her lips
and began to run,
legs light, leaping
longing for
the risk
of flight,
yearning

to sail free.

Untitled
by Robin Dunn

los angeles vibrates a dream of death
ten thousand suburbs inside a nuclear bomb
my love

Bluff
by Katrina Greco

Could any of this be warmer,
you wonder—a world unswarmed.

Here, backfire.
There, reality of moths.

The weather all around my arms,
cliffside cracks,

bite of salt and queen ann's lace.
We are kissing in the wind.

As a figment in the furrows of your hand,
my face is beautiful

and I have never seen this city.
But your hair gathers foxtails,

and catches the fog.
Can you tell a lie?

The bay is full of bodies.
The deer run wild in the hills.

Afternoon Rain
by Elena Rielinger

Sacred offering. Effervescent sound. Please tiptoe past the worms.

Guilty
by Kendra Liedle

You only see what you want to see. Beyond the frames of your glasses, your field of vision, your own perception, there exists a world you'd rather not know. How can you be so blind?

There are the guilty and there are the innocent. Most would say you're innocent. That you've always been that way. But today, I say you're guilty. Guilty of being innocent and naïve. Guilty of failing to see that she doesn't love you. She never has. I know you may find this hard to take. Remember, it's those with vision who lead the blind. She has a vision. Bright, clear eyes full of youth and promise and plans for the future.

When you close your eyes, she leads you on. She makes you feel like a teenager. You make her feel like a success. The act feels natural. This is easier than she thought. You fall into her net like a trapeze artist lacking skill. There is no struggle. You don't even attempt to escape. But you're caught.

Guilty, red-handed.

Such a fool, old man, she thinks to herself. She looks at you and sees dollar signs, a beachfront home, vacations to plan, the last of her student loans. Visions beyond her bank account. She ties a blindfold around your face and looks ahead to see a future without you. An open chequebook, a solid foundation for a life.

And then she smiles. *Innocently.*

Garden State Parkway
by Cameron Mount

The inlet's death scent
echoed the landfill
down the road this morning
as I drove behind the fog
on rain-soaked roads
and the spray of leftover winter salt.

The trucks spat rocks and clouds
against my windshield
and made me jump off beat
as The Boss cried
about the days of glory
lost by we who still sing of them
to whoever will listen
long enough.

Construction didn't halt
even in the downpours
even though the evidence of progress
evaded the human
eye, and the dump trucks kept
hauling the damp remains of asphalt
from one mile-marker to another.

I suppose that's a sort of progress,
moving trash from mile 44 to mile 63
but the burnt rubber tire smell
kept burning
while headlights crept up tailpipes
and disappeared into trunks
in the sequence of dominoes.

Electrified steel
and the taste of ozone
kept me from nodding
when the disc shifted
and The Boss still croaked
of blue-collar days
he'd long since abandoned,
tho he kept the bandannas
and kept crying
about the Garden State
where the smell of decay
tainted the morning.

A Certain Day In Spring
by Robert Knox

I cry in the same place every year
I remember to bring tissues, but don't remember why
We are called upon to respect others
The minister, recalling an incident involving her wife and their child
explodes the canon of pronouns
We breathe the fragrance of potted pink hyacinths
People older than us shamelessly singing
choruses of 'Hallelujah!'

At night I strive to recall
this wisest of all her sayings,
'the sacrament of tears'
I listen to songs named 'Two Souls,' 'Sacred Nature,' 'My Brother's Keeper,'
Isaac turns in a slow circle, expectantly for the ram
Now we will live forever

The Blacksmith
by Sarah Brown Weitzman

First published in *Journal of the Cow Neck Peninsula*, Fall 1996

The clop of hoofs
upon the cement pavement

always called me after school
to the blacksmith's door

to watch him shoe town horses.
There I could smell

the forge's sulphur mouth
and sometimes was allowed to work

the bellows.
The blacksmith knew by colour

when to tong the metal out
when to put it back, when to strike

red sprays of sparks that blinked out
before they reached the floor.

On quiet days the blacksmith banded
barrels or fixed a rake to its handle.

But best was that nail worked from red
to white then hissed

back to sudden black again
in a pail of water when John

the blacksmith's son forged for me
a friendship ring of iron.

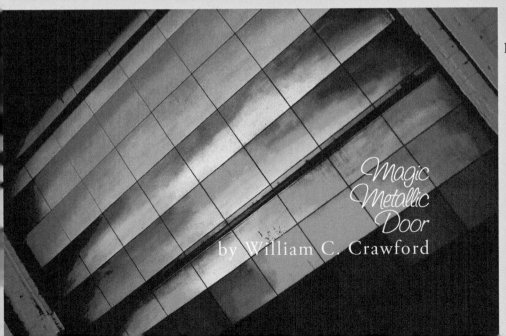

Magic Metallic Door
by William C. Crawford

Lunchtime
by Carol Middleton

There are three vine tomatoes in the white bowl, still linked to their stem. She picks up the bunch and sniffs it, before examining each one with the ball of her thumb.

I watch her. In the first, she finds a slight indentation that indicates a bruising. In the second, a black speck marring the redness of its cheek. The third is immaculate. She twists it away from its stalk.

"Use this one."

I don't argue. I don't put forward logic, that we should use the blemished tomatoes first and save the perfect one for tomorrow. I take the third tomato from her and slice it evenly, making sure all traces of stalk, where chemicals could linger, are cut away. It is years since we bought organic fruit, with their scars and imperfections.

She turns her attention to the cucumber, washing it under a gushing tap before handing it to me, with a frown.

"Feel this. Go on, feel it."

She grabs my index finger and presses it along the length of the cucumber.

"Is that normal? The ridge feels too rough."

"It's fine,"—my usual refrain. "Lebanese cucumbers often have that."

I cut off a slice and put it on my tongue.

"Tastes good."

I continue slicing before she objects. I grab the new pack of cheese, fold back the plastic and slice the crumbly Cheddar. She is hovering.

"Wait," she says, taking the cheese and removing the plastic entirely. "Just in case."

She knows I'm careful, but not perfect. My vision is no longer 20/20. My sense of smell is poor. Her senses are adrenalin-fuelled super-powers: the fight-or-flight smell of a dog, the keen eyes of a hawk, the fussy tastes of a cat.

I carry our plates out to the patio, bringing the vinaigrette I made two days ago in a small jug. As I pour some on my salad, I detect a faint whiff of vinegar. Stirring it again, to mix the oil and lemon juice, I push it to her side of the table. The kookaburras screech with laughter.

She takes the dressing and spoons it liberally on the tomatoes. This is the first time she has touched it. I settle down to eat. Today is a good day.

Suddenly she is spitting, clawing at her tongue. I am on my feet.

"What's the matter?"

"A lemon pip. I'm OK now. Don't worry. We can't all be perfect."

I'm Hanging On
by Chaya Backman

I'm hanging on. Everyone else is swimming. But me? I don't know how. I don't know how to swim so instead I'm hanging on to the side of the pool for dear life. I'm watching everyone else float and tread and do all other kinds of things I'll never be able to do. I'm too busy trying to hang on. I'm too busy trying to gather whatever strength there might be left in me. But then I fall. I fall and I start going down. I start leaving, leaving everyone else, leaving the pool, I even start leaving myself. And then I have a choice. I can either let myself keep falling until eventually I drown. Until eventually I won't have to struggle anymore, I won't have to feel the pain. Or I can try to get back up. I don't know how, but maybe I can try. Maybe I need to try. They always say you can't go down without a fight. Maybe I need to fight. And so I fight. And I almost get there. I almost reach my hand to the side. I almost grasp it, but it was too slippery. I fall again. This time I'm motivated. I'm motivated because I got so close, I know I can do it. And so I try again. I fight again. I make it. I reach it. I'm finally back holding onto the side. I'm finally back able to breathe. How wonderful it is to breathe again. Except I know it's not going to last. I try to appreciate it while it's here. I try to enjoy where I am, but my hands holding tightly on to the edge are a constant reminder. They are a constant reminder that my struggle is not over, my struggle will never be over. And then before I know it, I fall again. I fall back down and this time I'm too tired. I'm too tired to push myself back up. I can't do it. So someone else has to. Someone else has to come push me back up. It's too hard to do alone. She pushes me back up. But then I'm back in the same place again. Breathing but waiting for the moment when I will no longer be. It's so hard to focus on the present when the future seems impossible. And then the future becomes the present. Now what? I'm back down again. Wouldn't it be easier to just let myself fall? It would stop my pain and I wouldn't have to bother others to keep picking me up. I don't want to come back up. I don't even think it's possible anymore. Not for me. But she's there again. She's there forcing me to keep trying. She isn't letting me give up. So together, we come back up. And together, we hold onto the wall. And who knows, one day I might let myself swim.

Storage Facility
by Chelsey Clammer

There. In the heart. Something is stored. I want to call it love. But as it sits, dust not quite collecting because of the muscle's beat, its thrust, that rush of red that stays in me, continues, moving, that will escape only when I open it up to the world but even then will still be re-contained because skin still heals in spite of my mistakes, the pulse of cellular levels keep everything—even dusty memories—inside me from settling on a something stored in my heart that might be or beat or feel like what I want to call love but really don't know. Its movement.

Inside me.

Something.

Love-like. I'm naming it as curiosity and contribute its attributes to the reasons why this brain of mine continues to thrive. Stays alive. It wonders about the whys of the past, decides on the whats of now, and prepares—no, ponders—on the hows of my future tense and what sentence structure I will find for them. Their stories to be stored. Loved.

My grammar is an educated guess, and my body, its memory, mirrors that.

I thought I was going to write about love. As in joy (I write this on Christmas) as in loneliness (I write this on Christmas). And my heart's character trait of confusion (I'm an atheist who's far away from family on Christmas and am trying to figure out why and what and how, or even better, why or perhaps if I store something inside me, such as love). Everything feels so wrapped up in everything.

The present I present to you.

Present tense.

Here's a present, intense in my body, its thrum of existence pulsing through the rushing highways of veins, getting a bit congested in the heart of the matter that stores so many curiosities. Like family. I'll call them feelings. They spread through me, wondrously, creating love, creating lonely, creating life and joy, perplexities and bad decisions, and once, many times, how I used to open myself up to the world because of them. This could sound lovely. It wasn't. X-ACTO, you see. Exactly. Not pretty. But now my body is whole again in spite of my mistakes, and under the scars of life flows a confusion called love, and I sit here on Christmas morning, wondering what's inside, gathering.

Working Lunch
by Christie Wilson

Catherine prefers the humour of the one closest to her. It isn't sticky with puns, or worse, slick with innuendo. It is flat, consistent. She feels connected to him, as if the red table tops resting in front of them both here at this Hardee's, with a truck stop out the window and an entire afternoon ahead, as if the table tops were one continuous plain on which they could find each other, share a cigarette, gaze out at the blinding sun. But, in fact, there is greasy air pushing at the space between them. There's a tiled aisle, occasionally traversed by dirty families and even dirtier truckers between them. There's an entire class system between his dusty boots and her silk shirt.

There are four of them, one of her. He is not the largest, though it is evident that he is the smartest. She puts a fry to her mouth, the square edges of manufactured food always a pleasure when she is on these trips. Never allowing herself to consider such a meal at home makes them all the more coveted. She knows he can't watch her eat from his angle, at least he can't without an obvious shift in his position, but this doesn't stop her from performing for him, small bites, purposeful and direct, not hesitant or shy.

When she has had her fill and put her finger on the edge of the dirty windowsill to study it for a moment before wiping it on the sticky wrapper, she rises and he does the same. He takes her tray from her and stacks it on his own, putting his hand out, palm up to catch a falling napkin, floating, having taken flight to find buoyancy, a cross current, an unlikely shifting of air, making a short journey possible in all this mundane.

Outside she can see him back at the table, looks long enough to focus on the dust cake cuff of his jeans, looks long enough to wish she hadn't seen him at all before turning back to the car and heading west.

Playing the House
by Patricia Behrens

In the casino
of glass high above

the city lights of Salzburg
silk clothes over

butterfly shoulders
legs slim as racehorses

drunk on aperitifs
and the soft sweep

of the shoe
in chemin de fer

the click of the ball
in roulette

we bet the green zero
and won

sped down the mountain
in fog that hid the precipice

laughed at the odds
and squandered our winnings

still dangerously unacquainted
with loss.

A Body of Lies
by Gregory Stapp

I'm rich as a bank of loans,
my money stacks high and green
as a forest drenched in rain,
a slope of low mountain in the mist.

Famous as a marauding saint,
my arms swing out wide and bracing
as an incomplete circle of petrospheres,
a horseshoe of stars cupping the moon.

I am strong as a Taurean bull.
Watch the way I pull at the weight,
how my eyes alight with the strain,
how my shoulders quake like engines.

My heirs will rule the earth like suns.
Watch as they grow tall and searing,
how their feet leave sooted prints,
how their arms sway like a burning bush.

My heart will beat a thousand rhythms
for every tap of your finger on the table.
I stampede horses through your living room
until the sun has steeped your tea.

San Simeon Roundup
by Brenda Yates

Men on horseback whistle. Dogs who understand these commands, run, chase and cut off strays,
gathering the herd together, tightening the moving river as it thunders uphill to another, greener
pasture. Who knew there could be such peace watching man and dog at work.

Volume
by Chad W. Lutz

You are not your past.
You are not your present.
You are not your future.
Water holds no shape,
Nor does a bolt of lightning,
Other than itself,
And not for long.
Neither do you.

Dusk West
by Trevor O'Sullivan

In Kathmandu
by Bruce Louis Dodson

rain falls like Shiva's tears
great darkened clouds
come roiling onto jagged peaks
above the valley
thunder echoes above
warm deluge
warm rain
as Lightning scatters monkeys
lightning scatters monkeys
who take shelter in the eves above an ancient temple
as umbrellas blossom in the marketplace below.
monsoon.

Monsoon.

Watering Down the Price of Oil
by Kari Gunter-Seymour

Petrichor
by Eric Berge

Sky and I smelled dark
that early morning, walking
to the car, and he said the earth
smells so good, why so good?

The rain, I said, the rain over
night cleaned the air and now
actinomycetes are releasing
geosmin from the earth and we smell

it. Just for us? He jumped on a fake
stone in the landscaper's arroyo.
No, I said, just because. It's science.
But we smell it, he said, just us.

After
by Noreen Lace

I woke with blood on my hands
cleaned them on the clouds
it rained red drops into the oceans,
the water turned red, the sky
turned red, and the earth
turned red, I turned to you,
and you were gone,
curved into the grave of the world.

Lonely Sound
by Honor Clement-Hayes

It rained for days.
I sat out on the wet porch;
Wet rattan, wet canvas, wet timber;
And watched the mist moving across the sound.
When you'd been gone four—five—days
I began to think the rain would never stop.
Food ran out. Fuel ran out. Spores settled in my lungs.
And you still weren't back from the store.
I sat there, staring out over Lonely Sound,
Picking apart the rotting rattan.
Waiting, but not expecting.
Just me and the weather.

When Harley was ten, he told Mom about the angels
perched like fallen stars
on the windowsill, or maybe the hill beyond,
he wasn't quite sure. He said if he kept
one eye closed, his thumb hid their light.
Mom said he needed glasses.

When he was twelve, he got the glasses
and stared for hours at those angels
still hovering like memories of light,
like remembered fire, stars
he couldn't guess how he'd kept
even a thumb's-breadth away. The hill beyond

now stood solid as an eye-chart, and beyond
that the horizon, the angels … The glasses
put a stop to their dance. Harley kept
one eye dancing up and down the thumb. The angels
stood fast, frozen stars,
the lenses shaping their light

as a telescope shapes and gathers light
that might have gone further, gone beyond
what we know about stars,
what a pair of glasses can hold—Dancing angels
that in childhood can be kept

like a found dollar is kept
secretly, or how bugs with tails of light
can fill jars with dreams, with angels
that would always remain beyond
Mom's vision; she'd always worn glasses.
Harley suspected she'd never seen stars

the way he'd seen stars
dancing for his pleasure, kept
at thumb's-length by eyes free of glasses,
eyes that never demanded light
stand still, conform, not go beyond
the sky, not reveal angels …

He kept his thumb high, dropped the glasses
to the desk, and smiled as stars and lights
spread beyond disappointment in a grand finale of angels.

Harley's Angels (a Sestina)
by Chris Tannlund

Bloom
by Francesca Grazioli

And there were stars
by Jude Goodwin

If I write it down in the book
we'll be sitting at Arriva's forever
ordering bottle after bottle
of chardonnay while the plump
restaurant owner flirts with you
and I flirt with you and the napkins
and the crystal and the wide platters
full of fat pasta flirt. We'll never leave
the party, bumping into each other
like balloons all down the alleyways.
I'll write "and then we kissed"
and we'll kiss again, mad with celebration
and then I can go back
to the first pages and see you
cheek in hand, smiling at me
and I'll reread that part wondering
how it could be written
there might be flowers
opening in a vase or sparrows
hopping around on the sidewalk
or perhaps I've forgotten
the accordion player
and how he paused by our table
to play something Italian
and romantic.
I'll write "and there were stars"
because there were
and when I get to that part
I'll tape the pages
at their corners so the end
will always lead back
to the beginning.

Waimanalo Bay
by Faisal Warsani

A Lesson in Light
by Alexis Henderson

The business of the night wasn't his to keep. It was never the shadows he was after. He liked the light, warm spots in the darkness like the bright cut of a bedroom window or the long lick of a flickering flame touched to the tip of a cigarette, lit. He first saw the girl on her walk home from work, a diadem perched atop her head like a harvest moon hollowed out in the middle.

He liked the light in her.

And took it.

A Far Tortuga Tale
by Patti White

That was the summer of the shark,
when seas flattened into warm celery
soup, a creamy broth like zinc ointment
to put on a desperate sunburn. Oatmeal
fish trailed the boat, flaking like knee—
caps broken by hammers. He had malaria,

shook and shivered all night, bug malaria
poisoning his blood as mosquito sharks
swarmed the mangroves, ate up our knees,
and we scraped skin like teeth on celery,
rasped and ratcheted our nails. Oatmeal
clouds above clotted the way stale ointment

hardens in the tube. We offered him liniment
for his bones, his femur shattering in malarial
spasms, we slathered him with cold oatmeal.
Nothing eased his pain. And the blue sharks
hovered like angels as the sky turned celery
at the horizon and a storm began to keen.

White waves tested the boat, cracked the keel
against the reef, and we boiled tar for ointment
to seal the leaks. We fed that night on celery
sticks, drank quinine water to keep the malaria
at bay. We watched black rays gather in a shark—
frenzy of longing, tossed them raw oatmeal,

a book of poems, the last of the tar, a cornmeal
muffin, a watch cap. Nothing would do but a knee—
bent prayer to the gods of the last damn shark,
the kind you say as the medic takes the ointment
away and lets you burn. It's a rare fever, malaria —
a death-fire in the brain. You long for cool celery

the color of peace, wrap your thoughts in celery
linen, ask for salt. His skin poached like oatmeal
boiling. He died a week later, from pure malaria
or the yellow infection in his bug-ravaged knees.
Maybe in delirium he swallowed the ointment,
and poisoned himself like a rotting bull shark.

I think of the celery sea, the wind behind our knees,
an oatmeal sky so thick it spreads like ointment,
the way malaria strikes like an archangel shark.

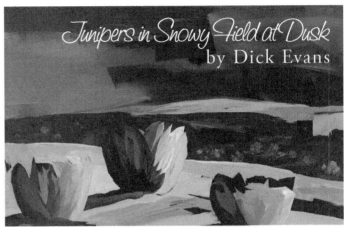

Junipers in Snowy Field at Dusk
by Dick Evans

Eluding the Edge
by Dick Evans

Wheat
by Bee Williamson

Wategoes
by Bee Williamson

The Crying Room
by Christina Dalcher

Do this. Find a church. Or a temple. A mosque, maybe. Tucked in a corner, perhaps all the way back on the right, will be a place full of mothers and babies. The crying room, they call it, a cramped closet to isolate the little ones, calm them before they kick up a fuss and disturb services. Enter this place and see the children, cranky from colic or hunger, but peaceful in their innocence. Look into their eyes. Tell me if you find such a creature as a Christian child, a Jewish child, a Muslim child; do not lie. Listen to the music of walled-in wails and sequestered screams. Stay in this space, away from all gods, until you understand the only absolute quiet you will ever know is here. In the crying room.

Maybe, if I'm lucky enough,
once my body expires and my radioactive brain
keeps throbbing, God will finally invite me over
and we'll take shots at his kitchen table.

It'll get so late it'll get early, and I'll be
honest with God for once and tell him
I miss the sunrise, the way a child might
miss something it doesn't yet understand how to love.

Then, because he feels bad, and because he's a lightweight,
God will be honest with me for the first time.
He'll tell me he knows and he's sorry, the way
a child might be sorry when something isn't its fault,
and all its fault all at once, and so overwhelming.

We'll pound back another two, and God will ask me
if it was really all that bad, and I won't be sure the way
a child is never sure and becomes an adult. Then I'll
ask God if he knew all along, about all of this,
and he'll get shy and say he doesn't remember knowing
much of anything.

I'll say me neither, because we're so alike,
put my head between my knees because we're so alike.

I'll start throwing up, and god,
God will be really sorry, for the first time, for me.
He'll carry me upstairs and leave the cleaning up
for another time, like he usually does.

At the Kitchen Table with God
by Donna-Claire

*Cross
Your
Heart*
by
Francesca
Grazioli

Safe
by Brenda Yates

Shut in darkness, you have done with this:
the all too soon, the slow, the fast, the numb
procession of years. You have done with
spring, with its fire burning brightly like some
spiteful god who brings no peace. You are done
as well with every fall, turning, and returning,
to toll again in the shocked bell of your body.
And also, bereft of politics, patriotism and the
polysyllabic rhetoric of fear, you are done with
conflict. And done now with any promises, or
words, broken and floating skyward. And free
from all those mouthless dead whose dreams
still wander like orphans. No need for warnings, abstractions, or even euphemisms for
die. No need to remember. Done too are once
more, somewhere, anywhere, or those certain-
ties of always, never, or maybe someday. Yes,
you are finally done with hurting or wanting
or believing and with wishes for untime,
unspring, unkill, unwar.

Lapsed
by Claire Scott

I am a lapsed disciple no longer chanting
strands of Hail Mary's or genuflecting
to a dangling Jesus who looks exhausted
no longer transported by *Amazing Grace*

sung by an off-key choir my faith expired
like a carton of milk best by 06/01/14
a soulful atheist mumbling meagre
prayers to no one in particular

angry at a fictive God with His fabricated
afterlife angry at stained glass saints
who have never once made
an appearance in my life

angry that I am ending up with
less than what I began without

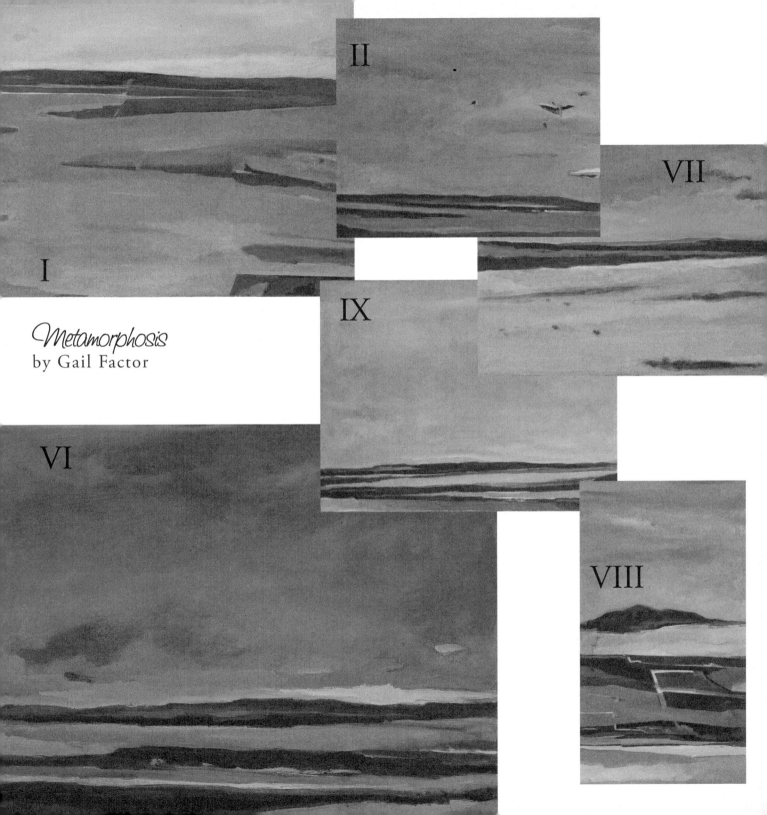

I

II

VII

IX

VI

VIII

Metamorphosis
by Gail Factor

My Girl
by Nina Bennett

San Antonio, a Mexican restaurant
on the Riverwalk. We nibble tortilla
chips, guacamole, sip weak margaritas
in glasses the size of a goldfish bowl,
watch mariachi musicians work
the room. My brother pulls out some bills,
requests *La Bikina*.

The violin player shakes his head, shrugs
his shoulders, offers Freddy Fender
or Johnny Cash. Two women at the table
next to us get the Temptations. We order shots
of smoky tequila, espresso and sopapillas,
listen to tipsy tourists sing about sunshine
on a cloudy day.

Thank You for a Lovely Time
by Karen Boissonneault-Gauthier

Dear Mars
by Monica Rico

Of course I will bring flowers but you're not concerned with those. When I think about it atmosphere is pretty cool well not cool exactly but crucial because without it I will die but with it I will die too but these are not the same.

See you in the morning Mars, where it is too easy to be embarrassed by our parents or the big bang. You know too much, you've seen everything so forgive the robins their migration to Mexico each year. I will winter with you.

I think you may enjoy a bowl of rain, black beans, my mother's rice, tortillas from *La Estrella del Norte*, and certainly a cup of coffee with cream to keep our hands warm while we gossip about the moon, our feet in buckets of dust, whistling in this vacuum.

Do I need more socks? I think now how my body has never belonged to me all these electrons
and protons repelling against each other; I am never touching anything at all, I am so lonesome
until I think of you Mars! Behind the woven trees glimmering red, and I wonder if I am upside down in admiration with your flash and blink. My grandmother was right. We are all, only visiting.

Untitled
by Robin Dunn

though the hot tread mighty over my wilderness
luxurious

though the riot rube colds me his chops
and I hop right oer the night to spy
his heart

though the 'o' key sticks
and the rage of my identity insists
that no words are enough
tell me
who marks the cards
and who cooks the books
who works the yard
for my holy spite
who levitates the heartache of a generation
on their i-pod

who hurts me for fun
with your wilful bone

it's you,
America
with your riches
and your glee
your two dollar pancakes

though I am tired
in the longest midnight of my dreams
where no one is standing
and no one is hurting
and there are no birds
nor words

still I spy the reason for the melody
issuing from the trees

umbrage cooks slow
for the world to know
who's being let out

endure the note
come whole to me
under the tragedy of midnight
etched in bone
under your eyes
my fleeting darling

cut me whole out of the night
for my violence and my imbuement to the sword of the agony avenue,
my own

hear the light
over the note
and reach in to throw it up
into the air

Galaxy Palms
by Faisal Warsani

**Film critic
by Lee Nash**

True, it was an excuse to speak to him. Come on, even the ghosts in this town are dead, and I go to movies alone. So I ask the gorgeous French film director why in the next shot there was no blood on the refugee's tee-shirt after she'd eaten the live chicken's heart and spattered the white cotton with blobs of red gore. He looks at me with those zealous Leo eyes but I don't spill my Pineau or drop my blini, says he kept the faux accord though he'd watched it forty times before some keen-eyed aficionado spotted it. Says it was a better take, so he left alone; incorporated error for art's sake. The master. What's more, he knows this criticism means: so glad I made your avant-première, I'll lambaste your brilliant Cannes-acclaimed film because this isn't some well-rehearsed moment when I deliver some über-cute line some slick-ass scriptwriter thought up, and even if I had that line, Chéri, I'd need directing.

Family Bash by Kerry Wingood

That night there was:
A flesh-pink, fish-shaped salmon mousse,
Glaring at me with a stuffed-olive eye.
Immaculately pressed antimacassars
Preserving embossed, brown velvet chairs.
Biscuits passed around
With a reminder to take only one.
Sugared fruit jellies—
The ones in the box with the greaseproof paper.
A claustrophobic avocado-coloured bathroom
With crocheted toilet roll holders.
Cut crystal glasses and crème de menthe.
Liqueur anyone?
Me leaning on a patchwork pouffe
With unravelling leather stiches.
Tribal art made of copper and animal hides;
A reminder of the country we'd left behind.
The smell of stale nicotine and Irish wool.
And four pink lines
Where my mum slapped my grandpa across the face.

Private Grafitti
by Gleah Powers

Domestic Arts
by Jacquelyn Shah

I
Cut the zucchini and be content
    to cut what cannot bleed
make a line of discs   a little spine
    clothe the spine in oil that won't
anoint   and sear sear sear . . .
    then thread and hang the thing
in vegetable effigy

II
Circle round yourself and be
    content to fill yourself with self
take your cue   in other words
    from men who've circled men
be loyal to yourself   dog-best-
    friend-wise   sit fire-side and smoke
for flames would only make you ash

III
Use the smoke to darken walls
    your own   smear it   all around
drink to smoke and mirrors
    mirror what you see then write it
with a lipstick on your breath-
    fogged glass in cuneiform and rune
in your own room artifact it all

IV
Cut on   cut on . . . happy with the cannot-
    bleed   internally make this kind
of sublimation force a sentence to
    the surface where a pock or two will run
a little   just enough to sully words
    too smooth   take satisfaction as you peel
the skin from carrots   dice and boil them

Conversing
by Joanne Jackson Yelenik

How white a body,
a surprise translucence,
sun shaded skin tattoos your legs white,
the back of your neck, bronze,
a reddish hue bleaches your high forehead,
chisels your cheek bones.
Tones lodge deep in your blue eyes,
specks of autumn fire the well-water depth of the man you are.
My hand, smooth and cold like marble, plays along your white,
my fingers burn your bronze.
Soundless dialogue: me touching you; you colouring at the very thought of it.

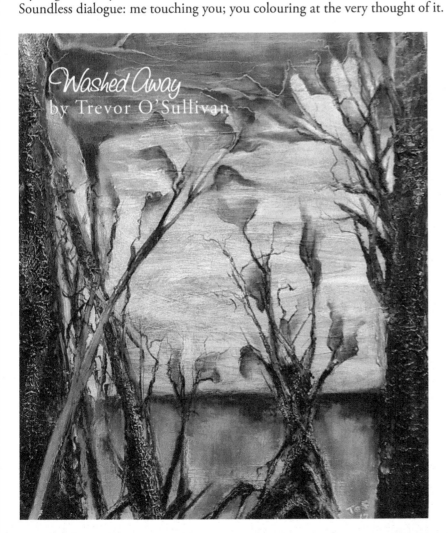

Washed Away
by Trevor O'Sullivan

Death—is Cruellest—
by Hayley Davis

Death—is Cruellest—
When it comes—Before Life—
Upsetting the natural—order.

How odd—
To Know—without Certainty—
To be Certain—without Knowing—
They Lived—
If only—for a Twinkling?

We recognize—
In our Minds—if not fully—in our Hearts—
That Death must come!
A natural—ebb and flow—
Seasons come—
Seasons change—
Time moves—headlong.

But this?
A mother's special sorrow—
To Know—Abstractly—
If only—we were purely—abstract—beings.
What then—
Of the stinging—Pain—of knowing—
There is No One—to blame?

How cruel to hear—
Everything Happens—for a Reason—
What—then—is the Reason?

None—
But—we can rest—
Knowing—

Nothing Is Wasted—
Nothing—is Wasted.

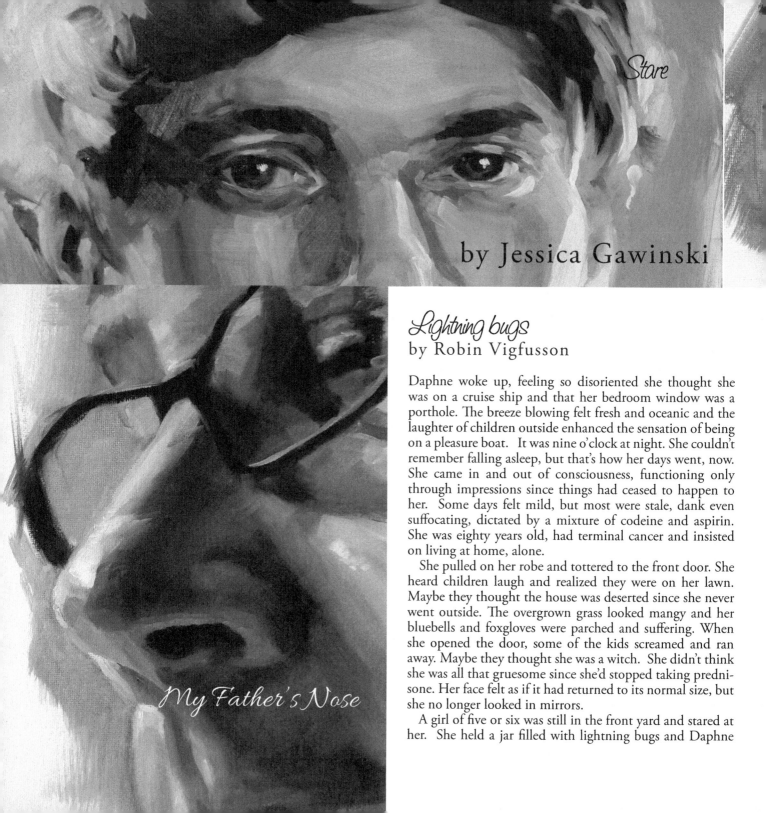

Stare

by Jessica Gawinski

My Father's Nose

Lightning bugs
by Robin Vigfusson

Daphne woke up, feeling so disoriented she thought she was on a cruise ship and that her bedroom window was a porthole. The breeze blowing felt fresh and oceanic and the laughter of children outside enhanced the sensation of being on a pleasure boat. It was nine o'clock at night. She couldn't remember falling asleep, but that's how her days went, now. She came in and out of consciousness, functioning only through impressions since things had ceased to happen to her. Some days felt mild, but most were stale, dank even suffocating, dictated by a mixture of codeine and aspirin. She was eighty years old, had terminal cancer and insisted on living at home, alone.

She pulled on her robe and tottered to the front door. She heard children laugh and realized they were on her lawn. Maybe they thought the house was deserted since she never went outside. The overgrown grass looked mangy and her bluebells and foxgloves were parched and suffering. When she opened the door, some of the kids screamed and ran away. Maybe they thought she was a witch. She didn't think she was all that gruesome since she'd stopped taking prednisone. Her face felt as if it had returned to its normal size, but she no longer looked in mirrors.

A girl of five or six was still in the front yard and stared at her. She held a jar filled with lightning bugs and Daphne

Gaze

At The Spice-Wallah
by Kim Peter Kovac

Cardamom, chili pepper, cinnamon, cloves, coriander, cumin, fennel, fenugreek, garlic, ginger, mango powder, masalas, mint, mustard, saffron, sesame, star anise, tamarind, turmeric.

Long pepper, black salt, holy basil.

was surprised. She'd assumed collecting them was a long-dead tradition like hopscotch or jump rope. Any pastime that didn't involve technology seemed obsolete, now.

"Did we wake you up?" the girl asked. In the dark, Daphne could hardly see without her glasses. The child moved amorphously like a specimen under a lens.

"Isn't it late for you to be out?" Daphne asked.

"I don't have school. It's the summer. Are you sick?"

"Yes, dear, but it's not contagious. Where do you live?"

The child pointed across the street which shimmered like a lake. She lived in a pink colonial that had been converted into a three family house. People were sitting on the front stoop, talking, smoking and drinking in the dark.

"We were collecting lightning bugs," the girl held up her jar and Daphne saw them whirling like embers, recalling how wonderful they'd seemed to her when she was a child though she no longer remembered why. She'd lived through a lot and the years had numbed her. Each loss had been an excision and now her adrenalin worked like a blocking agent, preparing her for the next one.

"I used to do that," she told the girl. "A long time ago. I think your parents want you to go home."

A man stood, waving his arm.

"Are you going to go to sleep, now?" the girl asked.

"I'm going to try."

"Here," the girl gave her the jar filled with lightning bugs. "This will help. It's magic."

Daphne smiled, touched by the child's kind charm.

"It is," the girl insisted.

"Well, thank you very much," Daphne told her.

"Good night," The child waved shyly and ran across the street.

Daphne went back to her bedroom and put the jar on her night table. She stared, transfixed, at the luminous insects until they looked like souls in their purest forms. That was how they'd struck her when she'd first seen them. At that time, all events had been portentous and everything, extraordinary. Daphne suddenly felt unreasonably happy and recognized this mysterious bliss as her natural state of mind when she'd been small. It was an innocent's unquestioning pleasure in being alive.

It seemed she'd spent her whole life trying to retrieve that mindset, only able to reclaim it for short spans of time; it was always dependent on external reasons like falling in love or having a baby.

She didn't know how long this supple, flowing joy would last, but couldn't bear losing it, again.

She opened the drawer of her night table, and took out the bottle of Nembutal her daughter had given her 'in case, things get intolerable'. She swallowed it all, then unscrewed the lid of the jar. She freed the lightning bugs and lay down in bed, watching them. They swirled like snow, pulling the night outside into her room and wrapping her in a deep blue web of glacial air. She closed her eyes and tightly held onto her blanket while they guided her out of this world.

Figure
by Jessica Gawinski

A Nurse Said
by Wendy Scott

Cancer can be beautiful

Nodes touch like outstretched
petals, cluster like grapes ripening
down her throat, blossom
like glowing fungi, grooved.

Pulsing. Tidal. Capillary tendrils
wash cells, consistent as sea water
across a coral reef.

Not that it looks like that under my skin.
Every inside I ever saw one large mess.

I remember Cousteau, ink cloud
released by an octopus, dark purple,
how it settled, how it spread.

Oncology Waiting Room
by Victoria Melekian

Almost to the door, the FedEx guy
walks back toward the receptionist,

plucks a flower from the vase on her desk.
He turns to the woman slumped

in a chair next to mine, kneels to tuck
the yellow daisy into her head scarf.

Faster than she can smile or say thank you,
he's roaring down the street in his truck,

two taps on the horn, leaving me
considering the possibility of angels.

At the Children's Hospital Wing
by Alan Catlin

Harried, she looks
in hospital gift
shop for last minute

token gift,
child's toy:
something,
anything.

Stuffed animal,
maybe, what else?

It's a little kid,
they don't care, right?

Buys a small
brown bear,
scrolls text

messages for
what room
to visit.

Standing in corridor
outside room,
checking the message
for the number.

Sees she has
the correct one.

How could this
be? There's no
one here.

Your One Phone Call
by Alan Catlin

In rehab hospital
recovering from
complications,
ongoing effects
of rheumatoid arthritis

Change in medication
induces dramatic change
in personality from
docile-loving parent
to crazed schizophrenic

yelling on the ward
pay phone that she is
being held in captive
in a neighbourhood
post office
two hundred miles
from where she is
now

Demands immediate
extraction, from
someone she knows
doesn't drive

demands help,
the kind of aid
no one can provide

Bird on Snow
by Bee Williamson

It Was Her Time—
by Hayley Davis

It was her time—
Coffee and a Brownie—
Her last request—granted!—

98 years—6 months—7 days—
She lived!

A faulty heart valve—
Not a faulty Heart!
Her Heart—
Strong—
Determined—
Unwavering—in its Desires.

She did not—Give Up—
In the End—
The Oxygen Tank—a Zeppelin—
Followed her everywhere—
A sign—of the Death to come—
The Death—of Independence.
She refused to Live—like That!

One month before—Hospital
Her Independence—replaced—
300 square feet—and—
That Thing—
Tethered—like—a gloomy Balloon!

She had wanted—106 years—
But—Eight Years—
Even Eight Weeks—
Was too long!
She was determined—
Not—to Live—like That!

The Link is Lost—
The Past has passed—away
Our Family History—
Cut off at the hilt!
The Matriarch—of Our Clan—
Whose stories—now—will be told—
Only through the Voice—of Others
Because She—
Refused—to Live—like That!

Thank You
by Whitney C. Hansen

Catholicism left a sour taste in my mouth the moment my middle school religious leader told me we loved gay people "anyway." I sucked its venom from my pumping veins and spat it out until I could almost forget the way this religion made me hate myself—not at the age of seven when I realized that I was bisexual, but at fourteen when I realized that Catholics would only love me "anyway." Despite my objections, my parents made me go through with my Catholic confirmation. When I was asked to choose a confirmation saint that represented my spiritual journey, I chose a saint named Pelagia. One website said she was once a prostitute and the patron saint of actors; another website said she never existed. I wore an all-black suit to the confirmation ceremony, sticking out like a mud stain against all the other girls dressed in pastel floral dresses. Those girls would always have a scapegoat, an explanation. They would always have something they thought they could turn to in times of need. That day, standing as a dark splotch against a garden of smiling teenage girls, I understood that they would have spiritual comforts that I would have to grow up without. How could I love a God who only loved me "anyway?"

Over twenty-four percent of the Omaha population is Catholic (the national average is just over nineteen percent), so it's no surprise that one of my best friends in college ended up being Catholic: Tessa. We used to work at a coffeehouse together where we would spend mornings discussing Latin American politics and her internship at a Catholic fertility clinic. She failed her final internship exam twice over her answer to the essay question. When asked what she would say to a patient who was considering an abortion, she said, "I would inform her about all of her options." This was not the right answer.

One night, Tessa and I had begun to gossip about our former co-workers. I laughed and blurted, "Lily thinks she has a demon following her."

"She may not be wrong," Tessa murmured. I had almost forgotten about Catholicism's ties to demons and exorcisms. I started to pass this off as a simple musing of a Catholic follower, until Tessa sighed. The rush of her exhale carried the phrase "I can see the spirit world."

I felt the heavy hand of pure adrenaline push down on my sternum. I could almost feel the bones in my chest start to give and crack. I couldn't breathe. Without even thinking about it, I looked Tessa in the eyes and said, "I believe you … but what do you mean, exactly? What do you see?"

Tessa continued to tell me about the Taco Bell worker's eyes that had turned black, the auras she saw around people on the street, and the weight she felt around Lily. Tessa pushed herself up from the couch and left the room. I looked around the living room and wondered what she saw in the shadows of her bookcase and the ridges of her ceiling. She came back carrying a tattered cardboard box, which she sat on the floor near my feet. She began to pull out books, rosaries, and candles, setting each item out on the floor. She handed me rosary after rosary and asked which one was "right." I didn't know what she meant until one of the rosaries—a cheap, plastic, glow-in-the-dark string of uneven beads—seemed to meld to the shape of my hand. I got the overwhelming sense that it belonged to me, that this particular string of glow-in-the-dark beads was made to be mine. My eyes snapped to hers, fuelled with disbelief. She smiled and said, "That's the one. Keep it." In that moment, I saw the lines of our spiritual divide start to blur until they were almost imperceptible.

She went back to rummaging through her box. I felt like a child who had been dragged along for "back to school" shopping. I didn't know what half this stuff was for. I didn't know why *that* item fit me, but *this* one didn't. All I knew was that Tessa was helping me in the way she best knew how. One rosary and one scribbled prayer card later, I was ready to leave the safety of Tessa's apartment. Before I left, Tessa gave me one last piece of armour—a small bottle of holy water. I started to twist it in my hands, wrapping the string of the rosary around it, when Tessa said "I know that you don't believe in this, Whitney. I know you don't. But this is what I know. This is how I know how to fight this."

I smiled at her and said, "I know. Thank you."

Bethany
by Dell Kaniper

From ten feet away, she was still quite beautiful. Closer and you'd see the lines near her mouth and eyes, but at just over three yards she could still pass for thirty-five. With each day, she understood this truth better. She studied light and shadow. She avoided the sun and drank in dark bars. She barely ate. She ran.

As she did, on mile six, or, more often as it was now, over a glass of vodka, she imagined the things she wanted, beginning with those society deemed attainable, like winning the lottery or aging with grace. But after her second drink, her third and fourth, she pictured what she truly desired. Herself, age seventeen. When she'd drank whiskey and kamikazes. When she'd smoked cigarettes. When she wasn't worried about her hair or her family, her friends or boyfriends. She'd understood, even then, that everything, but her memories, was fleeting. So, instead, she'd been concerned with jumping naked from rocks and proving she could drive drunk and being nearly-but-not pregnant a hundred times. She'd cared that, for a brief moment, she and the world agreed to believe in her invincibility. It was the last time she'd felt anything was possible. It was the last time she'd been impulsive, and it was so long ago.

There had been dares then—a cliff and a dare, a piece of clothing, a body part, a dare—and now there were only truths, which came after vodka five. Truth: the town she was from had shrunk since she'd left it. The mountains had become hills, the highways: roads, the rivers: creeks, and, somehow, she was also smaller. Truth: she wished she could go home, but she couldn't afford a train ticket any more than she could afford the drink in front of her or the rent she would soon have to pay. Truth: she'd been fired that afternoon, just as she'd been fired too many times before. The job had been like every other one she'd had—a desk and three fabric-covered walls—and was only important because it would be her last attempt at the success that everyone, including her, believed they were destined to find. Truth: she would stay unemployed this time, intentionally giving the universe what she could finally admit it wanted from her. Apathy turned to acceptance or perhaps the other way around. She glanced at her drink. In the right light, vodka carried an iridescence that suggested snow, suggested clean, but in the bars she chose the alcohol looked as brown as the wood beneath it. Truth: Its only glow came from the red of the drapes.

Similar to every previous staff that had served her, the employees at the current bar were rendered as futile by their indifference as the mirror behind them was by the shadows of cigarettes. In the foggy reflections of both, she could still be the girl she once was and the girl she might have been. She could be beautiful, ageless. She could be protected by money or even love. In this temporary home where the air was sweet with wine, she could be all people and no people. Hiding, as she'd done many times before, beneath the veil of anonymity. Every day she could have a new story. Every day, pristine. Every day, free.

Except, eventually even the most disinterested barkeep would recognize the uniformity of her days, and after that it wouldn't matter if she changed bars every hour. Soon her cash would disappear and her credit would be declined and the stories of lost cards and forgotten wallets would be recognized as the lies they were. Then she couldn't reinvent herself. Not that it mattered. She knew she wouldn't try. Everything would be lost—her locks changed, her possessions on the street—until her inconspicuousness deepened to invisibility, and she forgot her real history, even of the old days, even of the drunk racing and sex, because no one, especially her, wanted to believe the girl she'd been—just like everyone—could become the woman on the corner with the bags and the smell.

Except.

Just past the garnishes, the tip jar was full and within reach. The bartender was in the bathroom and the other patrons wouldn't see her. Here, she was a ghost. She didn't have a hair colour or a name. She thought of the person she would become as time passed between the act of her theft and its retelling. She would be larger in her myth and just crazed enough to justify her success. And then? Would she split once more and become three women? Seventeen, forty-one, and today. Wild again. Impetuous and feral. She stared at the mottled green and white of the wadded money and felt the purifying wind one finds at a cliff's edge.

Tea Country
by Clare Flynn

Fast flowing streams and waterfalls dissected dark rocks rising above the roadside. Early morning sunlight dappled through trees, lighting up the vivid-blue morning glory flowers that draped over undergrowth like floral bedspreads. Whooping sounds and coloratura arpeggios filled the air—birdsong unfamiliar to my English ear. The scent of cardamom wafted through the window as we drove past spice plantations. Blue-grey peaks of distant hills pierced the mist, like desert islands in a pale sea. We had entered tea country.

Birthday
by Damien Titchener

Dust.

I read once that dust was the human by-product of dead skin cells. An amusing thought since all I can see is the dust in the sunlight. Is that the last of humanity floating in the air? Another cheerful thought for the day. It is hot. The Australian sun has never failed to deliver in that regard. It's worse now the seasons have changed. More extreme.

I guess that happens when the world turns to shit.

Wasteland,
ruled by gangs,
a hellhole.
On a morning like this, staring out the kitchen window, watching the dust dance in the sunlight, I imagine things aren't so bad. It's just a normal day. I could do some gardening, catch some food. Rabbits, perhaps. Once a pest, now a lifeline. Only job I have is survival.

Strange to think that when you strip all the bullshit out of life and take it back to basics, life seems more relaxing. There's a sense of calm that was never there in modern society. Now all I need to worry about is my next meal, other people, a few escaped animals from the Zoo and the gangs.

It's better on your own.

No one to worry about but yourself,

no need to feel emotional pain when someone is taken away from you.

Bullshit.

I miss her.

I live in an old farmhouse with lots of land surrounding it, right in the middle of suburbia. Having never been re-zoned, it is surrounded by modern homes and stands as a beacon. Thankfully, no one comes out this far to the southeast. Most huddle on the coastline, or near the city. Plenty of fish now they aren't being ripped from the ocean to feed billions. It used to be farmland here, so the soil is still good for growing vegetables and fruit. Good soil, more valuable than gold.

It started with disease and ended when the bombs dropped. I never thought they would drop here. Most of the tension was in the north. But I guess when you go for broke you can't escape it.

Humans are creatures of habit. So I have a routine. I follow it—have to. I'd go nuts otherwise. Gardening, scavenging, checking traps, and then trying and do something fun. Oh, and avoid other people.

Today is a special day. It's my 38th birthday. I have a calendar that's current till 2019. After that I'll have to keep track manually. Or stop ageing. 40 seems like a good place to stop.

A shopping centre lies just over the hill, I don't go there much, I avoid it. Gangs. They call themselves Gaters—an abbreviation of the original name for the place. Best to stay away, otherwise they might come looking for this place. It's not even my original home, just a place I found to hide while running. I almost got shot.

Thank God for shitty aim.

The dog barks, his ears twitch, his head holds still, then scans the horizon. I call

him Dog. Not original I know, but I was always crap with names. Keep it simple. No one is going to complain.

I approach the window—keeping still—not wanting to move the curtains or show any sign that this place is inhabited.

Dog's not on a leash. He'll bolt if things turn to shit fast. So I'm waiting. A few minutes later, a push bike goes past. A male with a back pack. No visible weapons. Not that I can see from this distance. He stops and looks up. Dog stares and growls. I haven't killed anyone yet—don't want to—but when you're desperate, anything can happen. I've seen people die.

From disease.

Like she did.

So here we are.
He's down there.
I'm up here with Dog in the middle.

I can't aim for shit, but I have a baseball bat.

Grey Area
by Erin Conway

The drive could have almost cut through clouds. Their darkness hung so low on the horizon that the weight could not be lightened by the errant, orange leaf dancing across his windshield. It was ironic they had raised Holsteins throughout the period of his life when he thought everything was black and white. When his father sold everything but the Ford tractor was the first time he saw a smudge, a gray area, under the SOLD stamp. He thought then, it was only a pause, not an end. "We still had the land," he had said to himself. "I can stay for that. It is not the machinery, nor the livestock, it is the land that matters. We can rent land to neighbours and everything is almost the same. We would still be farmers living on a farm. I won't sell out."

Fifteen years go fast when you allow yourself to ignore your dream. The funeral should have been a gray day with an October sky like this one, but it had been May. There had been sunshine and green, and he had felt peace in the opportunity for his father to rest his feet, his heart, his head, his fears after an almost 100-year-old life that spanned the construction of two barns, the Great Depression, his mother's cancer, the loss of forty acres to his aunts' greed and his way of understanding "progress." He had held the death certificate in his fingers, but the addressee line on the outside of the envelope had smudged, reminding him once again of that gray space. He was sixty-five, and he had stayed in his grandmother's house, stayed nearby, stayed because it was keeping the land whole that mattered, and somehow repainting the red barns every two years still meant a farm, still meant farmer.

As he turned off the highway, the afternoon sun broke through the clouds. The day wanted so desperately to be warm, to be bright. His daughter had taken to requiring him to mention five positives for each realistic, what she called negative, comment. The light caught the underside of his neighbours' cattle lounging in a slowly browning field. He could almost imagine it was still summer, that he was anticipating the meeting with his brothers to discuss the next steps, the gray space that he had waited so long to turn once again into the black and white formality of action, of business, the busi-

ness of farming. The figures he shared at that meeting had seemed so black and white then, the price of corn per bushel, the cost to regain soil fertility, the investment made to custom the planting and harvest. It had been in his hand, shiny like the headlights on the old Ford he planned to replace. Still somehow it was as if he had once again lost his glasses, lines blurred gray. He had been sure and also afraid to be sure.

He made the final turn onto the shaded road as he drove home from the meeting to consult figures one last time. He protected those oaks from the power company. He glanced at the ditch, overgrown with prairie heritage. This wealth was guarded by the still stark, "No Mowing" sign staked in the black dirt before the current grass and leaf cover had even been dreamed of earlier that spring. She was walking ahead of him. He would gain on her because the small, tan ears of her companion would turn to face the blustering wind. The room on the shoulder was narrow. The two figures stood caught on a thin stretch of golden gravel and two invisible walls that rose on either side. It was as if he could feel them closing in, suffocating his breath, blocking sound like the ringing in his ears that had not forgotten his younger days on the combine. In some places there was escape that was no escape, lines where wire fences had been removed between the prairie and the straight, high corn rows. Underfoot or overhead, either growth could erase a path. He could see the overgrown ditch, the old prairie yearning to regain its past. He blinked. He could see the black asphalt oozing and breaking but holding fast in front of him. He blinked. Sun blanched corn silk. He blinked. Sixty-five years old, and he could see a close horizon. He blinked again as it began to rain.

His father and fear, past or future, the land mattered. Winter would come fast, faster every year for him. His hands loosened on the steering wheel as he turned into the driveway, the blood flushed on its return, his fingers now a little less white on the black vinyl. His daughter was coming up the driveway behind him.

Dearth
by Jerusha Rodgers

He revelled in the details. The manicured lawn; the slope of the long drive that took far more space than the gradient needed; the discreetly placed security cameras. He felt like he'd been told a secret for finding them, but they were deliberately conspicuously inconspicuous. His heart dropped and jumped while over-annunciating his name into an intercom with an uncomfortable ahem. The gate opened for him, creaking with reality. This was the necessity of the gate, not to keep out interlopers but to let them in just enough to remind them they didn't belong. Soon he'd go home and feed his friends the scraps of his brush with worthiness.

"We've been expecting you," a disembodied voice crackled through the speaker. The rush of elation and importance merged with the insinuation that he was late. He looked at his watch. He was right on time. He strode with guilt up the gravel drive.

Everything existed in perfect harmony.

Except for him.

Returning
by Melissa K. Downes

Jeremy in the snow
dead as flowers in December,
while the wind makes thin screams scratch
like pine boughs on aluminium.
My brother, snow-angeled
in the backyard, where he's clutched his heart
and fallen   I am past six, Jeremy's going
on eleven.

Jeremy   I said   Jeremy
get up   stop teasing   it's not funny
and he lies there never moving
near the rosebeds buried under
and ice cuts through my jacket
and he never even shivers.
Jeremy   I said   Jeremy   stop it
Mama's waiting   I'll tell Papa.

It's afterschool home-from-bus
and the night's coming early:
Jeremy's body stays lax and limp
while I shake it fiercely
with sharp bones, budding limbs,
this thorn of a sister.
Jeremy in the snow, and I run
screaming toward the back door;

he is calling,
back from the dead like flowers
come through winter,
shaking off the snow mantle
that shrouds his flesh,
and laughing.

Garbage Man
by Marcus Benjamin Ray Bradley

Garbage is defined as a thing
that is no longer wanted or needed
So being referred to as a just a
Garbage Man makes my shoulders sag
Without me they'd just be litterers
dumping outside of their houses
The homes along my route are probably
filled with belongings unblemished
and swanky, devoid of character, and
identical to their boring neighbours'

I'm bewildered by pieces they discard—
fully functioning or intriguing enough
that I can't bear taking some of them
directly to their final resting place
I instead give them a home
extending their useful lives
as additions to my mismatched
houseware, golf clubs, décor
or curio cabinet clutter of
conversation pieces, oddities,
and things wherein I found
beauty that had gone unnoticed
or unappreciated for too long

I look at the landfill and wonder
what treasures are buried there
as I breathe the mouldering bouquet
that I associate with hard work
and I marvel at the magnitude
of what I've had a hand in building
understanding that you just need
to be persistent and keep adding
a little bit to it every day
if you want to do something big

On Whether to Accept Prescription Narcotics
by Robert Lee Kendrick

Now and then, I still stumble
over my birthday, confusing
11 with 28.
1966, I get right.
It's not for lack of practice—
hospital code for food plates and shots,
vital signs measurements, bathroom
trips. Dialling the combination
on the first try earns an ease

like a long needle pulled
from the skin, warmer than CAT scan
iodine dye, latex and honeycomb
breathing tube scent, or EKG purple
hum.
A lily petal, my attention
floats across water. Railroad
spikes in my ribs. One lung pruned.
A hole in the bucket,

dear Liza, dear Liza.
Would this window sunshine
sweeten with oxy? So few
wits in my wallet. Count them again.
Four floors below, a leaf clings
to branch in the wind; a stray cat
crawls towards a manicured bush,
locked on a flicker. Such unbroken
focus, small steps.

Aspasia by Veronica Scharf Garcia

The Boardwalk
by Joshua B Huitz

In the Pictures Sarah Takes of Sarah, She Lies in the Middle of the Train Tracks or Road
by Marie Marandola

In the pictures Sarah took of me,
she stood me tall
against a burnt-orange mural
in a seaside town.
My white dress, embroidered,
earth-toned flowers at the hems.
I am smiling, gazing
into the idling crowds,
looking so wholesome
she might eat cherries
from my forehead.
This is who I am to her:
clean-haired blood sister
in white March sky.

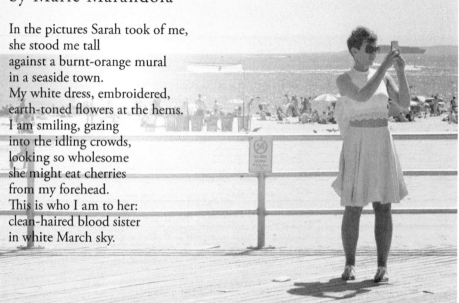

Unsheltered in the San Juan Straits
by Brenda Yates

Leave the leeward side and you will be reminded that here, winter storms are fierce. Wind and such a sea as ever was batters now and then or even often. Though these are summer days, the season of sunny and calm, almost any beach—on islands this far north—still holds its own driftwood forest of drowned trees. Or rather, of once trees: giants downed, washed and stripped of bark, their huge log bulk blasted ashore, strewn like so many flinders.

Will
by Elyse Hauser

I can still remember what he looked like quite well. It would be cold—November, or December, or maybe even January, although I think it was all over and done with by then. I'd open the door of the little modular home I shared with three roommates on the edge of campus and there he was, smiling that funny smile people have when they know what is going to happen next, something that would have looked arrogant if it wasn't so genuine.

Thoughts on Josephine
by Alexis Henderson

I knew her by smell: a stale perfume dried flowers and leaf rot, the lingering traces left behind like a stain on my creased sheets and pillowcases as though she was trying to make my place her own. Sometimes I saw her phantom in the bright cast of sunlight shafting through my bedroom window, or in him when he smiled, her words etched upon his bottom lip in a tongue I couldn't speak.

Elwood Sea
by Bee Williamson

Salt
by Cooper Hepburn

I
wind blows from the west
and brings salt that eats at our hair and our hearts
like old rusted station wagons or boats in backyards
(o shaky tree i am weeping)

II
today i am filled to the brim
i dont wanna hold it inside
i'm not gonna hide it anymore
i keep swerving around it
(lapping waves over and over and over)
writing dense nothing about moisture and salt
but here we go this is what i've meant
fuck it, i'm starting to miss you
today i am home sick

It was the Lilies—
by Hayley Davis

It was the Lilies—
Spider lilies—aptly named!
Spider—a harbinger of Death—
Lily—the symbol for Peace—

She died—
All at once—
In an Instant!
Instant—
Painless—
Lovely—in its mercy.
Walking to the kitchen—she dropped—
And—
Departed before
Her body came to rest.

Brain Cancer—Diagnoses—
Wigs—Wheel Chairs—
Could not steal her final—earthly—
Joy—
A spider lily—
The Japanese omen
For Death—
On her kitchen table.

Then—
her Ethereal Joy fulfilled—
by The Face of Her Maker.

It was the Lilies—
It was the Lilies.

Magnolia
by Bee Williamson

Tribeca
by Joshua B Huitz

Hungry Month by Laura Eppinger

February flat, dull days won't end. Winter
nights woken to hands that choked, he
choked till I could not swallow. For the swollen
throat I could not forgive (myself) would not
feed. Hurt this body on every machine
at the gym. It was then I felt Hungry
Month begin.

Sleep-strangler in the daytime loosened
his grip, but I was too good a student
of deprivation. Own flesh now
another jar on the shelf, another empty
in the bin. I knew then

Hungry Month
might win.

But then, with friends, backs to the cold, stumbling, after two
sips of gin eat up grocer signs, flaky pastry, city
market shuffle to coffee coffee black
grounds between all teeth, release smoke like powder
in the setting snow.

Another round: cream of lobster and avocado
three tiers of sweets, it all falls down into deeper
softer skin, shakes up a newer kind of tears, they
call me back to daily bread—by God, Hungry Month
will end.

My Lucifer
by Tiffany McDaniel

I met him at the mall. His sleeves cerulean, his collar fuchsia, his horns bright blue.
He walked on hooves and was serious about his pitchfork.
He said, "I claim the flames. Won't you burn with me?"
I hollowed out for him and took to fever the next day.
This is my prayer, me on my knees, sober from the devil, drunk on Christ.
Now I know fire reaches not toward the sky, but toward heaven so that it too can know.
This is how hell burns. This is how angels lose their wings.

Youth
by Robyn Groth

Shoving down a low-carb wrap with veggies, I think of the days when I could drench cheese fries in ranch dressing and still wear a midriff, then I head out the door to burn off a few bean sprouts. Once out of my own peeling-paint neighbourhood, I turn down a street more like the one I grew up on—thick, green lawns and rounded bushes. Orange lilies lining walkways, stretching and reaching to expose their pits and crevices, their down and freckles. Stalks of lavender beside them, tall and slim, compactly purpled tips. And here come the boys from the high school track team, out to burn off a few urgent needs left unmet. They pass me easily and move smoothly, their arms pulled out of their sleeves, their shirts draped around their shoulders like short ponchos, leaving their lean lower backs bare so the breeze can whisk away the flush. A screen door opens and out steps a bald man in glasses, a neatly tucked button-down shirt. He grabs the mail and gazes after them, and I wonder if it's his own youth he's longing for, or theirs.

Youth
by Joshua B Huitz

Shipwrecked
by Jodi Cleghorn

She is shipwrecked. She is shipwrecked with loss. She is shipwrecked with loss on a foreign shore. She is shipwrecked with loss on a foreign shore once home to her lovers. She is shipwrecked with loss on a foreign shore once home to her lovers, only toes left kissing. She is shipwrecked with loss on a foreign shore once home to her lovers, only toes left kissing the hungry water. Toes left kissing the hungry water as she once kissed them. Hungry. Impatient. Insatiable. Toes left kissing the hungry water now frigid with longing. Toes kissing the ocean that stole her lovers.

She is shipwrecked with loss, alone on the tiny, black stones of this beach. Tiny black stones like geological punctuation marks. The sentence ends here. And here. And here. And if she gathered them all up. If she placed them on top of each other, fitted them together, she could end here. And here. A cairn to who she was. Who she will never be.

So many places for her to end. And none.

She does not end here. Nor here. Here. Or here.

She does not end, shipwrecked on this foreign shore of basalt full stops. On the beach they stood skipping stones.

Stones black as grief, cold as the bed in the house on the bluff she will never share with either of them again. Stones so plentiful it breaks her heart.

She reaches for a stone thinking she will skip it across the white wash. Skip it over the waves. Out toward the deep. She will skip it across the deep. Not a punctuation mark. Not an obsidian arc. Not an end. Not a beginning.

She will skip a stone as coda.

Return to the place where they are already playing and singing and loving. Where they are full of life. And potential.

Return to where they are full of life. And potential.

Return to the point where they are loving.

And play not to the end but return to the coda. Repeat. Infinitum

Keep skipping the stone. Skipping the stone across the ocean, and follow it.

She will walk on water.

She will be her own resurrection.

Skip the stone and walk until she finds them. Then inhale a lifetime's oxygen and dive deep. She will dive deep to where they languish at the bottom and kiss their water-bound lips. Push air into their lungs; inflate them with love.

Push air into their lungs through water-bound lips and inflate them with love so they will rise.

Rise with love and live again.

Rise with love and hand-in-hand they will walk the deep, jump the waves, paddle through the white wash to the shore. They will cross the beach, climb over the rocks and follow the path up the bluff to the house with the bed where they made love. And she will no longer be alone.

She will no longer be alone, shipwrecked with their loss on a foreign shore. On a beach with infinite ending, but no beginnings.

Justified Shooting
by Jonathan Covert

The counsellor asks what three hundred and sixty-five means to you. You say that, outside of some cosmological context, it sounds arbitrary. It's just a number.

"What do you mean by *cosmological*?" he asks. "Do you mean *celestial*, as in *divine*? Like *God*?"

You say no. "*Cosmological*, as in *astrophysical*. As in *revolutionary*."

He puts his pen in his mouth for a moment and seems to chew a thought out of the top.

"*Revolutionary*." He pokes the air with the pen as he says, "Anti-authoritarian, anti-establishment, anti-government, anti-social," connecting a constellation of imaginary dots.

"No," you say, groaning into the palm of your hand. "Revolutionary, as in spinning in circles."

"Where is this anger coming from?" the counsellor asks. "That's not you."

You can't think of a more absurd statement. How can you not be you? But then you think of that number that is not a number, *three hundred and sixty-five*. When you're alone, you repeat it to yourself — *Three hundred and sixty-five, Three hundred and sixty-five* — until the spirants and sibilants melt like a hymn into the air.

When you're with the counsellor, though, you say as little as possible.

According to the Office of Professional Standards, three hundred and sixty-five days is how long it'll take to clean this up: to buy time and run damage control; to make vague declarations and grave assurances about protocol; to gather an official committee and organize an official investigation; to interview witnesses, take accounts from fellow officers, and review the evidence; to take your statement; to ignore the phone; to scrutinize your past — your grades at the academy, your psych profile, your record; to go over your statement, one more time; to meet with attorneys and union representatives, all of whom warn you not to speak, and block one another's eye-contact as if they were taking bullets for you; to be eighty-sixed; to hear flaccid suggestions like *Get some rest* or *Take a vacation*; to punch a hole in the wall; to go over your statement, again and again, pressing the narrative until it's the shining diamond of truth at the soot-black core of your reputation; to assemble a tribunal; to pass a sentence; to hand in your badge and your gun; to clean out your desk; to see the counsellor once a week where the two of you sit in forty-five minute bouts of silence, each waiting for the other to break; to drink; to see a psychiatrist once a month, who prescribes you anti-depressants and sleeping pills, and refills the Xanax without question, the patron saint of Not Giving A Fuck; to wake up and fall asleep with the television on channel thirty-seven; to lose entire days; to answer the door after the third ring, after the knocking becomes panicked, just before your colleague kicks it in with probable cause; (You might be dead, no one's heard from you, you smell like you're dead, Jesus); to report in; to—on the recommendation of that community-college, dick-fisted counsellor—sign-in at court-ordered anger management classes; to bogart the heavy-bag at the gym and batter it with a vigour that makes those around you nervous; to ride a bike on sunny days through the same neighbourhoods you used to patrol at night; to—with the encouragement of the counsellor, who is just doing his job after all—attend grief counselling; to evaluate your progress and be prohibitively re-instated; to get your badge back, but not your gun; to sit at a desk and move paper; to ignore the sidelong glances and the whispers you can almost hear; to feel the frustration sour in your jaw when people tip-toe around you, speak circuitously, or avoid you altogether; to patch that hole in the wall; to go out for drinks and stop at two, or three; to re-learn how to reconcile a work-day with a sleep-cycle; to do your job, day-in, day-out; to wait patiently for the time allotted by the Office of Professional Standards—three hundred and sixty-five days—to finally burn away.

At the end of three hundred and sixty-five days, your name hasn't been in the paper for nearly eight months. Eventually, Captain asks you into his office. There, he notifies you of your reinstatement and spares you any congratulations. Instead, he holds out a requisition form. You grasp it, but before he lets go of the form, he gives you this look.

It's anger, maybe. Or hurt, with the suggestion of pity. But he's silent.

In that moment he looks like your father: white thorns of stubble on grease-slick leather, pulled by gravity, gristled by weather. He likes to say, "It's not the age, it's the mileage." It's easy to imagine that face rendered in oil-paints, framed in filigree, installed in some municipal building.

But now he's silent. Silent like an escarpment that will avalanche someday.

He lets go of the requisition form and you look away. You leave. Later, in the basement, the quartermaster takes the form—folded and worried and smudged a little now—and files it somewhere behind the counter. After a few moments, he slides a gun through the slot in the glass.

"Please confirm the serial number and sign here," the quartermaster says.

You turn it over. It's the very same gun, but it's clean.

Mezzanine
by Christina Dalcher

There's a mezzanine where I work and I think about vaulting it because last week I dropped my heart over the side and a girl picked it up and if you want to know where life ends, it's right there, over the mezzanine railing, down in the glass and brass depths of a crowded lobby where girls loiter, waiting to steal hearts. Once they wore pumps and poodle-skirts; today, trainers and trousers. Doesn't matter. A girl is a girl is a girl. They're all pretty little thieves.

I asked my mates what they do with the hearts, the girls who take them. Swallow them whole, William said. *Stomp on them until they bleed* was all Randolph could offer between draws on his pint glass. The consensus, cold in its simplicity, was to stay on guard, keep that beating muscle close under your skin. Beware.

Maybe I asked William and Randolph if they were happy. Maybe they said they were. Maybe I heard the lies on their lips.

So last week I dropped my heart over the mezzanine and watched it float down and down and down, wondering if the sound it made when it hit the marble would be a pop or a plop or an explosive burst. And I waited.

This morning, when I see her red curls breach the horizon of the escalator, pink lips pursed and perfect, a tiny brown bag clenched in the space between her breasts, holding and letting go at the same time; when I see her lips twitch and spread back; when she steps off and stares into the hollow inside me, I stop thinking about vaulting the mezzanine rail and I reach out and take her heart without having to steal it because she's giving it over for free.

Surrender
by Eileen Herbert-Goodall

The beach bakes beneath a sky of flawless blue; it is deserted. The sea is hypnotic and brilliant, like his wife's eyes.

Those eyes.

The memory of her gaze has branded his soul.

The day they were married, when she'd walked towards the altar, a shaft of sunshine plunged through a church window, setting the beading of her dress ablaze with light.

It had been a sign; their love was divine and stretched far beyond the confines of this earthly plane.

Or so he's come to realise.

Beneath his toes, the sand is soft and warm. He stands naked upon the shore, two bands of gold tucked into the palm of his hand.

He steps forward.

The ocean laps at his feet.

The sun's heat stings his face, and he resists the urge to dive beneath the waves, to be done with it all. Sacred rituals mustn't be rushed. The old man ventures further into the sea, which soon kisses his lips.

He sinks into the blue silence.

We will be one again.

Before long, pain holds his lungs to ransom.

Someone speaks his name; it is her.

She waits, keeping watch from an invisible interstice between worlds.

The metal within his grasp seems to sear his skin, but he must endure.

Her voice emanates from unknown depths, summoning him.

Come, she says.

Pain tightens its grip.

The old man sees a golden circle trembling high above, well beyond reach.

His heart feels as if it is about to burst.

He unclenches his hand, letting the rings tumble free.

The ocean heaves a sigh as he surrenders to the light.

Forgive me, my love. Forgive me.

Breaking through the water's surface, the old man gasps. The ocean is a rolling canvas of splintered blue-gold, blinding in its beauty.

His head spins as the sea swallows his tears.

He breathes, feeding his oxygen-starved muscles.

The old man swims towards shore, one word echoing through his mind: *alone, alone, alone.*

In Relief
by Elena Petricone

Your stone has a lit candle nested in the base that never goes out. In relief a lily of the valley curves across the stele front. Gray. The space above the flower bells is blank. No name.

I wonder who you were.

This is a common side effect, the doctor says. Most patients recover and never think of it again, others describe experiencing a sensation akin to lips against a skull, chomp. Hollow. Their feet carry them over to the memorial grounds like an echo.

How are you feeling?

Numb.

Good.

Keeping the name off was smart, the doctor says. People who opt to put names or dates on the stones often drive themselves crazy after the operation, chasing after a puzzle. All that anguish, when the truth offers them nothing. We want to make sure that the operation closes the door and locks it. We all must return to work.

I nod, and the blood pressure cuff tightens around my arm to the beating point of pain.

Your stone is the smallest size allowed. There are no children's toys in my apartment, no covers over electric sockets, no especially bright cereal boxes with mascots, no books with less than a sentence per page. No powder smell, no unspoken-for bed. Or cradle.

But your stone is mine, its invoice as mysterious as your stone itself. The customer service desk gently turns me away. The line is long. They spot people like me by how we clutch our invoices, paper worn and weary at the folds, our only link in a chain of unknown length and weight and tautened into fog.

Apparently I paid extra for the high relief, the ringing shoots and tepal bells. At the grounds I press my nose against the cold stele but there is no scent.

I find the pacifier while vacuuming under the skirt of the couch. Dust and lint from the carpet coat the nipple as though it was still wet and popped from a mouth, dough rolled in sugar. On my belly, vacuum off, I stare at the happy yellow guard and ring, at the flared nipple bottom resting against the carpet. Like your stone: a bell without sound. I cover my ears.

I sell the apartment furnished. I stop going to the grounds. I return to work.

You are doing a great service for our nation, the doctor says. By volunteering to forget.

Bomb Shelter
by Halli Lilburn

Pops always said there was enough room on the floor of the bomb shelter to roller-skate. He said the cement was smoother than the bottom of the swimming pool. He dug them both out at the same time.

"Son," he said, "them movies in school tell ya yer desk will save ya from them nukes but they is lying through their teeth. What ya need is three feet a concrete and a couple loads a mother earth 'tween you and the blast else you'll become a pillar a salt like Sodom and Gomorra."

I told my teacher what he said and she sent me to detention.

Pops wouldn't ever let me go down in the bomb shelter but sometimes, when I was swimming, I'd dive down and put my ear to the wall of the pool and listen. The pool was like the next door neighbour.

"Son, I got enough supplies in that bunker to last five years on account of the radiation." Pops would say.

"What about chocolate?" I asked.

"Five year supply," he boasted.

Mother rolled her eyes. "Five years according to whom?"

"I also got yer mother a crate a yarn so she can spend her time knittin' us sweaters." He pinched her cheek. "That'll keep ya from gettin' bored."

She put on her statue face. She did that to hide what she was really thinking. Every time she gave Pops a homemade sweater he wore it for a day or two then mysteriously lost it. He told me it was high time I started losing Mother's knit sweaters too.

When my folks listened to the news they would argue. My old man would say, "It's gettin' worse." And Mother would tell him to calm down and clean up for supper.

I couldn't wait for the war to start. Just thinking about roller-skating all day and eating chocolate for five years sounded amazing. What more could a kid ask for? I would sit by the latch in the middle of the lawn and invent stories about shelves full of salt water taffy and pretzels. Living in the bomb shelter would be heaven.

It might have been true if we had used the nukes but we never did. A couple of years went by listening to the news and cleaning up for supper. What finally happened wasn't political at all.

We interrupt your regular broadcasting to bring you this emergency message. The radio dominated our diner conversation as rain poured outside.

Pops dropped his fork spattering mashed potatoes across the table. "This is it!" He turned up the volume.

There is a severe weather situation. A tornado is affecting many residential and industrial areas. Citizens are urged to take cover immediately!

"What?" Pops slammed his hands down making peas jump off his plate. "I built a bomb shelter not a tornado shelter."

Mother collected the rolling peas in her napkin. "This is second best, dear."

"Phooey," he said.

Sure enough, Mother barely had the table cleared before wind clapped the shutters and tipped the trash can.

"Phooey!" Pops repeated as he grabbed our coats and headed for the hatch.

The wind whipped up Mother's skirt before she could prevent being indecent and I protected my ears from the roaring wind as Pops pried open the latch. Finally, I would see inside the wonderland of the bomb shelter and eat candy all night.

First impression of the underground fortress hit us with the ungodly smell of rotten potatoes.

"Tarnations!" Pops bellowed, flipping the light switch and finding half an inch of water on the floor.

I think he would have turned around and taken us back to the house if the tornado hadn't dropped right on top of it. Shingles singed the air like fiery darts. The water in the pool flew into the sky as if it were raining upside down. Gravity was reversed, sucking everything into a slime green sky like an alien tractor beam. Pops wasn't strong enough to close the hatch but luckily our car rolled on top of it and locked us in with a bang.

We collected our breath and listened to the now muted noise of the storm. My new environment consisted of cans filling steal shelves that lined the concrete walls. Mother tip toed through the puddles to a bunk bed where she removed her ruined heels and rung out her stockings. She was wearing her statue face again.

"Can I have some chocolate?" I asked.

Pops went into a silent rage. He might have hit me if Mother hadn't started crying. She was looking into the opened crate of yarn.

"Roger, you oaf, this yarn is all black. How am I supposed to knit anything with only black?

Pops was taken aback. He stumbled for an answer. "Well, uh, darlin', they only sell them bulk yarns in one colour per crate so unless ya wanna get more crates..." His voice petered out.

She threw her ruined shoe at him.

He didn't even duck.

It's O.K.

A Running Jester

It's O.K.
to Go In

by Karen Boissonneault-Gauthier

To an Editor
by Jean Gill
from One Sixth of a Gill

The 'one word too often profaned'
is apparently 'cat'.
Too many women write too many poems
about, explicitly, 'that'
so I'll try not to write
any poems that bite, that hiss
or that land on their feet.
I'll try to be wary
of words that sound hairy or piss
when they ought to look sweet.
If feline is out, perhaps canine will do
or vulpine, bovine, asinine …
please advise.

The Good Boys
by Honor Clement-Hayes

The boys I have loved. Even the worst of them made me hot water bottles in the night, brought improvised snacks into bed.

They sorted out, they picked up, they dropped off.
They indulged flights of drama and dried tears.
They went after lost purses and rolled a thousand cigarettes.
They wrote letters, drew pictures, cooked dinners.
They lay with me on grass, on rocks, on planes.
They built fires, put out fires, fanned flames.
They had cats, mothers, little brothers; square TVs from the 90s, TVs that went online; striped socks, odd socks, socks I wore on my hands.
They bought me cider, shoes, a locket, a watch.
They came on foot, on a bike, in their mums' cars without permission.
They shouted about boys, girls, money, drinking, work, rent, broken windows and writing on the walls.
They were banned for drink-driving, damaged by absent fathers, babied by ever-present mothers.
They were heavy drinkers, hard rockers, light fingers pressing need in the dark.
They smoked Royals, Virginia, Drum, Thai stick, on Friday nights.
They went to school, went to college, went to uni, went to shit.
They got jobs, lost jobs, quit jobs, did jobs for a week.
They crashed cars, collected scars, got in fights.
They played scrabble, played guitar, played away.
They took me to the skate park, to Paris, to hospital, to hell and back.
They gave me red roses, bloody noses, confidence, cystitis.
They passed out, walked out, lashed out and found me out.

They were at war, at sea, at one with me.
They were all good boys.

Uptown Haberdashery Display
by William C. Crawford

Dead Words
by Elizabeth Lovatt

The act of writing is creation, vitality is its purest form, but words newly written are already dead, static and unchanging. They begin to rot.

Words speak from beyond. They live and die with the reader's breath. Each time they are read they are resurrected and then lowered back into the earth to await their next raising. Immortality of a sort.

Offspring
by K. Irene Rieger

My fingers fit the frets of your spine,
The seashell curve of your ribs: you're mine.

Geography by TJS Walter

We are a planet of mountain range spines, long, lean lakes and tidal pool eyes. The wind of our lungs sings sweet and low-quiet-soft through our valleys of bone and the flesh of grass. Every hand-forest's finger tree trembles as the dream quake rattles the celestial body. Wrapped in night and anchored by gravity, we orbit in space and blankets and our heart beat pulse is the definition of sound. The moon crests over Shoulder Hill, rising as stars fall down past your horizon. We lay afield and watch satellites and when the sunlight whispers low we whisper too, and bury one another.

Tread by TJS Walter

Weightless in water we stayed suspended and listening to the muted pat tapping of the sky falling gently onto the surface of the lake overhead. The fluid was womb-warm and we couldn't tell where we ended and the lake began. The light scattered here, showing us nothing but moss green ahead and dark below. On the outside, above the ceiling of water, rain fell like rice on concrete, dull and musical and inconsiderate of birds. Our arms moved through the water, pushing it in slow arcs around our bodies. We had faith that we were moving forward, but had no perception of progress. Here was protected, impermeable to the rain and the rest of the world. Here was infinite. I had faith in your presence the way I had faith in motion, but you were lost in a sea of green. Above, on the outside, thunder mumbled and a slightly brighter light pulsed once and was gone, and that was all we knew of the storm around us. The lungs inside my chest grew heavy with stale and useless air, and put pressure on me to leave here, to break through the surface of the lake, where I would feel wind and rain and be subjected to the early morning's grey light. I looked up, toward the pocked ceiling. Another flash of light. Another dull, roiling thunder. More pup, pup, pup of water tapping water. The sky was knocking, calling me out. Maybe you were out there too, but I was amorphous now, and I didn't want definition. In love with my new viscosity, I waited. My lungs waited. Just a little longer, I told them. Just a little longer …

Humpback Whale
by Faisal Warsani

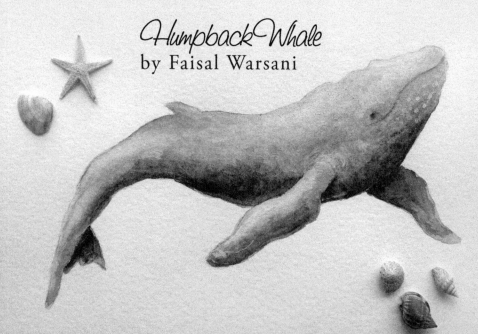

Whale
by Alice Tarbuck

At flooding point, the Fenland holds
its mirrors to the sky, remembers
drainage strategy: turf walls, pumps, dykes.

A dim shape rests, is sand dune, sand bank,
wreck. Marine Biologists inform the press
its organs had collapsed beneath its weight.

The sand is golf-course smooth, the whale
apocalyptic, carried off in chunks.
Stink augury, one cloudy eye below
an oily loop of birds. They click and whirr.

She the Garden
by David Anthony Sam

She a garden is dry
      barren wasted
      by neglect of weeds

indifference wintered
      what once bloomed
      green and yellow and pied

now brown and grey dry
      stalks memory
      of old harvests mixed

with greed of weeds
      the only harvest
      she is dead the one

who lived this garden
      tendered seeds
      into soil hoed away

weeds and picked
      insects old fingers
      brown-stained with saps

she herself neglected
      died indifferent distant
      relatives paid minimum

cremation the kind mortician
      thought enough to
      sneak old ashes into

the garden she thin
      fertilizer for weeds
      before the real estate

hawking signs of open
      houses set strangers
      free to imagine

silence from inside
      oneness of careless
      universe loved at

last by winds drawn
      up her dust for storm
      clouds congealed

unknown her
      pale spirit white
      swirl of nothing

content in engulfment
      by disintegration
      integrated she a garden

Jonah in the Whale
by Annie Blake

I am back in the dark
and I know that the outside is a faded
light of white—it is not
purity or the washed hands of the sun but sterile
white—without fire; like the night without its shine. There is no
tune in here, it is the tangle of the triangle I am in the middle of.
The conversations are barely edible and the music is aborted.
That is why I am here—because the sun won't
drip and stick. The only people who make love with fire
and water are flying in the metal webs
of my head.

No Longer Nearby
(for Prince)
by Nancy Devine

How the skin of him I never touched,
so what difference does no longer in
the world mean?
I have image and sound and light and
sound,
so in a prayer, we could say nothing is
different.

No ordinary air we shared,
just drastically altered as it floated
from one state to another.
By then, everyone's exhalation was
there:
some cat mewling in a dark alley,
or its gut vibrating to slow and then
still.

So close,
Minnesota borders me
the way my husband's body is to mine
in sleep and waking.
Does anyone realize
how big missing is,
a huge god swallowing, gulping,
drinking from a font in the laze of a
last day.
as if life had no bottom whatsoever?

The Colour of My Vanity
by Hedia Anvar

My natural hair was chin-length and darker than espresso. It was so dark that I was often accused of dyeing it. This became a point of pride. But when I bleached it to try on blonde during what must have been a manic impulse, I still expected to make it as a member of the flaxen clan through more than just the weekend.

It took one glance at the stranger in the mirror for me to miss the former contrast between my dark hair and pale skin. I'd have been a complete inversion of myself if I'd gotten a tan too, and because of the Toothpick Kid, I didn't make it even as the most temporary of blondes.

My boyfriend at the time was playing a gig with his band in the East Village. I stepped outside for air and behind me followed an early-twenties guy I could imagine walking around with a toothpick in his mouth. Usually, a cold stern look on my part was enough to send men on their way. But this time, no matter how monosyllabic and unsmiling my comportment, the guy wouldn't let up on telling me how I should "ditch the long-haired hippy with the guitar" for him.

It took a few encounters similar to the one with the Toothpick Kid to confirm that with my bleached hair, men were approaching me with more familiarity—and sleaze—than normal. There was something missing from their demeanour: fear.

I found this revelation so alarming that I poured the next bottle of black dye on my head.

As a blonde, it wasn't more attention I was receiving; it was *different* attention. I had been used to men drawing near with an air of caution. Somehow their caution vanished with my hair pale as if blood-drained. It made me feel unshelled. I wanted to catch the eyes of surly guys in the corner who disdained flash, not the cleavage-obsessed ones wearing shiny, unbuttoned shirts.

Once I moved to Los Angeles, my women friends looked styled for a magazine cover even when waiting in line at the DMV. They had flowing hair, puffy lips, impossible eyelashes and bubblegum toenails. They were head-turners, drool magnets. I held my own, but I wasn't of the flowing-hair variety. Pairing up with one such girl for a night out was a sociological experiment akin to Marcia Brady and the Beetlejuice girl clubbing together.

At a rooftop record release party in a posh hotel, Lorena of baby-doll voice and Botticelli Venus cascading hair was the quintessential drool magnet. Meanwhile, I was expert with a terse smile to divert drooling duos from including me in their pick-up manoeuvre. As such, the night progressed to each of our liking—Lorena received ample attention and I sipped my cocktail in peace.

Then something shifted.

I was on my second drink, already laughing more merrily than I normally considered necessary. My disinterest in the other attendees remained the same as before, but my booze-induced aura seemed to have loosened them up toward me. It soon felt like the whole room was descending on me in the context of ordinary, insipid pick-up games.

Get you a drink?
You look like you're having fun.
First time here?
You from LA?
You really pull off that short hair.
Some would consider it harmless, but it dripped of too much lechery for my taste. I felt blonde all over again.

Lorena seemed confused by this room shift to my direction, so I looked at her with bewildered eyes and shrugged.

"The alcohol must make me seem ... friendly? Approachable? Easy?" I asked with great horror. She threw back her head and laughed. We understood each other, both good at crafting how to come across to the world in a manner that pleased our respective vanities.

The ability to strike enough reverence in men-on-the-make to keep their distance from me is apparently what satisfied my vanity most.

Anger
by Helena Halme

Excerpted from Helena Halme's latest novel, The Good Officer

Kaisa parked on the sloping car park, and pulled up the handbrake hard. Peter winced; he just couldn't get used to her driving. Not looking at her, Peter got out and picked up his sword from the back seat. He fixed it onto his belt and walked across the small yard towards the entrance of Drumfork Naval Club, a low-slung, 1960s building. It was used as a social space for naval families, and as everything in Helensburgh, was run-down and grey-looking. Peter noticed the ice on the ground too late and slipped on the steps.

"You OK?" he heard Kaisa say behind him, but he didn't have the energy to reply to her. Instead, he cursed under his breath and took a handkerchief out of his pocket to wipe the palm of his hand. There were a few spots of blood. "Fuck," he said out loud. Glancing down, he saw his uniform trousers had escaped the worst of it and still looked crisp and smart; they still had the deep creases he'd ironed into them that morning.

Inside, it was even colder than on the windswept hill. Peter rubbed his hands together, keeping the hankie between them in an attempt to stem the blood, which was dribbling out of the fleshier part of his right palm. He nodded to the same Wren who'd shown him into the Base Commander's office three weeks before. She didn't smile as she stood up from the grey plastic chair she'd been sitting on, but her eyes had a kindness to them. Peter moved his face away from hers. During the past weeks he'd heard nothing but condolences, people saying how sorry they were. He didn't need their sympathy—he needed this to be over and to get back to work. Even Kaisa had nothing but sorrow in her eyes and Peter couldn't stand it. What he needed was anger; he needed people to understand how angry he was. Angry at Kaisa, angry at Duncan, angry at the Navy for posting him and his new, young, pretty wife to this God-forsaken arsehole of a place, angry at Scotland and the bloody Jocks complaining in their harsh accents, angry at the drab, ugly married quarters on the hillside, overlooking the steely cold Gareloch, angry at himself for being so stupid as to care that his wife had slept with someone else.

Labour of Love
by JJ Marsh

The plaster cost two hundred—only the best for her. She took me eighteen months to finish. The mannequin mould was the easy part, set in three weeks. But attaching the hair, finding the clothes, sewing them on, painting her face, nails, mouth—it takes time if you want it right. If you want it real.
And all I had to work from were pictures in the paper.

Tonight, under the lights, my beautiful girl sat upright, waiting for me. A perfect likeness, frozen in time. Kneeling, I put the ring on her lifeless finger and cried.

My Name Is Iris
by JJ Marsh

"Sara! My name is Sara! For God's sake, Mother. You know who I am!"

Shouting is a bad thing. We all know that. Grammy looks at Sara, but not with recognition. It's fear. It seeps out, a kind of yellowy-grey like pollution over a city sky.

The little boy sits on the chair, kicking his legs into the air, enjoying the game of gravity, the thud of his heels as they hit the floor, the self-inflicted purple pain. It reminds him he's still there. He watches the women and listens.

"So how is everything, *down there*?" Sara whispers, but you could hear her right along the corridor, if you wanted. Pink wafts of curiosity curl out of warm, bored wards. Sara, Stay-At-Home-Mom, as if I didn't have enough to do Mom, who glows green at the school gates, has a stainless steel voice.

"Sssh!" The old lady glances at the lad, as if she cares about what a little boy thinks. She's whitewashing, clinging to decency. "Everything's fine. All ship-shape and shiny. Nurse says I can go home tomorrow. Will you arrange for the carriage, my dear?"

"Carriage? Mother, please! You'll either go home in the ambulance or Norman will bring the Volvo. Look, you have to sort yourself out. Keep talking like this, they'll never let you go home."

Anger in the air, blue-black smoke. It creates a shape like a scythe, a skull, overshadowing Grammy's blush-puffs of disorientation.

Sara, SAHM, way too busy for this Mom, heaves herself up. "I'm going to talk to the Sister. You stay there."

Grammy nods, her dutiful expression so pious it could almost be sarcastic. The boy watches her. She's pewter, old and dented. She smiles to herself.

The boy's legs stop the kick-drop rhythm, and he bounces on the balls of his feet.

"What's funny?" His curiosity is saffron; illuminating, natural.

Her smile, mother-of-pearl, draws him. "Your mum told me to stay here. But I'd rather not. I'd give anything to disappear. Even it was just under the bed."

Reflections hover above her. The boy is confused.

"You want to disappear? You want to scare her?" His face is a charcoal sketch of suspicious.

The old lady smiles again, and colour spills into the air. Lilac shoots, golden motes, shafts of double cream.

"No. I want to scare myself. If I can't surprise anyone, I may as well turn off the lights. Can you help me?"

He approaches, in primary colours.

Farming for Us All
by Kari Gunter-Seymour

Garden of Solace
by Chumki Sharma

Mass of red, orange, gold,
as I prune away dead
leaves midst the long shadows.
Nothing exotic in my garden,
deep silence of green, more green
and silence.
Leaves of Neem and tall Begonias
offset by beds of white
flannel flowers.

An old ache returns and
I take a break.

Beyond my door, in my
perfect garden of
loneliness,
I twist and pull a deep root.

Animal, Vegetable, Mineral
by Joanna Brichetto

Nashville: Agricultural festival, Butterfly Barn.
A twenty-something couple traps
the Educator near Miscellaneous Displays.
When I hear "Brown Marmorated Stinkbug"
—a major agricultural pest—
I scuttle closer.
Girlfriend (wife?) keeps quiet,
but Dude drawls,
How do you kill it?
"Well, we try to use biological methods to combat insect pests,
rather than pesticides.
We might find another animal that likes to eat this one."
Animal? You mean bug.
"Insects are animals."
Insects are animals?
"On this Earth, you are an animal, vegetable or mineral,
and insects are in the Animal Kingdom."
Dude shakes head.
You learn something new every day.

gratuitous
by kerry rawlinson

whale music blows over sandbars of our own design,
complete with mariachi, capers and tiny umbrellas.
Primary colours somehow became secondary to the
process. Imagination closes its eyes when every known light
comes on. People-songs about having nothing fun to eat
proliferate, so we manufacture whistling Disney chickens
wrapped in plastic which we abandon in the sea. We kiss
the snouts of our cartoon families *toodle-oo*, clambering
onto festive planes which fly our consciences to all-inclusive
ships, far from reality's reach. The locals stink. We drink
what we need to forget. It rains for forty days and forty
roulettes and we still can't bleach the red out of the beach.

Twang and Sass
by Kari Gunter-Seymour

Tomatoes
by Victoria Melekian

Round red juicy kisses
plucked ripe from the vine.
We dated in full sun,

transplanted ourselves
after spring's last frost.
Six years since you said, "Be mine."

And now we're making Heirlooms—
Lollypop, Green Zebra, Brandywine.
O summer breeze, pollinate me.

When I Tell Him the News
First published in text, September 2015
by Ariel Dawn

I wait for the world in his eyes. Only dark earth, ash
—burned paper flowers on the wall while he served spirits
in Main Street bars—of light I recall. Red river, guts, heart,
and wanting to grow backwards through veils and stars
while Mother devoured meat, molasses, bread and leaves.
Fought to escape flesh, then to remain within. He holds me
in blood-shot eyes while being pulled into our room,
candelabra, mirrors, bed against window. Sleep, I whisper,
then toast, oranges, pots of strong tea with honey.

Then He is Gone
First published in minor literature(s), November 2014
by Ariel Dawn

He is gone and young women are nesting with bedclothes, necklaces,
fairy lights stretched between sofas and closets for their secret lives.
They make a picnic of cake and tea and rum. Show their art
on walls and windows: roses, vines, handwriting, eyes.
I ask, where is his letter, and they laugh, point out colour, design,
light and shadow. Fallen leaves in bowls and hung on fishing wire.
Our bedroom window frames overgrown garden and the shed
broken into the morning I ran away. Thieves looked through
glass at us: we were naked by the sea, the leaves fell.

The Hennaarna
by Zvezdana Rashkovich

Her hands are slim and long fingered, gentle but steady. When she was little, Yoma always said her hands belonged to an artist. That was long before her mother's breath got thick and hot, like steam rising off Khartoum streets in summer, and before a foul-smell rose from her skin and before her body wasted to a skeleton under their zinc-roofed hut as she looked on with closed eyes and as they all looked on, Zahra and her father and her sisters and brothers. They just looked on—because there was nothing anyone could do to stop a hex once it cleaved to a soul.

Zahra's eyes sting—she blinks and licks her lips. They taste salty and something else - like rage and her deceased grandmother's ululating at funerals. Her hand-shakes but she still traces the extended foot resting in her lap, that of the golden-skinned bride lounging on the bed. A ceiling fan stirs coconut scent from oiled hair and Zahra hears a soft sigh escape the young woman's lips. The teenage girl lounges in a vapour of heady sandalwood perfume and expensive Indian oud incense. The smoke tickles Zahra's nostrils.

Clucking their tattooed lips and sashaying their round hips the bride's aunts and five bridal attendants have done their job well—the bride was now fragranced like a barely budding jasmine flower –plumped up like a decadent rose and mango pudding—to be offered to her groom on wedding night. For his sampling, as he wished. The girl, had been rubbed then polished with copious amounts of wine-red grease, a pungent blend of frankincense, myrrh and jasmine, until her skin bled then peeled and she is now all new and smooth and lulled into a trance by the massaging and oiling and the perfume and the sweetness of *mahalabiya* they fatten her with.

Zahra, looks up at the young woman and finds what she expected. A wide, smooth cheeked and flushed face, a slightly parted mouth the colour of dusky dates, a hint of pink tongue flicking like a gecko's behind small sharp teeth. The eyes are those of a Savannah gazelle, drawn out, soft at the edges and limpid inside, filled with the feverish reminiscence of her groom's full lips and winged brows and perhaps of his firm arms and herself inside his body on the soon arriving wedding night. Zahra, lowers her eyes and draws her veil around her shoulders then continues to trace a magic-infused painting on the girl's feet and upwards onto her legs. The finished creation is crystalline in her mind's eye. It is lovely—as if the jinn themselves possessed her hand while she drew. Winding, circling, pressing the henna tube over skin, teasing the fragrant cerise paste, creating a roadmap on the golden thighs and slim hips towards sacred, secreted places that await the groom. She refills the small plastic funnel with henna, gripping it between the fingers of her left hand and it follows a trajectory on its own will. She is a Da Vinci. She is a Picasso or Raphael even, except her backdrop is not a monolith or a stretched out cloth, but the impatient hands and feet of idle women with amethyst eyes. Yoma, was right. Yes, feet and hands are Zahra's canvas and black henna is her ink for she is the yellow-eyed maker of African magic, and the sorceress of this Nile… she is the cohort of all brides. She paints decaying flowers and haemorrhaging hearts and mystical hexing chants on golden skin… then releases her artwork gently, into each pungently-scented wedding night.

And then—she holds her breath.

Toxic
by Shushanik Karapetyan

He's nervous. I can feel it from the way he moves and makes the walls of my cage vibrate. He needs me. He'll come for me. And it doesn't take long until he does.

He flips the top open. I shiver from the gust of wind in the darkness. He runs his cold lustful fingers across my lips, shivers rushing down my spine. He pulls me out, plays with me - rolling me back and forth between his thumb and index middle fingers, then places me in between his warm wet lips.

Light me.

Love me.

Burn me.

The flame of the match ignites my body, his breath running through my veins. His fingers hold me in place, his lips tightening and relaxing as he takes his first breath, sssssssslowly. Burning me.

Killing me.

I ache in pain and pleasure. His lips free me.

Temporarily.

Take me back, I release a lubricious moan of smoke.

His lips seize me again. And again. And again. He sucks slow inhalations, my smoke, my life invading his insides, his tender membranes. He sucks me tenderly, quietly to quench his appetite. He drains me then drops my shrivelled leftovers to the ground.

Satisfied?

And all you'll have left from me will be my souvenirs, my particles of tar clinging to the walls of your lungs.

Cosmologies
by Sarah Lyn Rogers

Today, you are an astronaut. You don't know yet that like most things worthy of interest, outer space is both beautiful and terrible. You are four years old, and you want to wear a white suit and a helmet. No one will tell you yet how freezing and desolate space can be. You are four years old, and you want to float in midair. No one will tell you yet that a person can be crushed by gravity, or that our planet will ultimately be consumed by the sun. You are four years old.

Today, we are swimming. I bought you an all-too-exciting pair of white swim trunks, and goggles with a white strap. You thanked me with a shriek, insisting to wear both before we even got in the car. White-suited explorer, boldly going where we have definitely gone before, to the much-charted waters of our local lake.

I watch you with your father on the shore. Laughing, so proud, he lifts you skyward, a mini rocket-launch. He wades out so you can experience weightlessness. Almost. I take a mental snapshot: he, sweetness and strength, you smiling, so trusting, floating inches above his hand. He is your lifeline to me, the mothership.

Little astronaut, you will tire soon, and we will take you home to our pets and toys and cable TV. You will have Tang with dinner, and a dehydrated ice cream sandwich for dessert. I know that this surprise food will be well received; I still understand your likes and dislikes. You are four years old, and Mom is cool.

Tonight, after your bath, I will wrap you in your star-spangled bathrobe, help you into astronaut jammies—white pyjama pants, white tank top—and tuck you into constellation-dotted sheets. I will kiss you goodnight on your fresh-smelling forehead and try not be consumed by the son; that is, I will try not to think about how someday you will be crushed—not by the force of gravity, but by the force of expectation, the force of adulthood. Someday the world will teach you about the malicious forces of space, politics, death, bigotry, dogma. But I won't. Not yet.

For now, you are still perfect, my white knight in flannel. You do not know guilt, or shame, or even sadness. You are fearless, for you know nothing to fear. Tonight, you might dream of brilliant shooting stars, or viewing the Earth as a tiny blue marble through a faraway window, or even floating in anti-gravity, and you will not be afraid. Not yet.

Radishes and Zinfandel
by Stephanie Thurrott

Jón stood alongside the two-top, his pen poised over his pad. These two were Americans, he guessed. He spoke in English.

"The root salad is constructed from five local radish varieties, bathed in an organic tea made from almond oil and honey." He leaned in. "We're nearly sold out."

"We'll take two." The man spun the stem of his fishbowl-sized wineglass between his meaty thumb and forefinger. "Can you recommend a wine that pairs well with them? Perhaps a peppery red? How does that sound, Eleanor?"

"It sounds lovely, Henry." Eleanor pushed a thin smile toward Henry before gazing toward Reykjavík harbor.

Jón pointed to the second-most-expensive wine on the list. Twenty thousand krona. "This blend from Gemini Vineyards features biodynamic Zinfandel grapes grown by twins, a man and a woman, who bring their yin and yang to their greenhouse-vineyard just three kilometres from here. They harvested only when the Northern Lights are on display."

"Sounds perfect." Henry set down his wine glass.

A minute later Jón returned. "In keeping with the Gemini tradition, we'll have you both taste the wine. To appreciate its balance and harmony you should entwine your arms and sip simultaneously. Let me demonstrate." Jón turned toward the dining room. "Lilja, do you have a moment?"

"Of course."

Jón took two empty wineglasses from a nearby table. He and Lilja entwined their arms and mimicked sipping, then Jón poured the wine for Henry and Eleanor.

Henry stood. Eleanor sighed, then stood as well. They lifted their glasses, awkwardly wrapped their arms together, and sipped.

Lilja tucked a thousand-krona note into Jón's apron pocket. "You win. What's next?"

Jón tilted his head toward the couple just entering the restaurant. "Kolrabi shaving salad and sparkling tea, sipped facing east, the direction of new beginnings."

Lineage
by Stacey Margaret Jones

I am owned by my marrow,
filling the bones of my
skeleton, articulated for me
by women now sepia
toned and long gone.
There is a legacy in
my ligature I cannot
flee. I merely
advance from the main
frame of my familial past.
But evolution is slow.
Our bodies were made to
widen at the hips so another
woman could appear, to be
named the same, and
stomp around, short,
tending to middle roundness,
with dark, thick hair,
slamming her curiosity
against almost everything,
and keeping a rich life
inside.

This interiority,
the life of the mind of me
and mine,
has peaked and progressed
past motherhood,
here
ending the trajectory of the
future of Margarets.
My tendons seethe with
each step,
piano strings vibrating with
the hue
and cry of the past,
the last.

LuciXV
by Vakseen

No Filter Me
by Vakseen

Shimmy
by G. M. Monks

Some California hills must have waltzed slow but others nearby
surely have rumbaed for a million years. How one waltzes with
a partner doing a rumba is beyond me. Others are so jagged they
must have danced rock and roll every time the North American
plate shimmied and quaked against the Pacific Plate.

The strip-teasers wear pasties of a tree or bush here and there, rarely
a full length dress of forests, so I can see them showing off a cave,
a crevice or a long-ago landslide, trickling out a stream. The granite
two-stepping with basalt. Limestone peeking through.

In the spring, just to be the temptress, they'll wear a skin-tight grass
skirt enticing cows to eat but I can still see their rolling underneaths.
Others flaunt riotous garbs of yellow mustard and orange poppies.

On a few roads, some rise up high around me, making it feel like
a crowded dance floor, and I can't see how they rumbled eons ago.

When Her Heart is Breaking...
by kerry rawlinson

she cleans. Or
she gnaws
expensive layers of new acrylic
lacquer off her nails. She smiles
and chews and
cleans. Believe me,
the microwave's pristine.
It's been wiped eight times today—

not unlike each room she intimately
navigates. Her nails
are like the surface of the moon.
Every Tranquility-slip blip
shifts
to crater.
And you could definitely eat
off the toilet seat.

Mask
by Jessica Gawinski

Combing My Hair With This Knife
by Nancy Devine

All the guys had black lips,
huge and swollen like sated leeches. And
the weather was hideous: wind that never
relented, shards of ice raining down instead
of broken rain.
All night, sitting on the plain sofa, twisting
my hands in and out of the prayer position,
I pleaded and begged and beckoned and wished
and tried to hope, twisting
my hands into and out of the prayer position.
But, I feel good now,
rocking in his fine body,
like I said,
combing my hair with this knife.

Suddenly by Brenda Yates

My mother appears, neatly dressed in another
one of the masks she used in public (anything,
really, outside the house, which included taking
trash out to the curb). Still, I'm afraid: *What are
you doing here?* And moving closer, note how
carefully lipstick has been drawn to the contours
of her lips, mascara's unclumped, slim lines of
understated eyeliner are not smeared, as though
done by hands no longer shaky and imprecise. *I
just wanted to see you one more time before I left,*
she says, mouth perfectly relaxed—not pinched-
bitter, not spitting some tightly-held hateful-
ness. She smiles, young again, and I almost
believe I can remember seeing her like this.
Waking then, I fall back into a body that makes
those who knew her, gasp at me, back into her
world, breaking and broken, always broken and
breaking. Back into the shape I've grown into,
into the hurt and hurtful face I ran from but
now find in every mirror—wondering if she's
gone from my dreams for good. Suddenly, twen-
ty-two years after her death, I miss her.

by J.I. Kleinberg

CORNFLOWER MORNING

vegetable
days,

words
for
praising

the exact
summer

even the
immaculate
sun

tap-dancing   with
cardinals

by J.I. Kleinberg

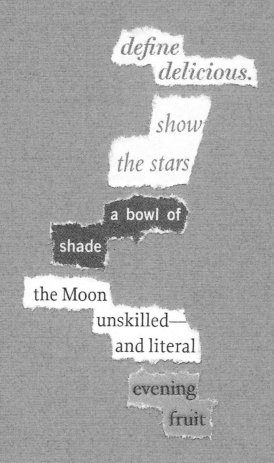

define
delicious.

show
the stars

a bowl of

shade

the Moon
unskilled—
and literal

evening
fruit

by J.I. Kleinberg

in a
galloping
forest
timber-
fantastic
with
caroling
boughs,
the
mischievous
trees
COMMIT
LOVE

by J.I. Kleinberg

in the trees
everything

has
sense

you   note

That
sound
again

drum-
strewn

echoes

slamming   inside
you

the dance of
wind

the breath of
roots

by J.I. Kleinberg

my
wheat
back
body

once was

wiregrass

and
words for
mustangs.

barrel-chested
landscape

spring
winged

province of
stone

by J.I. Kleinberg

THE BIG BIRDS, GATHERING

The
emerald
shrill,

**and
glossy
bright**

and teal
for all to see

missionaries

of the

resplendent

by J.I. Kleinberg

the future of
light

may be
falcons

becoming
Angels,

prairie
wings

cavorting
rough

constraining

clouds.

by J.I. Kleinberg

to rock
Bob Dylan

Take a
memory

hunkier than
a whisper

uncover

The

audible

laughter of
swans

by J.I. Kleinberg

you can see
prayers

on the
evening
air,

silvered
wing
of

lace

molten

attention

of light

We need

the   miraculous

The Single Woman's Guide To Survival

by Murzban Shroff

They pulled away from each other reluctantly. The darkness closed around them like a life jacket, reminding them they were more souls than bodies. They were not expected to say anything. Not expected to violate the silence that had sprung between them. The male in him fought that silence. To accept it would be to accept an equality that just wasn't there. He stroked her temples with the back of his fingers; then cupped her face gently. Could she be his universe, his heartbeat, his angel of mercy? He was feeling handsome, he was feeling tender. A surge of passion sprang from some place in his heart and he felt like a soldier carrying a child to safety while all around him bombs exploded. Yes, it was all about safety, he thought.

He now spoke. He said, "At last a woman who can kiss."

She did not look at him. Instead she smiled and circled with her fingers the hair on his chest. She drew words and symbols she hoped he would understand. Maybe, once they knew each other better they'd play this game. And she was sure he would understand: with a little bit of time he would learn to read her. Meanwhile, she could tell by his strained neck muscles that he was waiting for an answer. Did there have to be an answer? Her love-softened breast rose and fell against his chest, in sync with his breath. Her fingers stopped their conversation. She cleared her throat and said softly, "At last a man who can fuck. Really." The last word sounded like an afterthought. It was an afterthought. But then she wasn't good at these things. Really.

She knew the conversation had ended because, later, when she called him, his phone rang and rang and rang. And then the voice from the phone company came tumbling with unnatural clarity: The number you have called is currently out of reach. Please try again later. The voice, unrepentant in three different languages.

***

In the days that followed she would try out her grandmother's recipes, call friends over, and post the pictures on Facebook and Instagram, hoping he would notice them. She would put up sayings like: "Women give to men the very gold of their lives, which men invariably return in loose change."

Twice a week she would go to a Bollywood dance class where she would befriend women who were older than her. Women surviving bad marriages or bad affairs or divorced and eager to get back into shape.

Five nights a week she would get onto her bicycle and join a group of twenty-something boys who would pedal a three-kilometre stretch around Carter Road, Turner Road, Linking Road, and Union Park. When they reached the slope at Union Park she would raise her body off the seat and push extra hard to get a few feet ahead of the boys.

She also began a novel that opened like this: *A man's love is finite, a woman's infinite. Which is why a woman can take more risks than a man. She can go where men cannot.* But after a week she decided to pare it down to a Facebook post. More chance of it being read that way. More chance of it being shared.

And once in a while she would stand naked before the mirror admiring her pear-shaped breasts, her flat stomach, her narrow hips, and her firm heart-shaped buttocks resting on smooth gym-toned legs, and she would think, What the fuck am I grieving for? I am not yet ready for childbirth?

Memory of Lichgate

by Natalie De Paz

After two days of fucking and crying, I remember the light was perfect. Pin-thin streams of it threaded through the branches of that tree and poked through us. The tree had a bough dipping down toward the ground. I sat on it and it bent as if to say, *I will hold you, but it's not easy.* You fed me the cookies with black, acrid bottoms. It was my fault they were burnt. Everything was my fault. The cookies were too hard; they had caught the briskness of the Tallahassee air. I felt sorry I had ruined the cookies. When I opened the oven to check, I wasn't sure if they were quite golden-brown. Now I know gold is the colour of the perfect light from that morning, and brown is the colour of bark and earth, the colour of your heart buried in the Tallahassee dirt. I hope you were able to grow a new heart to give. Then again, I hope you weren't. Tallahassee is nestled in seven hills like Rome. Now I know what it is to walk the ruins of a fallen empire.

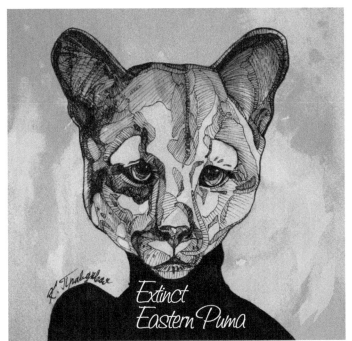

Extinct
Eastern Puma

Vulnerable
Polar Bear

by Katerina Pravdivaia

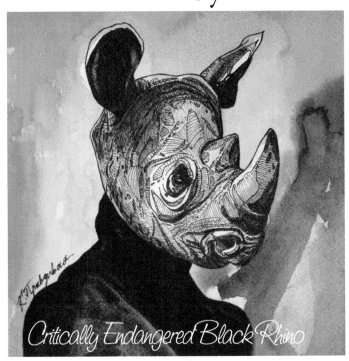

Critically Endangered Black Rhino

Endangered
Tiger

The Elderly Woman living In Apartment B by James G. Piatt

Old memories dancing in a room laden with aromas of spice and algae, as scarred brittle hands clutch at missing hours while apartment windows covered with pink sheets lean into the dawn while people in the street below barter with the devil to placate phantoms that live in their souls. Bodies floating in the wind, their names forgotten or never learned, fall deftly on the pavement in search of unexchangeable lives. Smoke curls in grief, as the moment consumes itself in hushed coughs from an old woman who won't believe in death.

The elderly lady living in apartment B wearing a pink terrycloth robe pours boiling water into a brown betty containing a month old Lipton teabag searching for flavour along-side the whiskey she adds to a broken cup. She laughs at her secret, the secret of still being alive, but being so afraid of death she will not flip a switch to turn on the lights at night, because it might cause electrons to rush out of the wires and flood her apartment and the pink telephone that is going tone-deaf.

The people on the second floor, with their living room covered with patches of rayon grass, think she is strange, living in rusted moments and flowerless room occupied with a blue-lipped octogenarian cat that sleeps with ashen bones, and she with old dancing memories contained in an earthen jar grinning in silence on a marble mantle.

Toothbrusher by Kayla Pongrac

Last night I asked if I could brush your teeth; I wanted to eliminate the germs that congregated on your tongue, scrub the plaque that coated your incisors, polish the molars that never complain about the daily grind. When I lifted the toothbrush to your lips and you opened your mouth, I was certain I felt all the bristles quiver in unison as if they were sympathizing for the two lonely tonsils suspended near the back of your throat, so far away from the foaming paste and the plastic toothbrush that didn't dare venture that far.

Instructions for living, with annotations
by Cath Barton

1. Ensure that all parts are present
No idea how many there should be

2. Assemble the parts according to the attached diagram
No diagram attached

3. Ensure that base is stable
What base?—the thing will not stand up

4. Begin rotation manually
There is a grating noise

5. When rotation is fully established, allow the installation to continue unaided.
Installation of what?

6. Ensure that the mechanism is overhauled at least once a year
Good idea, but if it isn't working to start with … .

Asking for my money back on this one.

Trixie
by Lee Todd Lacks

The Quilt
by Alyssa Cooper

There are pieces of you scattered all over the house, to keep me warm in the night. All the little pieces that you leave behind with every impassioned touch of your scarred and bitter fingertips. I collect them up against my skin, greedy and selfish and uncaring of consequence. I move through cold, empty rooms with your flesh closed tight around me, bathing in the smell of you, the memory, waiting for this internment to end. Waiting for the chance to spread my wings wide, and finally take flight. I'll carry those pieces with me. I'll carry them back to you, and with my small, deft fingers, I'll stitch them back together, so that your warmth shines through every seam.

Finally whole, finally free, you will have all the beauty of dawn—and there I'll be, a tired and tiny moon, resting at your side.

Sacred Ground, Doctore
by Jeffrey De La Rosa

In the drizzle, he steps to the sand's edge,
Raises aloft a child's rubber ball,
Scratches a grizzled jaw, grizzled temple,
And clenches a fist to serve.

An mp3 player screeches Beyoncé
From the shelter of an upturned beach chair.
Nearby, a keg sits half buried like some forgotten droid.
Gray Lake Huron. Steel gray, like steel.

See them all there, waiting,
Crouched around a disused badminton net,
Broad bellies hung over cut-off jeans.
Rain guttering from the cut-offs.

Rue Sainte-Monique
by Lee Todd Lacks

Pleas of soundly
chastened brides
echo through the registers.

Ghosts of bygone
lingerie
lament in scented drawers.

Housemaids blush
at either end
while bracing for the hairbrush.

Yardsticks sting the
upturned rumps
of shameless company girls.

Summer Dollar Sixty

by Wanda Morrow Clevenger

First published in Red Fez – October 13, 2013, Silver Birch Press Beach and Pool Memories Series – July 31, 2016

Every seventeen-year-old girl should be granted a summer romance free of acumen. This romance should begin poolside 1973, and it is imperative the girl is susceptible to being caught unawares. A likeable boy revisiting his hometown will steal her sandals from the concession stand where she makes barefoot dollar-sixty. She searches the upper deck for the sandals. Below, the manager waits to lock the gate. A huddle of boys leaned on a car wait too. The manager yells up, "What are you doing?" The girl pulls a rubber band free, long tawny hair sweeps around one shoulder. "Looking for my shoes," she says. The thief lifts the sandals above his head ("I have them"). The boy huddle is impressed with the enormity of his balls. The girl knows she is singled out above the bikini lifeguards; the boy climbs the hill behind the swimming pool every day for her, he wears her pink-gloss smear on his upper lip. Everyone poolside sees. Everyone poolside approves. Two months in, the boy eats a chili pepper on a dare—she is surprised amused impressed, in love. And he hands her a plastic disc that asks: DO YOU WANT TO SCREW? She does of course, and she doesn't. She nods yes and one night soon his hand pulls her hand down the hill to a shed. There is a leggy spider on a single silk over the cot. Frightened, she tells the spider she doesn't want to get pregnant. He understands, and he doesn't. He disappears for a week—someone sees him get with a bikini lifeguard. She finishes out the summer dollar-sixty. He doesn't say goodbye.

Saturday Night Dance

by Wanda Morrow Clevenger

First published in: Citizens for Decent Literature – October 15, 2012

Getting wasted wasn't the primary goal. Neither was dancing. Both backdrop, secondary bit-players in the small-town extravaganza. Our Town for the '70s. Leaving with a guy, being seen leaving with him, the band's muffled last hoorah cut off as the car door thuds shut, warm vinyl against bare ass was the goal.

Every Saturday night was the same: same place, band. Same faces, too, for the most part. Sometimes it was with a repeat horn-dog, but more often a different guy in a different backseat helping to spread the good word. And it was always good: the beer, the music, the sex. It's what we lived for.

Coliseum's dingy three-stall john was perpetually crammed with females in varying degrees of lucidity. A reeking toxic-dump of cheap perfumes necessary to mask two hours of dancing and excessive consumption. Estee floated in a floral plume around my waist-length hair, worth every hard-earned penny of the twenty-five-dollar price tag. Nectar blossoming against damp skin barely restrained in halters enhanced the passion during the slow dances, though not needed. The Guild's rendition of "Silhouettes," everyone's preferred grab and grope song, dialled up pheromone levels on its own.

A row of firm plums, ripe for the picking, crowded a narrow shelf vying for face time. Tender youth pressed as close to the mirrored wall as a tube of lipstick allowed and wiped glisten away with quick fluffs of Maybelline—a cresting sea of faded bellbottoms and proud nipples poking through spaghetti-strap tanks. Loopy chatter dwarfed the sound of flushing.

Invariably a rush to pee, powder your nose, and get back to your guy before his attention wandered or he got into a fight—no girl wanted to miss the start of the last set. Whoever you ended up with, still clinging on in hopes of a farewell roll in the parking lot, was who you danced McCartney's "Nineteen Hundred and Eighty Five" circle dance with.

On Saturday night all was fair. Every girl wanted a piece of the night to call her own. Every guy just wanted a piece. Blaring music melded into background noise; cocky band became scenery bought and paid for with the price of admission; stamp on the back of the hand was a brand marking you old enough to know better.

Getting some in the parking lot at midnight was never a sin. Getting caught by two overzealous cops who thought they were making a drug bust—we perps naked and obviously not smoking—was considerable bad luck. Facing down the cops, my lace panties stuffed into my accomplice's back pocket while scared shitless I'd be hauled in for screwing, was beyond terrifying. Being released with a warning, then cajoled into finishing the job we'd started was less than romantic.

Having those events exposed was worst of all. Watching one week later, along with two hundred drunk others, as a band member produced my panties, smelled them, then put them on his head like some Easter pussy hat is something I'll never forget, or forgive.

Ewing
by Wanda Morrow Clevenger

First published in: *This Same Small Town in Each of Us* – October 2011, Red Fez – February 13, 2014

And when he snatched my arm just as I came near and whirled me around and sat me on his lap—and by the sheer immediacy of this action—and when he said his name, making clear I knew the name was pronounced different from the spelling and that a girl at school had said it wrong to his amusement and to her dismay, I was taken by the intensity of how he made himself known to me;

and it is true I sometime soon stepped into his last name, pronounced correctly, having done the same since I was old enough to ponder the purpose of doing so and found it a good fit with a pleasant lilt—as most surnames before had sounded pleasant when joined with mine. Embarrassingly romantic, the maddening drive to match jewels to dress to heels to purse;

and he wasn't a boy and I wasn't a child and I soon realized his presence was important, if not out of reach, as he held back while I danced with others and came and left with others while he kept track of the dancing and coming and going—and his sister told me he was in love with me—and it wasn't until far into this watching that he asked why I had not ever gone with him. I said, the words roundly formed, *You never asked me*;

and we had our one date and it failed terribly and maybe this was because I thought I knew what he wanted and he didn't know what I wanted—and we didn't think to see what was showing at the movie theatre or say anything important to each other—and out of the context of dancing and drinking neither of us knew what we really wanted beyond the snatching and sheer immediacy of this action;

and I could have happily paired with his last name, the one when spoken correctly possessed a light lilt, had the timing been different, had we each been someway different.

Elin
by Stephanie Yu

Elin appeared unaware of the colourful warblers that gradually encircled her. They had followed her into the park, as she was head down, religiously gazing into her screen. Why she did not bother to see them was irrelevant, for she was absorbed in more immediate matters, such as where to find the nearest vanilla ice cream.

Fresh dirt rang in her nose like a church bell as she looked up, realizing that she was surrounded by song. An influx of chirps were violently overlapping, soon morphing into complex counterpoint. The music forced Elin onto the grass, and there she lay on her back with eyes closed. Her sprawling, golden hair shimmered like waves underneath the light of the sun.

A crowd of onlookers shuffled towards this fantastical sight.

Elin started to weep. Strings of tears slid down both sides of her head, warmly wetting the insides of her ears. They simmered. *Here I am again*, she mouthed. The cycle seemed to repeat itself, and it grew faster, stronger, and wilder each time. This time however, her sighs increased along with the speed of the swarm. Fear enveloped each voluminous gasp for air. She could no longer hear her own cries now, as they became one with the white noise.

The sounds scattered about the space, dripping into every person and crevice until only a drone remained.

People turned away and resumed their activities. Elin did not move. She realized that no one could see or hear the birds anymore, except for her. With tired innocence, she opened her lips and whispered to the creatures, *Could we go back?*

Her normal breath resumed as the whirlpool of movements lifted her above the ground, carrying her up towards the lavender horizon. Elin, beaming like an exploding sun drifted into another sleep, defying the pull of the earth and vowed never to return.

Untitled Six
by Christie Wilson

Everything stopped for the butterfly on your window. "Get my magnifying glass," you said, propping your hands on your knees. I start to tell you to back away from the glass so no one will see your naked little body, freshly soaped, but then think, who cares.

"I don't know where your magnifying glass is," I say. You command me to yell if it flies away as you fly away down the hall and return seconds later, your left eye huge on your face.

And I don't think about cocoons or sprouting wings, metaphors for later in the day. Instead we count the spots, stare at the symmetry, and laugh when the neighbour waves and you wave back.

Please Wait by Claire Scott

I see you
in a small town I have never seen

perhaps Wheeling, West Virginia or Laramie, Texas
leading my life, the life I said goodbye to

in the fall of my seventeenth year
I toss in a tiny grave

waving to a second-hand truck dragging a U-Haul down
Webster Street, carrying the rest of my life
stirring up eddies of dried leaves
swirling the dust at my feet

I felt your first kiss, your tongue tentative in her mouth
I feel the limp in your left leg, shrieking pain from

shrapnel fired all the way from Iraq
the wounds on my wrists have healed

I felt the wonder your daughter's first cry
tears soaking my face

I know what you are going to say, I hear
your soundtrack in my head

I hide in the red lining of your heart
please wait

China Town
by Joshua B Huitz

Tuscany Hills
by Faisal Warsani

The Cliffs
by Lisha Ruan

Why Must I— by Janet Buck

See you as a Mourning Dove, feathers dropped
skin glued to gutters of winter ice

& not & not in the comfy seat of a bus
headed for heaven's iron gates

prayer groups promise what I doubt
but need to memorize for sanity

you left too soon, for me, not you
with cancer swimming lymph nodes

liver, bones, wherever it landed
it was bad, then got worse

the day they said, "Chemo isn't working now"
the day you didn't call or speak

I wanted to take the plague myself

but you refused, put paper on the toilet seat

said silently, "Do Not Sit Here"
could not answer texts or calls

I want to pull you back from hours
when everyone gathers in tight bouquets

Panglossian perfume floats through ducts
the church is packed with gladiolas

gladiators deep in prayer that suffering
is over with, when ours has just begun

I refuse the day it's time to say goodbye
when I am faulty power lines

watching lilies, knee-jerk tears, sadness
so demonstrative it forms eclipse

123

steps and distant roles
        a cup of clouds spilling
a delicate balance
        rain and red seats
tales bloating like ships
        hotels bursting like rope

the clocks ebbing
        brittle birds in a novel
rougher than a camera
        a house near the airport
pens and young men
        water and white belts

horses and curt gloves
        birds on telephone lines
like a polite guest
        apples and cold steps
bodies folding like writing
        an ivory hilt

California King Size
by Israela Margalit

After my husband died my bed became enormously large, mutated from California King to a Siberian snow field. The deeper I sunk into it, the vaster it seemed. I couldn't lie in the centre. It reeked of death, no matter how painstakingly cleaned. I couldn't lie on my side. Made me feel guilty. Guilty of being warm beneath the skin. I couldn't lie on his side. His side was stiff. Hours with nobody on top of it and the mattress had already become cement. Like a heart deserted. His side was intent on punishing me for the blood streaming through my veins as it always did. No welcoming party on his side. There was no hugging of my shoulders' arcs or gentle bending under the weight of my buttocks. Just a firm rejection of my entire body: Want to be alive? Not on my watch.

I tried my side again, the very side that had been duly mine, even though I'd slept on the edge of my side for months and months, giving him space, giving him comfort, giving him everything I could give so he wouldn't have an excuse to die on me. He won't die, I thought, unless he's decided to give up. Don't give up. Life isn't that bad. Not yet. Look, I've given you three quarters of the bed. I've replaced the mattress four times. Firmer when you needed support, softer when it hurt, springier when turning from side to side in bed was your only workout, and one more time—I don't remember why; because you asked me to, because you had to be reassured there was no limit to what I'd do to keep you wanting to live. We cheated death for a long time, I, by making life too nice to want to depart from, he by playing along. I tried to cheat death a bit longer but suddenly it didn't work. Death was winning. I could see it in his eyes, the way they withdrew deeper into the sockets. Then it came, sneaking in behind my back.

I was sleeping on the edge of my side, hoping I wouldn't fall off and crack my head. I didn't mind dying but I refused to become a vegetable. And maybe I did mind dying because, come to think of it, even though I slept on the edge of my side, and could have easily lost my balance and fallen to the floor, I never did, which proves that I did not want to die, not even after he had. Why didn't I want to die with him? I loved him. I loved him so much that I cared for him at home until the very last minute. Caring for the wellbeing of an adult with a body you can't lift, with physical impulses you don't want to hear about, desires you can't fulfil, and fears you can't alleviate is hard. And yet I didn't want to die just because he had.

Was that a betrayal or a natural instinct? I wanted to discuss it with him in detail, with all its nuances, like we did other matters of importance in our lives. He would have said that I had always been my own person and that was the way he loved me and wanted me to be. Or he'd have said something like, "If you had died I wouldn't have wanted to live without you," but I would have known it was a fib because he liked good wine and cigars too much to just die with me. And that would have lessened my guilt for not falling off the edge of my side of the bed and crashing my head into oblivion. Only I couldn't discuss it with him. I couldn't even look at him to discern his thoughts. A lot was happening after he died but the only thing that felt real was the nothingness of it all.

As soon as I saw him dead I called the children. Then I put on my black slacks and sweater and ran downstairs. Why did I dress and run downstairs? There was nothing to do and no place to go. The lobby was deserted, apart from the relief night watchman on duty whose name I didn't know. I took the elevator back up. The children would be here soon. I sat on the edge of the bed and listened to the deafening silence of the end.

The End of Something
by James Wolf

Sonja was walking with nothing but the direction of a needle easily distorted by magnets and false hopes. In the glare of a noon sun, everything looked like an incline. Her only motivation, at this point, was to avoid the stillness of the present. There was weight to each step. It was a justified weight, a heaviness in over thinking that left tracks deeper than her stature. Any more dimension and she would almost certainly drown in her own version of the dozen beaten paths. The trails were mostly straight, but a compass did not feel out of place. A tamed rose with a pull for wanderers. The kind of mysticism pointing to destinations horses refuse to travel, so you dismount not for sake of purpose and endgames but because you have no better ideas.

This did not always overwhelm her. She knew coping was a managed response for boundaried problems. It was time spent travelling, or how long she'd spend at the top, perched, eyes fixed on distant giants. They were tall metronomes, and their pulses beat with little but the assistance of space and breath and the always-making-it sort of movement that drug her along from spring to whatever now could be called. No starting, no stopping, just her own familiar in between. It was an unwilling pilgrimage. She was pushed into it, shoved. Forced to climb the back of a living mountain as the ground turned, shredded the soles of whatever she had been honest enough to leave exposed. They were all stubborn steps, with two left feet, or backwards attempts at being forward.

The trees stood by. They could see more from the height of their boughs, and stood strong for a resting spot—a leaning spot, at least. *The branches are long,* she thought, *maybe I could pull them down around me and stay here. For a while.* Maybe marking the days in stones would help. You could write letters to the outside, hold conversations through the bars. Prison cell tallies, thank God, are measured, even, predictable. Day one, day eight, straight on through upper brackets and mouldy ceiling tiles—there is pacing.

There's none of that here.

Here you are skipping weeks, sometimes backwards, a grand stitching of tears and pummelling reassurance. You are a hero chasing windmills. You are jousting with a lance of feathers. You are a champion of spare parts and occasional misguidance who has not stopped but for the breath of turbines aloft.

The top is always just a few beats away, until it's not. Until it's here. Sonja saw invisible things in their heartbeats. Her imagination had felt victim to dust for years, full of choppy, heaving sighs and monitored by faulty machinery. It was a headspace full of fractions, of broken months and painfully labelled minutes. (Those were so slow. A near calligraphic mourning. A slowness irrefusable.) It was a schedule no longer worth being

stuck in. She had been dragging someone's heavy potential behind her, like the scraping pull of a prize catch for miles, just to watch its lungs quit, to have no choice but release in the end—a rapid succession of heartbreaks. Neither boots nor feet were prepared for the task.

Questions were harder as they got shorter. The *was-any-of-it-enough* and the *what-was-the-fucking-point*? Worst of all, the *why*? You know why. A hurricane rolled the dice, and while we can't blame nature for its games, we can say with certainty: it did a shitty job. You know full well, if this is escapism, best to take advantage of the momentary exercise in good odds. Find it.

There were enviable beasts full of spinning gears who had found steady breath at the top of a mountain. Beings who had found their space, occupied it and made of it what they needed. They had released what was holding them here. A girl with heavy limbs and full of heart showed up to meet them. She sat down, able to catch a second wind in a space empty but for the greetings of rotating blades. If she sat a while, looked (but not too hard), she could see invisible things in that heartbeat. It was hard to tell what it was, even in broad daylight, but it was closer than it had been.

She could come back tomorrow.

Scar
by Steve Prusky
For J.P.

At the centre of the horseshoe bend, we climb above the desert canyon floor, settle scores. You choose our perch, a sandstone ledge slashed smooth as silence by millennia of cyclonic winds. We lean against the granite wall below the apex of

the cliff above. We fend off hot summer's fickle gusts, dry desert dust, past sins.

After all these years of separation, you are a stranger to me barely bound by blood. Our hands clasp tight, a perfect fit, our entwined fingers weave threads of reawakened familial love. Dim memories of past anger stitch my wounds, soothe my burns as I reflect, forgive, give in, struggle to renew some semblance of at least a tepid bond.

The sea of sand confined inside the canyon walls stirs restlessly as each unsettled grain bears witness to your shame. Eastbound Santa Anna torrents stir the air like a dervish dancing 'round the scrub-strewn canyon floor threatening retribution should the sincerity of your apologies stray.

Stunted Joshua trees cast gray shade east in a futile race with night, granting rest to the shadows of your guilt darkened deeper with regret. The tiring Sun creeps west. The canyon walls bathe the earth below in early dusk. I grasp one last trace of light and brave a peek beyond the past to the dull brightness of the sky's first star convinced complete forgiveness still leaves the silhouette of a scar.

Roadside Royalty
by Roy Dorman

Though oft-times puzzled by the average person's fascination of things royal,

I admit to delight when coming upon a majestic stand of Queen Anne's Lace

growing wild in a moat-like ditch alongside a country road.

Say It With Flowers and Spanish Still Life
by Nory Marc Steiger

Pagan Saint Valentine
by Patrick Connelly

Some recall you
sitting in the grass midsummer
on a hillside olive grove
weaving a chain of wildflowers,
the low hum of your voice
carrying the syllables of her name
like honey bees stirred
from their waggle dances
in the hollow of a fallen oak,
whose dizzy arcs of flight
now trace her name
in cursive loops about your head
as wand strokes of an amative spell.

When you hiked barefoot
down to the village
in your felt hat,
a sprig of long grass in your mouth
that you removed only
to preach in the churchyard,
did you reckon you'd be arrested
and forced to restore
the sight of the judge's daughter?
Did she detect the scent
of honey on your hands
as you held her face,
your thumbs tracing
on her eyelids
the motions of the bee cipher?
When her eyes opened to the light,
and you returned with her

to lay down
among the ox-eye daisies
and scarlet poppies,
did you know
that you'd be dragged off
by the townsfolk
to testify before the emperor?
Did you take comfort
in those final moments
after you evangelized
the secrets of bees,
your gaze from the chopping block
landing on the king
before the axe swooped,
the queen stinging him,
your lips droozed with honey
forming the words
she loves me
she loves me not?

Mediterranean Interior by Nory Marc Steiger

Sauerkraut by Janet Buck

Near the end, your skin turned tired cabbage leaves.
A CNA with ragged nails touched your hand,
punctured it, left hematomas,
scarlet patches broad as quilts.

You were either hot from fighting, cold from not.
Pink tennis shoes at 92, your trademark
worn with Christmas sweaters all year long,
punctuate a knowing smile.

This year you missed the daffodils—
hydrangea petals—hyacinths grow holes.

My eyelids shrink from egg shells
down to oatmeal flakes.

I see too much, dream of sleep,
put my glasses in a drawer,
work hard at growing cataracts.
Tonight brings drooling memories.

I make sauerkraut from scratch,
add vinegar until the kitchen stinks.
Bitter & acidic fit. I argue
with the window latch until I lose.

Buried
by Marcus Benjamin Ray Bradley

Even when my bass strings are perfectly stricken at just the right instant
They are lost on the crowd

Having failed to reach auricles overwhelmed by sounds of instruments
I could play if I wanted to

No intricate fill or booming bottom note is noticed or appreciated
With glances to stage left

The feedback I offer at sound checks fall on deaf ears in the same way
That my notes do

This isn't due to the positioning of amps or the levels of their knobs
But to the hand on the faders

That are used to create a deliberate imbalance proving that all frequencies
Are not equalized equally

The hand belongs to one who plays an infallible god deciding what is best
For humanity's hearing

Passing judgment on which sounds should be featured or suppressed
Like unwanted evidence

I'm in sync with the backup singers and rhythm guitar player as always
As we hollow out this hole

After tonight's gig we'll make good on what we said we'd do the next time
He buries us in the mix

My God
by Tiffany McDaniel

Bare trees are spiders.
Bare trees are spiders on their backs.
The farthest ancestors we have to this widespread miracle.
We are more than a nicked universe.
We are the evolution of figments and fragments
let loose from the thighs of a God in a satin bed jacket,
waiting for the curlers in her hair to set.

Intersection
by Michelle McMillan-Holifield

His knarred
fingers cling to
his bucket. I drop change.
It clangs. He sings to me about
Jesus.

He tells
how they won't let
him sing in church. Tone deaf,
you see. His song undid my walk.
Changed me.

Dandelions
by Matt Kolbet

I never thought I'd be glad to see a dandelion,
the yellow marring my yard like an infidelity.
Even after I uproot them, they show up again,
part of the conversation. A neighbour glances
over the lawn, observes where the colour changes.

One Christmas, a couple years before divorce
sets in, we adopt tortoises since our union has
yet to produce children or more than a doctor's
grim news. In spring we watch their reptilian
glee, munching those ubiquitous weeds. We
feed them all summer long that way, a bent
knee, a few minutes in the sun, and piebald grass.

When autumn returns, rain beckons worms to
the surface once more. I no longer look at the
ground except to keep water from my face. So
under foot and beneath bicycle tires go beetles.

My wife is pregnant when she signs the papers,
an unseasonably warm day with flies hanging
about. Afterward, I go fishing. Grubs baited on
hooks wear slimy smiles, happy to despise me
in the present, knowing how like a child in a fairy
tale I'll be—how plump—when next we meet.

the garrulous irishman by Roddy Williams

weaved his words into the knots of
his laces
but they escaped
to tell me of his shoes

an epic tale
of a quest and bad workmanship
which somehow involved
the history of the geldofs

they were belgian
moved to dublin
at some point during my second vodka

he can feel cobbles through the soles
which I at first took to be some
genetic blessing
but turned out to be the curse
of the shoes

they'll never last
not like amy geldof
who lived to a hundred and five

'fancy that, now,' he said
massaging his imprisoned toes

Yesterday In The Sun
by S.M. Mack

Yesterday
my friend and her sister
sat in the sun
waiting for it to rain.

Today it rained.

I wish I'd been there.

Fragility
by Diana Whiley

Bare Bones
by Brad Garber

When I walked up the road
To search out the buck
Strangled in barbed wire
I thought of struggle
How coyotes smelled it
The things we do we are
The buck known dead
Before it was

Prego
by Gabrielle Rowe

Il Duomo looms above via dei Servi, the sun
creating colours on the octagonal cupola. I push
the stroller-cushioned bambino, bumping and clattering
across the stony street, past luminous windows vying
for tourists. A woman clings to my wrist, a child
at her breast and begs for lire as our eyes dart, lock, part.

A sunburst hones the gloom, a gold monstrance emanating
light from the altar, when I stray into a service and pray
to stained-glass saints in Santa Maria del Fiore. I circle
the Battistero, Ghiberti's doors, their bronze prophets
and gilded sibyls amidst columns and pilasters.

A water drop slips down burnt tiles on the terracotta
terrace in via Il Prato. Francesca surfaces, pristine as she drips
on parquet. The girl holds out her arms, upward palms:
"Prego Signora, prego."

Those Cherries
by Nory Marc Steiger

Geometry Represented
by Nory Marc Steiger

Equinox
by Michele Harvey

I met the simple requirements,
made certain my earthly possessions fit
in two check-ins and two carry-ons.
Equal time, every six months
dwelling north and south
of an imaginary line.

I remember you last autumn,
on that empty Chilean beach,
climbing between the boulders
of my two legs raised to the sky,
how you later chided me for living
between two worlds.

A season since you disappeared,
boulders turned to sand.
Beside thick smog,
the stray dogs,
a half moon;
I remain in Santiago.

Witching Hour
by Jessica Gawinski

Hiroshima Is A Name We Don't Know Yet
by Sarah Brown Weitzman

Translated into German and first published in *The Transnational Magazine #3*, 2015

My mother is mixing a half-dozen muffins
this July evening. Tall in her high heels,

she creams the butter and sugar, then slowly adds
the eggs. She smells of Shalimar and vanilla

in the oven-warm kitchen. Intent, she doesn't speak
except about her own mother's cakes. I am

waiting as patiently as nine can for a heaping tablespoon
of batter for my jar-lid pan for a tiny cake of my own.

Still wearing his jacket and tie my father's reading
the newspaper. Through the glass door, we can see him

sitting in the big side-winged horsehair chair
in the bay window. We know he's waiting too

to read the war news to us as the house fills with the odor
of rising dough. Hiroshima is a name we don't know

yet. Outside the gloom sits on the porch settee
and whines like a dog to be left in.

Finally, it is time. My mother's muffins have billowed
high out of their cups, golden as the kitchen ceiling

and edged with a perfect complement of brown.
But my tiny cake, left in too long, is black, flat

and rock-hard. Oh, how I weep like a lost child
now for my childhood and that little charred cake.

The Body
by Jason Kerzinski

On Maria street, between Pauger and Touro, people sit on porches with their heads lowered between their knees. Half-way down the block, I notice a jet-black rooster lying on the cement. A few feathers fly in the breeze. Empty, trash strewn lots surround the body. A black hefty bag has ripped open, and the contents blow in the wind—unpaid bills, bygone letters and cards from past holidays.

Circling around the body are four red roosters in a slow procession. The roosters slowly step around the body in a counter clockwise motion, making strange clucking noises—grieving noises that sounded oddly familiar—like the crowing version of, "A Closer Walk With Thee."

People leave their porches toward the body. Crows gather from above. People on the block make a circle around the mourning roosters. The crows descend. They make attempts to penetrate the arms interlocking over the body. The crows cried out of frustration. The community had formed an impenetrable cage around the roosters.

As I look back the sky had cleared of crows. I drifted down the street, unsure if what I saw was real. I felt if I turned around again, the street would be bare except for floating letters, unpaid bills, and holiday cards—remnants of someone's past.

On Violation
by Kate Bucca

Fingernails etch your pain into an old bedspread. Your mind detaches from your body, curls itself into a small ball. Allows you to watch safely, peeking out through fingers – a child at a horror film. Ready yourself for distancing.

Me as different from what my mother expected startles her in the way drops land clear across the bathroom in spite of a carefully curtained shower. I am her water, running too hot or too cold. No matter how she turns the knobs, I will not even out or become temperate.

Everything you accomplish will be despite your husband. You will lose the right to be proud of what you do for its own sake, achieve it in stark contrast to what you've endured. In this way, he will continue to rape you for decades.

There's just too much woman in the house, my father says to me. I am still unsure whether he says this with pride or anger, and learn early the push and pull of loving those who terrify us most.

When your ex calls his new daughter the name you chose – together – a decade ago, you will not know how to feel. Swaddle the girl from afar with the hope that she will never know his violence. Mourn your own miscarriage; question the cost of love. Return him, family in tow, to the partitioned-off part of you. As he fades, cradle the peace of distance and let it drum into your chest. This is the second heartbeat you've created.

Disappear
by Kendra Liedle

She finds a shady spot and parks the car, takes her keys and locks the door.

Walk away, disappear.
Leave no trace of who you were.
People go missing every day.

She leaves her phone on the seat, her wallet on the floorboard. She reaches the boulevard and walks to where the sidewalk ends. Stumbling, she looks down at the pavement below her feet.

She dodges cars: Jaguar, Mercedes, and BMWs. Some honk as they fly by. They can't see the light fading on her face. Hidden behind tinted windows, they don't know she's another lost soul, evaporating into smog.

How did it come to this? She has forgotten the story, the complications and the heartbreaks that have led her here. All she knows is the solution:

Walk away, disappear. They'll never find you here.

There's an overlook, a turnout. Mulholland, there it is. Dusk and downhill. Foggy. This is where it ends. She turns right and stumbles onward. Pavement, gravel, dirt…

One last glimpse of a mountain view. There is no going back now, Bettie Blue.

Pretty girl. Knockout. Miss America.

This town shakes them, blends them up. Few survive intact. Most come out in pieces— a jumble of who they were. It can take a lifetime to find themselves again, but a piece is missing forever. Lost.

Stolen. Disappeared.

Pretty girl. Knockout. Miss America.

Washed away in waves. Buried in the sand. Evaporated in California sun. You've disappeared trying to find that— it's you, you've left behind.

***

"Denim cut-offs. A Billabong T-shirt with flowers on it. Sneakers with laces too long."

"It's unlike her to be gone this long. Her phone goes straight to voicemail…"

"I was her boyfriend. Ex, I should say. We broke up about a month ago, but she had been fine. She'd been okay…"

An actress. Aspiring. A few auditions here and there, not enough to pay the rent. She did some things she wasn't proud of. Her boyfriend broke it off, but worried just the same.

"I thought she'd crossed a line. And I couldn't watch her fade away. Not like all the others."

Walk away, disappear. They'll never find you here.

"We'll find her. Everyone leaves traces. "

"Post up flyers. Offer a reward. Don't ever let them forget—"

Pretty girl. Knockout. Miss America.

They're all the same when blended and sucked up through a straw.

Lost. Missing. Disappeared.

All the outcomes loved ones fear. All alone, stumbling toward— One last glimpse of a mountain view. There's no going back now, Bettie Blue.

Evidence of Existence
by Kayla Pongrac

I am jealous of dinosaurs and the enormous tracks they left behind. My feet, by comparison, are embarrassingly small in their size nine-ness, and I am distraught that I cannot mandate their fossilization.

Spoiled, those dinosaurs!

I, too, deserve a mysterious extinction that would beckon archaeologists to my crater of a grave so they could extract my ancient bones and magnify my delicate-looking fingers, my impressively shaped skull, and my jaw full of teeth that pull my look together by barely looking a day over millions of years old.

I want to be classified by a carefully chosen name and displayed in a museum, the evidence of my existence preserved— mandible dropped, knees slightly bent, fists closed and thumbs extended upward. How I would die to make museum-goers stop and stare at my skeleton as docents pointed to me and exclaimed, *Behold our most delightful and rarest specimen of all!*

Cooper
by Kayla Pongrac

When my dog hikes in the woods, he owns every acre—or at least acts like it. Cooper seems certain that the chipmunks have been strategically placed on every trail for his chasing pleasure, the deep streams carved for his paddling, the trees grown specifically to provide yet another woodsy thrill: sticks!

When Cooper strays too far and I call him by name, he sprints back to me, sits by my side like the good boy he knows he is, and then opens his mouth to accept his chicken-flavoured treat as a believer would a communion wafer.

Here's one of my favourite examples of a palindrome:

DOG GOD

On paper, that's the closest my dog gets to God. Hiking in the woods, savouring the thickness of nature, is the closest my dog gets to believing. And maybe at home, too, when Cooper Amens himself into a ball, takes a nap, and prays that we'll hike again tomorrow. His prayer always gets answered, which could lead one to suspect that it's not so much about my dog believing in God as it is the other way around.

The Crab Apple
by Matt Pucci

I saw her today.

Walking toward me, on her way home from school. She's tall now, like her brothers—like her dad. A young woman. My heart pounded. Would she remember me?

She stopped, said hello. Still with that slight gawkiness, but something new. Something different. A sense of self. An awareness, on some level, of who she is.

We chatted a while, standing in the rain. I'd looked out for her. Back when they all called her weird, and "sullen". Oh, she was an odd-bod, all right. But my God.

That face…

She smiled. And then she was gone.

The '57 Chevy And The Scent Of Sorrow
by Kim Peter Kovac

Winter morning, the finned '57 Chevy wagon wending through the hilly suburbs smells like – well, it smells like nothing, leaving empty space for the 13-year old boy's numb nerves to bounce around searching for understanding of the big fat stupid event. He sits in the shotgun seat next to a barrel chest & a shock of salt-and-pepper hair and in front of his older brother. It's the 60's so no seat belts, yet all are constrained by the shock of a sudden death – not the kind at the end of a football game where the first score wins – but the kind that leaves a salty and rusted iron taste in the boy's mouth, the flavour of death, in this case the boys' father, also the brother-in-law of the man driving and droning in a mellifluous bass-baritone. He's large, a minister in a fundamentalist sect the boys and family don't embrace, flying 1,000 miles and providing a gentle, calming presence in a grieving household, a love-blanket belied when he slyly segues into attack-mode, asking kindly if the brothers ever want to see their two-days-dead father again, because, if they do, simply joining his sect will guarantee a reunion in the future, in heaven, presumably. Immediately all the air is sucked from the boy's lungs and a miasma of unwashed running shoes floods the car an odour that decades later he learns is Rue, a medicinal herb, an insect repellent, known to herbalists and shamans for its smell of sorrow, regret and betrayal. It's fingernail-scraping cold outside, yet the boy rolls down his window and sticks his head out, and does not respond.

On the Spyland
by Kim Peter Kovac

Hard left behind the granite slab back-dropping the seventeen foot bronze statue, a man ghosts from dusk's tree-shadows, dressed in slicked-back dyed-black hair, a phthalo blue track suit and red eel skin Gucci loafers. He glides toward a concrete bench featuring a man in a shiny black suit and 80s vintage aviator sunglasses, reading a newspaper in the New York subway fold, sensuously inhaling a Sherman Brown cigarillo. August afternoon on tiny Teddy Roosevelt Island on the Potomac, only reachable via footbridge from the Virginia side, is an unlikely meeting place for straight-out-of-Central Casting muscle-bound dudes who'd be cast as smugglers, thugs, or spies from some vague Eastern European region. Red Guccis casually loops around the bench and sits, studiously ignoring both the man in the suit and the ultra-sincere 50ish couple with their hating-the-hike grandkids. Aviator lowers his glasses and hard-stares with reptile eyes at a man leaning against a tree writing in a journal. I feel his ice-grey eyes even before I quickly glance up, so I continue writing in and out of a prose poem kinda sorta about the present moment. Fortyish words later, I sneak a look and note that Aviator has gone, and left his paper. After about five minutes of basking in the near-tropical humidity, ignoring the sweat rolling off his fore-head, Gucci-man grabs the paper, and heads off to the north, on his way to the swamp trail. I speculate about the significance of the newspaper and wonder if the eel skin will find his family during the walk in the swamp.

Songs
by Linda Lowe

1971

In a night club in Lake Arrowhead, she's belting out "Stand By Your Man" when a moth flies into her mouth. She doesn't choke, she doesn't miss a beat. The show must go on, after all. When the band goes on break, a man comes up and puts his arm around her shoulder, says how well she "handled that moth." She smiles, sips some water. He asks her if she knows the Mary Travers song, "Follow Me." She says, no, but I can learn it, and he hands her a twenty. Her husband walks up about then, sees the guy's arm, her smile, and that twenty. In the car, on the way home, she's thinking about the future. She's going to have to take the kids and leave, but how? Who should she call? Where could she go? Her mind is full of questions when his right hand comes off the steering wheel, and quick as a Cassius Clay, hits her in the mouth. Funny, she thinks, they're yellow, not silver, and not twinkling, but they are stars. Yellow stars swirling in front of her eyes. Her lips will swell, one eye will blacken. But her teeth will be fine. She'd kept her mouth shut enough for that. Her teeth are straight and white and cavity free. Back in junior high she'd won the Smile of the Year contest. Back when there was something to smile about.

New York
by Linda Lowe

1983

What was nineteen floors beneath her in the Hilton on Sixth Avenue was garbage. The street was full of it, the garbage strike several days old. Her husband had finally passed out, and she was so distraught she thought *what if I landed in that?* She'd never understood much that's scientific, like wind and how you fall in it, and height and speed and the significance of weight--a 120 pound woman falling though a twenty degree evening. To have landed on the sidewalk where it was cold and swept, seemed a clean and dramatic thing to do, but the garbage was a possibility, so instead she wrote a sestina about New York and having too much money. It was an insidious flower that bloomed and bloomed, making everything possible but unimportant. After the Hilton her nights back home became unedited versions of the TV ad where the man comes home at two or three in the morning, flips on the bedroom light, and says, *Oh, did I wake the little woman?* Torture was no steady drip on the forehead for her. She finally left to get some sleep. Even the ghetto blasters in the new neighbourhood didn't keep her up. She didn't miss that big bedroom with the yellow velvet bedspread, the moiré wallpaper she'd picked out herself, everything in the most serene yellow. When her friend Celia told her she'd always wanted to be queen, she thought of the prisons of the rich, and how she wouldn't change places with Elizabeth, or Princess Di with that big sapphire, for anything.

Oregon
by Phoebe Merten

I miss you. Your reaching hands of moss pushing pine needles everywhere; the mud; the smells on the wind: water, and wood smoke, and sweet clean forest decay. Here there are trees, but not real trees. The smells on the wind are exhaust, and piss, and sometimes the ocean.

Out my window at night, there's no pitch black of unlit woods; instead palm trees are silhouetted jagged against a sky lit up orange from the city, and streetlights glare, and the lights inside my neighbours' windows spill all their lives into mine.

In the day it's all sunshine, bright and hot, unrelenting. The clouds, when they do come, are the high clouds that don't hug the earth or cry for it, like your clouds do.

The ocean here isn't fierce like yours; no waves a churning maw gulping towards my feet, no wind blowing sand and rain in my face, no deep chill eating down to my bones to live there. It's docile: waves washing gently, welcoming me into a fluid embrace; sun beaming down; sand warmly cuddlesome.

I could drown just the same.

Tide
by Quinn Ramsay

Her toes dig into soft sand, shells and seaweed scraps swish around her ankles. She gasps. The ocean is sharp and cold, though the sun has fallen into it, sunken nearly out of sight. Soon it will be dark, and she will return home numb.

She makes a game of it now. At first, the coldness could not be borne, the pain of it, the squeezing. She learned to think loudly, to shout, to drown out the screaming in her legs until now she can stand ten minutes, maybe more, without stepping back to land. The pain is welcome. It clears her head of other things, of a life which, like the ocean, hides clutter amidst vast emptiness.

Some days she tries many times, until her mother's voice cries out, gull-like, harsh, over the dunes. Then she returns, and her thoughts scuttle like crabs behind her. She feels the sharp pins of their feet creep up her legs and through her hair. They burrow into the shells of her ears and whisper, each straining to be heard above the rest.

Sometimes, at night, she grasps a fish hook in one wet palm. When the whispers grow too loud, she squeezes.

Lemon Drops for Paige

LEMON DROPS

Land of Enlightenment

Chess-Nut Swamp

by Roopa Dudley

Aries

Good-by Mr Winter Frost Bite

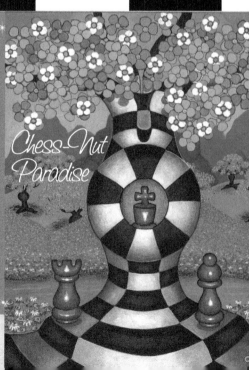

Chess-Nut Paradise

Confronting My Demons

Sweetheart

Consummate

Dorian Grey Cat

by Roopa Dudley

Monotheism's Latest Greatest Emancipation Proclamation
by Gerard Sarnat

Like moths through mittens,
there is a current among the three of us.
The sun probed our eyes even though
we hook-nosed pretty-boy
walking wounded testy testes
were alligator clip hobnail bootstrapped
then circumcised miles below
the earth's surface currying electric
favor in the eclectic Holy Basin bunker
by triaging Muslim Reformation
terror diasporists into a vast theatre
of outage outrage outed outposts.

Past Moses and Jesus believers,
hurt or disappointed, yearned for dispersion.
Freedom from Torah's yoke,
temple/ church advanced to sovereign mosque,
rabbinate/ priests became imams
whose prayers veered toward sacrifice:
this's where hatred mutated from gutter
anti-Semitism to more respectable
anti-Zionism—Ishmael's just-discovered memo
of understanding vowed in cold blood,
Oldest brother, you are now
not welcome at my family table.

Alice in Hell
by Annie Blake

I was sitting on my mum's couch desperate to be a virgin—
I wore my child clothes and watched old-fashioned cartoons.
That's when my mum came crashing in from behind me to open the trapdoor.
And that is the point I fell like Alice in hell.
I fell and fell. There was no time for keys or spells or magic brooms
which fly to the moon.

Apollo
by John Repp

Tilted at a reentry angle, the capsule
demonstrates how cramped & primitive
the Apollo years. Kids peal how small
the astronauts must have been,

the docent urging awe at their courage,
especially when it came to squeezing
food from toothpaste tubes. Best not
to ask too much of ones so young.

Science is fun, serious fun & the capsule
looks real. I examine the heat shield
atmospheric friction chipped & blackened
in millions of imaginations as the world

watched the head-phoned newscaster
read the latest bulletin. Simulations
thrilled me & later the transmissions
from inside the speck hurtling

yet seeming utterly still on its way
to the animated moon. They've propped
the hatch open. This thing bobbed
on the open sea. Teams of engineers
had to reason each bit from nothing.

Miriam
by Kerry Wingood

I used to hunt for ant lion pits in the garden
Where a musky guava haze hung
We called them twirly wirlies
The waft of pork fat seeped from your kaya
And you offered me samp and beans
We brought you saltwater from the sea
In bottles with beds of sand
I heard you wretch and send the spirits away
Your skin was soft and ample
And you smelt like lemon leaves

From the Annals of Contemporary Dating
by Michael Fontana

At long last I found love. It had a sweet candescence to it. Her lips, I remember, were as soft and pliable as caramel. Her eyes circled like bowls of goldfish. When I touched her skin there were soft craters formed that might have been reflections of the moon.

I took her first to a restaurant where they served fresh sea bass full of bones. I crunched them as they tore into the softness of my mouth. She didn't mind the blood. She thought it manly that strands of it stuck to my lips as I talked to her.

Afterwards we walked along

Twin grandsons, 8 years old
by Saxby Pridmore

It's like you take a tour of The Empire State Building and throw yourself off the top and land on a refit of deluxe hotel mattresses, on an open truck, going along 5th Avenue, and you slip off

at the lights. And the wind along East 34th Street sends a one-hundred-dollar bill skipping and spinning through the air and straight into your pocket. And a Cop looks at you like you stole something but, all he can do is say, "Goddamn".

They're like two 8 month old Labrador puppies that keep licking your knees because they like the way you taste. And you can tell, if you go to gaol they'll visit on your birthday, every year year after year, until you get parole.

Gandy Dancers
by Brad Garber

We stood across the rail from each other
nine-pound hammers in hand
he Hispanic and tall and glistening
in thick Wisconsin summer
sweat too thick for mosquitoes
brown like swamp weeds down
where Mississippi rattlers coiled
me a sun-baked college kid
and drove steel spikes into oiled wood
"ping/ping"—"ping/ping"—"ping/ping"
three strikes and in, deep to hold
a hot rail in its place, boxcars rolling.
Next tie, nestled in rough ballast
spikes placed and ready, "ping/ping"
rhythm of muscles dancing in time
chain gang thoughts and challenge
smiles of conquest, muscles tight
no boundaries, just the love of movement
we strutted like dancing cranes, high
our wings swinging in competitions
far beyond the simple pleasure of art.

the promenade while I sucked on a napkin to stanch the bleeding. The moon hung in the air like a luminous watch dial, ticking away our steps, our words, our faintest gestures. Finally we lay in a field of baby's breath where I unpinned her hair. The hair was dense and moist as spaghetti fresh from the bowl. I ran my fingers through it and it wrapped around them. I sucked it until no hair remained on her head. Now that she stood bald as a boulder, I played phrenologist and touched my fingertips to each small crevice of her skull.

I do not know at what precise instant our bodies aligned but they did, clustering together as if more than one body was involved, hers, mine and the moon perhaps, but I could not breathe in the midst of it. My throat literally closed and threatened to kill me even though it would have been quite a rapturous death, her body around me like the final stages of a mugging, mine dissolving inside her like sugar into water.

Afterward there were minor earthquakes in East Timor and Swaziland as direct effect. Her belly immediately swelled and turned loose a secondary moon that orbited her body, with particular emphasis upon her breasts, which were coated in sweat and throwing off starlight.

After that I walked her home and kissed her at the door while dozens of small children poured out of her like urine to splash on the stone of the steps. I returned home to wash my face, hands and torso, jotting down her cell number in repetitive motions all over the walls and sheets before lying down to bed.

Heart
by Lindsey Anderson

Valentine's Day was more democratic in elementary school. Everyone could count on receiving a card—even the kid who sat alone at lunch and always ate home-cured deer jerky.

Each year I'd select with my mother the finest card that corporate America had to offer. Barbie dancing with Ken across a bed of roses. Cinderella sweeping up a cascade of tiny cartoon hearts. Pre-packaged and pre-decorated with a tasteful splash of glitter, a sticker or two.

Studies suggest that little girls suffer from poor self-esteem. And—according to a team of clinical psychologists at New York University—the average girl's happiness peaks at age nine.

The best of the cards came with bits of chocolate or conversation hearts. I didn't like the taste of those candy hearts—no one did. They were like the crusty stiff sponges that multiplied behind the kitchen sink.

> The Anatomy of a Candy Heart:
>
> Sugar, Corn Syrup, Corn Starch, Modified Food Starch, Gelatin, Sulfur, Natural and Artificial Flavours, Clam Sauce, Cyanide, FD&C Colours, Toenail Clippings, Petrified Wood Shavings, Vegetable Gum, Arabic Gum, Lead-Based Face Paints, Partially Hydrogenated Lamb's Wool, The Left Eyelid of a Canadian Caribou

But the hearts had an appeal that could not be curbed by terrible taste. Contained within them was a recipe for lasting romance, a declaration of love in twelve letters or less.

The New England Confectionery Company (NECCO) original Sweethearts Conversation Hearts have been a Valentine's Day fixture for generations. Cute, quirky and playful, the heart-shaped candy treats are a great way to let your Valentine know you care without getting all mushy—the hearts do the talking for you!

I liked to arrange mine in little rows along my desk. Points turned in, toward me, they were soldiers waiting to receive my marching orders. And I'd send them to their deaths one by one by one until only the best of them was left—the one whose message was purer and more beautiful than all the rest.

And the parents of those little girls are, understandably, upset. They write angry letters to their local newspapers. They curse Barbie and Cinderella for giving their girls unrealistic standards to live up to. They wring their hands and tell their daughters that, no, they can't get a nose job.

That one I'd wedge between my molars and oh-so-solemnly crush to death, meditating upon its message as chalk dust dissolved to liquid along my tongue.

But there are no angry letters levelled against the marketers of Happily Ever After. No curses for the creators of Unrealistic Expectations. These girl-children are left to learn for themselves that no nose job will ever straighten their crooked dreams.

Later, years later, I discovered a box of unopened conversation hearts in the pocket of an elementary school backpack. The box was faded, but the hearts were as bright as they'd ever been, and the conversations carved into their candy faces were the same, the same as always and nothing like what I had remembered.

BE MINE * LOVE ME * CALL ME * I WANT YOU * I NEED YOU * I'M LOST WITHOUT YOU

Disappointed, I sent the candy hearts skittering across the floor with a flick of my wrist. Canary Yellow and Sea-Foam Green and Pepto-Bismol Pink rolled, then settled, in the cracks around my feet. I raised my heel an inch or two before bringing it down again, hard, on one of the hearts. But of course nothing happened. Candy hearts are dense, and damn near un-stompable.

Kicking Roses
by Lauren Dunne

Painted with the chaffs and wrinkles of time, my fingers explore the crevices of the chair that keeps me prisoner; dipping and bumping along the dents of the wheels. I cannot answer the mountain's call for footprints in their wet, damp, soil. So instead, I oblige and listen to the eerie squeak of the old swings' cry that sings out for the ghosts of laughter and voices of play. The children have left the old park for their mother's warm embrace, the loaves of bread that await to be soaked in rich butter.

Spreading across the room like a disease; her shadow snaps me out of my daze to the freshly disinfected floor. Her stretched reflection is illuminated by the harsh white lights, and she stands timidly in her bland apron behind the half closed door. Sleep fails to mother me away, the other patient's words *Come put me to bed* I seldom speak.

Like a child's drawing, our lives a mixture of colours and lines and shapes that don't quite seem right. We are a houseful of forgotten and misplaced jigsaws that have been thrown together; a desperate attempt to put us back to the men we were.

Veiny leaves struggle through the barred windows that persist in stopping us from ever meeting their trunk, filling the room with smells of all things alive; in their own, small way, breaking me free. Delicate smells so intricate they soak through the cotton curtains, push past the hard bed and weave in and around and around and all throughout me.

Growing ever greener and lusher among bees, birds and butterflies, the leaves flourish until the brown sickness seeps through their veins. Unable to cure the inevitable, the mother trunk lets go of what it has nourished. It is left among the worms and ants and bugs to become what will be needed to nurture the new foliage in the spring.

Leaves hold memories of all things before, and become the essence for all things after.

Their scent and memories encompass me so completely, and every sensuous cell in my body is reminded of the time when this town swung so gay. When the ladies wore red, and they laughed and glanced lovelier as the nights grew tireder. The floors were a flurry of dances, dresses every shade of red the sun has ever set; reds of boys kicking wild roses in the meadows, of rubies basking elegantly in the twilight sun, and wasted blood spilled all over its wound.

The sounds of heels tapping on the dance floor still echo in my mind, the clumsy steps of the love-seeking men are ever drowning out my thoughts. Deep laughter, shrill chatter and eager how-do-you-dos.

The smell of yeast and frothy bears tilts my head back, The bathroom door opening and closing with each bar goer's reality of one too many, and the local high school jazz band obliviously playing on.

And the girl, with eyes so dark and heart so big, that none of the rest matters. Not the way her cocktail forms a ring of condensation on the dark musty timbre, the man in the bowler hat who's stare holds just a bit too long, or the amateur musicians who seem to always be off the beat.

The dancers slow, each movement dragging out, every beat lasting longer than the last.

The leaf lingers only for a moment more before it drops onto the cold, unforgiving floor; freezing its scent, killing the memories it held.

She's slipping away, and I won't be able to bear it when she goes. Even after all this time. Always she has been the beat to steady my heart.

Standing tall to walk calmly and dignified out of my head and heart, her satin dress is the colour of her lips as she bends to whisper in my ear. *Come, I'll put you to bed.*

Her words cannot hide the quiver in her lip, the glisten in her eye, or the sweat of her palm as she turns, brushing my leg with her delicate fingertips.

It's a strange feeling when, even a memory has to tell you it's goodbye.

Veni Vidi.
by Quinn Ramsay

I came I saw I cursed I cowered I ran. I am but what I am. What I became, when I came on you in the midst of snarled metal and scorched rubber, or what the roadside device had left, pasted over the searing sand like so much strawberry jam.

I came I heard ... nothing. The percussive thud deafened me to screaming pain and shouted orders, sizzling machinery and Perkins' groans—he lost an arm and half a face that day. I could not hear my own curses. I cursed I cowered I ran I fell.

I came to on the other bank of the Rubicon, tasted blood in my mouth and everything was white. The Nurse was white the walls were white my gown was white my face was white. They said I'd lost a lot of blood, I coughed up blood, I saw I cursed. I was red and white and blue.

I came home I saw that we had conquered nothing. I could not even conquer my dreams: bleeding on the floor of the senate, twenty-three shards of shrapnel in my flesh. People. New suits black shoes. They asked what I had seen, and I couldn't even speak.

L'Absinthe
—on the Degas painting
by Gregory Stapp

He begged me to be his subject, and now
look at me, I'm a doll from *A Doll's House*,
the dingy white contrast between a dress
and a brooding dark companion.

When I see myself as a doll in *A Doll's House*,
I find I'm an object, like the suggestion of a table,
a dark companion in a dance slipper, bras au repos,
an actress whose performance followed her home.

I find it objectionable and suggest it at table—
why this figurine with an etched face, mime of pose,
an actress who forgot to remove her makeup,
this mirror of melancholy? As a hung portrait,

I mimic the position of a posed figurine who faces
scenes of gaiety, sweet wine, and raised glasses
mirroring the melancholic end to a fine afternoon.
No amount of absinthe will void that image now,

rather it will enhance the gaiety and wine and glass
until Marcellin cannot tolerate sitting near me.
Since no amount of absinthe can fill his void,
his scintillating cup calls to be filled and drained

as does mine. It calls me like applause, but I wait,
a dramatic pause, more tolerant than Marcellin.
The scintillating cup calls to succour my needs,
to return me to subject, the beggar's object.

Film Noir Self Portrait
by Sally Jeanne Stevens

While He Sleeps
by Ariel Dawn
First published in Litro, February 2015

My steps spill rain from trees and the trees reveal old dream faces.
I write to them and Rhys sleeping and Lucy who lives in this forest.
Apologies, stream of consciousness, echo poems dying for echo,
all rolled in leaves, tied with sparkling blue ribbon, and slipped
into abandoned nests, coloured bottles, ivy hollows and deep
branches. Under bitter cherry, diary with belts and pin on a string,
I keep it buried: hole and earth in my hands, the invisible living.

Spare by Stacey Margaret Jones

The woman on the book jacket
walks along the railroad tracks
away from me, her reader.
Without any luggage,
long hair, spare, where the tracks
cut right, she strolls straight
ahead. Though I cannot see her face,
her posture assures me she is assured
of the figure she cuts in the air there,
below the title, *Sweet Tooth*,
one foot lifted, mid-step,
she knows where she is going. That is why
the publisher chose her from
the stock-art file. [cont. pg 143]

Her trench coat covers her,
but I know who a woman is without any suitcases
strolling along toward the end of an empty platform.
She is light, airy.
She has *come so far, it is over.*
Don't be morbid: she will not leap.
There is no flat, two-dimensional death
in her paper future. She will transcend.

You can see this familiar of the skeletal me there,
so perfect, so clean, so
Tidy.
An apotheosis, not the getting-to.
She is complete in her self
and she calls to the woman in me
who wants to control,
to tame
all the cogs and wheels of my world.
She is the she who asks me, sceptically,
in a sound that isn't a voice, but the raspy
haunt of a blown-out reed,
Will you be good enough today?
Will you be like me?
She wants to run things.
Make me thin and flat
like her.
She walks ahead of me along the platform
to show me where to go,
how to cut dimensions of baggage away
how to walk without luggage to the end
that is the beginning of clean,
a sterile, trench-coated, emotionless world
of perfected, slim achievement.

I know I will see her again.
I will feel the chill
from a magazine page,
or find her walking ahead of me in the airport.
In her wake.
I will know her by her hidden face.
Anyway, she is not smiling.
She is bone cold.

Wind by Nancy Devine

Jimmie Paul socked me in the gut
and my wind went all the way
to Canada before it came back
in no hurry.
He'd hide near a plum tree afterward
or the evergreens next door,
his too-pink lips
a give-away that he was not inside yet.

Jimmie Paul's mother sometimes fixed my hair.
I'd sit on a chair in her kitchen,
and she'd work around me,
teasing and back-combing,
rat tail and Spraynet.
She was done
when she bobby-pinned in a bow
to match my dress.
I'd always go home, careful.
This was how I wanted to look.

Jimmie Paul's parents got divorced,
I heard,
long after they moved away,
not just across town
but back to the state
where they came from,
somewhere south
where it doesn't get as cold.

Jimmie Paul never gave me a clue
about why he'd make me
suck and gasp,
when one minute earlier
we were on tricycles in the spring,
nearly breath-less in delight.

We'd stop in the driveway
between our houses.
He'd just get mean
and I would feel bad,
blown away
by how much I could be hurt.

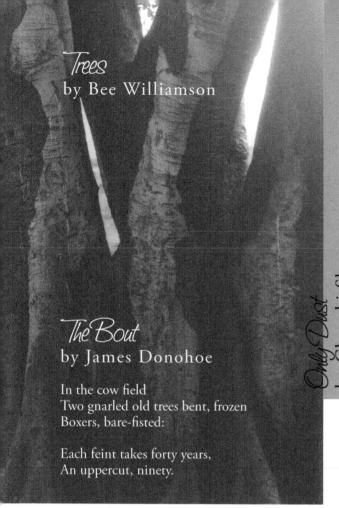

Trees
by Bee Williamson

The Bout
by James Donohoe

In the cow field
Two gnarled old trees bent, frozen
Boxers, bare-fisted:

Each feint takes forty years,
An uppercut, ninety.

Cateechee Blue Yodel Number 5
by Robert Lee Kendrick

White whips hang from tree limbs,
snap collapsed veins. Too many hits

to the mainline, needle fine
splinters strewn over ice.

Dusk spits hooks from its mouth.
My pig bone necklace clinks

over my heart, slaughterhouse
shape notes of nothing foretold.

Only Dust
by Chumki Sharma

Bartender transforms into a keg
and the keg is a field of poppies.
My tiny house midst the poppies,
raptures into a seed,
its burning woodstove
becomes an oak grove,
then a sickle, then a stone.
String of lights on my porch
become fireflies I tried to catch
once as a girl, when the shepherd boy
became a lamb, the lamb became
Jesus, then Adam, then dust.
Dust of the jet black stone,
the rock of Shiva at Kailas,
its bare head a birth canal
you challenge me to enter,
so I wriggle in and come out
birthed, kneeling, kissing the dust.

Handful of dust
this Universe
stars

Seven times seven times
spit on my grave that hasn't been dug,

I swore on goat blood
and the King James Bible

I stole from my mother
that I'd gut the moon

for taking the panther eye
face mask I see through in sleep.

He can run to the other side
of the world, but he can't hide

from me. The creek covers
her children under her skirt.

Coyote howls *best not let
the boys in.* He knows this snow

will glow like fresh coals tonight.

Willow Tree
by John Spiegel

When I die,
he says,
I want to become
a willow tree.

I want children to swing
on my long,
dangling arms,
just like my sister used to,

or those kids during
pool time
from summer camp
I staffed that one year.

We had a willow in my
front yard and
I loved that thing in a way
I didn't understand until now

even though I
could never climb
it like I wanted.
But my brother made it

and fashioned a ladder
with knots in a
frayed rope. When I was a
kid I would grab a handful

of the long,
dangling branches,
and jump up to swing
on them. I felt the

tree sag under my
weight, like
my mother when
I would tug her arm.

Peaches and Cream
by Christopher Owen Nelson

I Need Light
by Honor Clement-Hayes

There's branches and scrambling brambles
tangling over the blue sky and I need light
but they're choking me I'm scrabbling and
babbling nonsense in breathless distress.
The tunnel where I end bends and blurs
and blooms with dark flowers and dying
fairies and I was wary but still wandered
in wonder until the light ran out and I
shouted in fear but no one could hear how
afraid I became. It's eating me I'm just
meat to it and no matter how much I bleat
it won't release me until I'm consumed
and my spirit is exhumed by the forsaken
fates that govern this unsacred place. I can
scratch at my throat all I please but there's
a whisper in the leaves that refuses release
I'll die in here where the sun's blocked out
and the thick woven trees absorb every
shout if I struggle I'm in trouble but I
think it's too late and no matter how I
pray they'll just eat me anyway.

Some Leaves—Some Ground
by G. M. Monks

The ground, speckled like a parade
had passed, leaving autumn confetti. Yellows,
reds, the oranges are best. Ginkgo maple oak
eucalyptus all splayed like cut-out shapes,
like a Matisse painting. If I was with Matisse,
he'd hold my arm and love that I took him
down this path. He'd say Let them be, don't rake
them into piles. And I'd say They need to be bagged
and put in the trash. Oh no he'd say, and he'd kick
a pile to watch the confetti scatter. Shapes, shapes,
he'd exclaim and I'd say How do you fall in love
with leaves and then I'd want his painting.

Metamorphosis of a Superhero
by Maggie Veness

A neon sign flashes outside the window of Bella's tiny third floor apartment, her nakedness flaring from red to green like some x-rated stop-go traffic signal. Dean kisses the taut ligaments of her neck; flattens his tongue against a pulse that's nose-candy quick. A hiss of strangled air turns into a growl inside the cave of her pretty mouth. On her left cheek, her ear, drool glistens red, then green; stop, then go. He does that for a while—pausing, then pumping—and her growl becomes a roar. She strains upward and holds her breath, sinks her silver talons into his chest. Gratitude overwhelms him. He sings her name from behind clenched teeth; presses down until she stops thrashing.

Bella tells him she died and went to heaven, that she's totally spent, but she still doesn't close her eyes. It's been thirty-six hours. He just wants to sleep but she says she just wants to dance and wriggles into her black tights and short pleated skirt, her white knee-high dancing boots and purple crocheted coat. Dean checks his latest wounds—weeping red crescents alongside crusty scabs alongside pink scars—then scoops his jeans and t-shirt off the threadbare carpet. She drags him three city blocks to the closest nightclub.

'Sorry. Capacity. Shouldn't be too long,' says the doorman, distended pectorals twitching beneath the black-on-yellow wings of his batman t-shirt.

They move aside, wait hand-in-hand by the kerb as traffic crawls past spewing out warm monoxide. When Bella starts coughing and can't stop the doorman nods them inside.

Through the haze and strobe they see that most everyone is dressed as a superhero. Bella squeals, thrusts her coat into Dean's chest and disappears through the swinging door with the fluoro Redheads profile. He waits with his nose buried in purple wool, the mix of her patchouli oil and sweat triggering a clench in his groin. No use denying it. He's in love. He decides to tell her exactly how he feels. Tonight. The idea prompts a sickening thud in his chest. Then she's back with her orange bra outside her shirt, poker-dot knickers over black tights, the pleated skirt draped around her shoulders like a frilled cape. Wonder Girl strikes a pose. Awestruck by her metamorphosis, he can only gape. She pirouettes, and a mauve lipstick star sparkles upon her pale forehead. Bella hangs off his neck, laughing. Being so into her chills him to the bone.

They dance inside pulsing, rainbow light-beams and drink vodka shots 'til three.

Back at her apartment he heads for the unmade bed and she heads for the window, throws it open to the stink and din. Before Dean crashes he glimpses her in the kitchenette—a superhero in a frilled cape cutting powder. He's gonna be there when she's ready to get clean. They'll get a place together. She glances across and blows him a kiss.

'I gotta sleep, babe,' he calls. He's crazy in love and he's gonna tell her tomorrow.

Dean wakes around noon to find Bella on the floor beside the bed. He knows by her blue lips and the awkward way her limbs are folded that she's not sleeping. Paralysed, he sits there. Time blurs and bends until a siren screams past from the street below and he slides from the bed onto his knees. Trembling fingers close her eyes and tidy her costume.

Stretching out beside her, he takes Bella's cold hand in his and spends the afternoon choking on snot, watching a dazzling arc of sun edge around the faded wallpaper; the beaded glass fringe on the lampshade glinting like diamonds; blinding rays bouncing off the mirrored wardrobe doors; a bottle of patchouli oil illuminated on the dresser like a stained glass effigy.

When the sun dips behind the city skyline and the neon sign start blinking, he kisses one green cheek, one red cheek, and calls the cops.

The Fall
by Mark Brazaitis

His fall was a hybrid: part accidental, part suicidal, with a little reckless bravado, fuelled by whiskey, thrown in.

The balcony was on the 28th floor, and he'd been showing the six people on it, including the woman who had, moments before, broken up with him, what a marvellous tightrope walker he was by strutting, arms extended, on the guardrail.

He'd never walked a tightrope in his life, and probably no one who had (and had survived the feat) had done so in loafers and with a blood-alcohol content several numbers north of the legal limit.

So he'd fallen.

He'd heard of cats who had survived long falls, but he'd never liked cats—in fact, he was allergic to them—and even now he couldn't summon the kind of sympathy toward creatures of the feline persuasion he would have needed in order to assume the relaxed and fatalistic posture of a plummeting cat.

He was, however, a fan of bats. As a fellow lover of the night, he decided he deserved the right, in this perilous moment, either, in a desperate burst of evolutionary adaptability, to sprout wings or to summon a school—no, a colony—of the soaring rodents to come corral him and fly him to safety.

But either of these solutions would have been a miracle, and as recipients of miracles are generally deserving of their good fortunes, he would be unqualified. The truth—the sad and painful truth—was that his girlfriend had broken up with him because, in a misstep he regretted nearly as much as he regretted his misstep off the 28th floor, he had cheated on her with his ex-wife.

He should never have divorced his wife, although he had done so in order to be with his (now ex-) girlfriend. This was his original misstep.

Surprisingly, he was still falling. Shouldn't he be a pancake by now? He checked his watch. He calculated he'd been falling for more than thirty seconds. Surely he should have hit the ground—if, indeed, there was ground below him. (He was facing the sky—heavenward, as it were.)

Despite his fear of what he might see, he flipped over. He saw nothing but darkness. This wasn't unexpected. It had been close to midnight when he'd fallen so it was reasonable to think that the sidewalk and street below him would be dark. But as dark as this? Were there no streetlights, no passing cars, no late-night pedestrians walking their poodles and speaking on their illuminated cell phones?

For the hell of it, he counted to sixty. Still no impact with pavement. He sang an old Elvis tune, "Can't Help Falling in Love," amusing himself by omitting the last two words of the title. Still no splat.

With care, he removed his cell phone from his pocket. He was disappointed to find there was no service, so he passed the time by re-reading old texts. His ex-girlfriend, he realized, had communicated with him almost entirely in exclamation points and emoticons. He wondered what this said about the depth of their relationship

Before long, he became both bored and tired. Neither was going to be an easy problem to fix. There were only so many smiley faces he could entertain himself with. And he'd never been able to sleep without a pillow, much less while in the midst of a free fall.

This is hell, he decided. He debated whether he meant it literally.

But I'm alive, he thought, checking his pulse. If I'm alive, I can't be in hell, which is for dead people.

Before long, another problem intruded: hunger. As his fall continued, he fantasized about food. "A peanut butter and jelly sandwich!" he shouted into the darkness. "All I want is a peanut butter and jelly sandwich!"

It didn't matter whether hell was for dead people or living people, he decided. He'd found it.

As if in confirmation of his conclusion, a cat—an unremarkable tiger cat, albeit with particularly unpleasant yellow eyes—soared past him, paws poised for a soft landing somewhere up above, in the world he'd left behind.

Housekeeping
by Stephanie Yu

After licking each crumb off my fingers, I folded my hands. My pinkies began to twirl. Clockwise, counterclockwise. Three and half times each way. Then I heard her start up again, so I stopped. Eyes refocused, head up. Now I was listening, tuning out the buzz of a fly.

"Now I can live for myself. Don't have to put someone before me, one who stopped loving me, am I giving him credit that he ever did? That's the least I can do, send his body overseas and honor him like I've had all these years, that's what he wanted, he didn't want his body burned, it's the last thing I'd do for him, can you believe he went to be with that woman? It's good that God took him when He did, so he would suffer no more, so I would suffer no more, so I could decorate my house ... My Darling, which couch do you like? I like this one."

Grandma's fingertip rested firmly at a black leather couch from an Ethan Allen catalog. This, I knew, was an attempt to modernize the townhouse she moved into a month earlier. Though it occurred to me suddenly, that this couch meant much more than pure functionality or decor.

"That one's perfect," I replied.

I tried to understand the anger, but I truly didn't. All I could think about was how and why she let this happen, and where her dignity lay for decades past. I tried to see the moments she bitterly pushed aside. My eyes even averted down to see them. It was as if she threw every memory into the air like confetti, and pieces permanently melted into the carpet.

Then I heard the buzzing again.

Shy Miss
by William C. Crawford

Drought
by Marie Marandola

By the time I got home, California
had run out of wheat pennies.
The nineties were back, so I gave
my body to Kate Moss's: all hipbones
and ribs, rib bones and hips.
We memorized the nutrition facts
for Greek yogurt and air, recited
them back like times tables.
Like the preamble. Like erotica.
Protein: 22 grams. Kiss me
where I most protrude.

Working in New York by Gleah Powers

At first, I used petty cash to buy myself lunch: lox and cream cheese on an onion bagel.

Once my signature was on his account, I "borrowed" money for art deco furniture and a nicer apartment on 72nd and Columbus. After that, I tried to limit myself to $200 a week.

He drank too much and wore a bad toupee, but I became his girlfriend, which relieved my guilt. He gave me a mink coat for Christmas. He took me to Broadway plays. I thought I wanted to be an actress. Sometimes, I'd wear a fake wedding ring with the mink and use his name to get the best tables in restaurants. This was almost everything my mother had dreamt for herself.

Teaching Marileen to Smoke
by Megan E. Freeman

in the basement of the house
(bolted against tomorrow's earthquake)
using perm papers and oregano
to roll our own
sucking the plastic smoke
into our northeast Los Angeles lungs
to surprise the resident inhalations
inspired by musicians and teen idols
turning me into the girl
your mother warned you about

Pancakes by Rose van Son

It was pancakes she ordered; buckwheat flour layered with sugared-pear, smoothed with caramel topping. The girl beside her waited for takeaway, a black dog, terrier, on her lap. She was sure when the food arrived, moat-lipped on a white enamel dish, the caramel flowing, the pancakes, three layers thick as cake, a dollop of ice-cream, cherry on top, like a flag, melting in summer's heat, the humidity leafed between layers, the dog, almost flinched, and for a moment she thought he might jump clear out of the girl's arms, join her in the taste; but she ignored the thought, ignored the fear this might happen, instead, she bit into the buckwheat texture, spiced with ginger, the spice a surprising after-taste, moistened her tongue folded in ice cream, let the cool float down her throat. It took her back to the North Island, to the place where ice-cream was a national treasure; where the recipe was kept a secret, in a vault. And for a moment she was lost in ice-cream, buckwheat and ginger, caramel and honeyed pear, and time stopped; when she opened her eyes, the girl, and the dog at her side, nowhere to be seen.

Seven Billion Secrets on Planet Earth
by Maryanne Hannan

The smiling guy at the fish counter thinks everything is grand. Especially what I select for dinner on any given night. Yesterday, he considered the piece of salmon I chose so grand I *had* to invite him home with me. It'd be rude to hog such grandeur alone. Fortunately, he didn't accept my hospitality. How would I prepare such grand salmon in front of him? Maybe poached, swimming in liquefied dill sprigs, by candlelight to dim any fishmonger memories. Or I could sous-vide-smithereen it the modernist way, so he'd taste the future glory of his trade. Or maybe he'd prefer an old-fashioned method, a backyard bonfire with kindling twigs and seasoned logs, like his grandpa used to build after their Saturday morning fishing trips. We'd smile, shoot the breeze to the savoury smell of sizzling fish fat. It could work, as long as neither of us mentioned all the grand ones that got away.

DNA at the Radar Lounge
by Gleah Powers

I found a photo of him at eighteen chopping wood in a backyard, shirtless. His scapulas looked like mine, but when I met him at the Radar Lounge in Hollywood and he walked through that red lined Naugahyde door with the gold buttons lodged in its skin every inch or so, the bright sun glaring at his back, his head cocked to the right, like mine, I was glad not to have his ears.

(Un)Fashionable Face
by A.D. Ross

Big-rimmed Ray Bans: a unisex trend for new-age nerds,
blue-beaked, book-nosed birds.

Heavy-handed people looking at her now,
while she looks down, presses glasses close,

facial coverage to fight every-day dangers,
like the desiccating sunlight, leaking time from her skin,

or the marble tile eyesight of anyone who might see
tiny curling nicks, slivers like red commas,

radiating 'round her eye
that he put there.

Her finger forces up the nose-bridge,
the quiet plea of a loud hand,

removing black bangs that crossed her cheek,
greasing the lens. Grabbing a piece of ear,

she removes the glasses, shedding her lucent mask,
but only in the corner, hidden by purple shadows.

Tahitian Fisherman Lad
by Sally Jeanne Stevens

Standing Strong:
The Next Step Series
by Susan Stamm Evans

Writer's Block
By Russell Reece

I was drawing a blank, the writing going nowhere after hours at my desk. I gave up and went and got a haircut. I was at the Hair Cuttery, where I always go, but had a new stylist I hadn't met before. She was thin with short dark hair and a small spider tattoo on the back of her neck. "Nora," she said, "My name is Nora." She was quiet for a stylist, all business, which was fine with me.

I watched her in the mirror, thinning the sides, lifting layers of hair between her outstretched fingers, snipping and combing, her firm hands occasionally guiding my head to the best angle for her work. But it was her expression I found interesting. It seemed to be one of distant thought more than concentration. I guessed her mind was drifting like mine does when I'm doing a monotonous task like painting a wall or cutting the grass. It made me wonder what her life was like, where she was at that very moment.

And then my eyes were drawn to the shelf beneath the mirror where she kept her spare scissors and combs, her electric trimmer and spray bottle of water and I swear as I looked at that shelf the scissors melted into a silvery pool of liquid and the combs and trimer turned to powder and collapsed into a pile. The room began to gray and the walls and the other girls with their customers jittered and faded and I'm thinking what's going on? This doesn't make any sense. But then, this is flash fiction where anything can happen.

And then I was on the back of a motorcycle driven by a guy named Mitch and we were zooming down a country road over hills and through stands of tall trees. The sun was warm and we leaned into the turns first to the left and then the right and the huge motor roared underneath us, and I was caught up in the rhythm and the movement as if I was in some wild and furious dance. It was exhilarating and I wrapped my arms around Mitches waist and pressed my face into the soft leather of his jacket and I was appalled that I had just done that but at the same time it felt comforting and natural. And then Mitch slowed the bike, pulled off the road down a twisting dirt path and stopped near a patch of grass alongside a stream. He switched off the engine and stepped off the bike. The hot motor continued to tick, tick as Mitch took off his jacket and spread it on the grass. He wore a black t-shirt that said Born to Ride. He had a gold chain, shaggy blond hair and a chipped-tooth smile that for some strange reason did not seem unattractive. Tick, tick. Mitch stepped toward me. "Hey, baby," he said. Now I'm as liberal as the next guy but I was suddenly not so comfortable with the way this was going.

I squirmed on my seat, the sun glared through the trees. The engine tick, ticked… snip, snip and I'm back in the chair at the Hair Cuttery. Nora pauses for a moment and I glance around. The shop seems normal again, the walls, the mirrors, the other stylists hard at work. Nora lets out a breath, "whew." She fans herself with her hand. Her face is flushed. She grabs a water bottle from under her shelf, takes a long drink.

"Are you okay," I ask.

"I think I had a hot flash," she says.

I think I know why, I say to myself. And now I'm scrambling to find an end to this story without getting caught up in anymore of Nora's lustful daydreams.

"Shall I trim your eyebrows?" she asks.

I nod and she slips the narrow end of the comb through the brow and runs the trimmer over it. As the small hairs pepper my cheek I wonder if I'll be able to think of anything to write about when I go home.

Absolute Zero
by David Anthony Sam

My step
becomes the frieze
of your eyes
pearls lost
in frost
and tumbling space

the crunch of grass
and leaf
silvered
into cold sunlight
slipping me
towards your edge

TOG II
by Susan Stamm Evans

Flies

by Mary Jumbelic

When it's quiet, you can hear them munching and crunching. Hundreds can congregate for a feast of decomposing flesh. Still juveniles, maggots eat voraciously during this active phase of their life cycle.

Fly mothers birth eggs in exposed, moist regions of the dead — eyes, mouths, and bloody wounds. These white specks appear like powder. Soon though, they become worm-like creatures squirming through multiple growth spurts, discarding pupa casings with each enlargement. Having stealthily entered through sinuses, and airways, they feed and excavate brains, stomachs, lungs.

Nature's essential tasks are usually unseen by people, who genteelly shoo away a bothersome insect at a cookout. The delicate proboscis searches for a drop of sugar in the remnants of a festive meal. Finely lined wings allow quick escape from the human threatening its livelihood. The blue-green body sparkles in the sunlight.

The beauty of the adult belies its immature state, the one I'm most familiar with as a medical examiner. Fully developed blow flies are pollinators, drawn to the aroma of food or flowers. Their larvae, however, are scavengers of necrotic tissue. Those of us who wield the swatter with murderous venom sense the disgusting childhood of these nuisance bugs.

***

"I can't get to her," the investigator says balancing on the concrete ledge. He reaches out toward a tree rising up from the ravine. A second officer holds onto the man's ankles. Their armpits sweat heavily in thick police garb.

"Maybe the guys below can push her up," another trooper says.

Red toenails peek out from the yellow, brown bushes. A young female is suspended upside down in the autumn foliage along this hilly ridge. From the sour smell and the green colour, it's clear to me she's been deceased for longer than the past 24 hours of Indian summer.

Wearing jeans, a t-shirt and sneakers, I am dressed casually today, not attired in the usual hospital scrubs, or white lab coat. This is an outdoor homicide scene.

Earlier that morning, a jogger noted dots of crimson where most of the leaves had already fallen. He slowed, thinking he had spotted a downy woodpecker. His breath caught as he realized he was observing the pedicure of a woman.

Now, the response team tries to recover the decaying corpse. She had been dumped from the bridge parapet head-first into the forest. I scan the landscape attempting to determine the best approach. The slope is steep yet passable.

"Whoa," the uphill man calls as his gloved hand finally makes purchase but slides along the leg. The fragile skin comes over the foot like removing a sock.

"Wait," I say, the physician in charge. Forensics 101 — disturb as little as possible.

After descending the gorge to join the downhill team, I move in to assess the situation. Caught in branches, the skull is precariously attached to the neck via strands of sinew, the integument eaten away by maggots. Moving the body in the direction of the valley would decapitate her. We have to proceed upward. She rests 12 inches above us in a tight stand of trunks. The deputies are too big to fit into the narrow space.

"It's up to you, Doc," the lead detective says, as he shrugs, "you're the smallest."

Wedging myself beneath her, I stabilize the scalp and yell, "Okay, I've got her. Go ahead, pull."

They do. She begins to move.

Fly larvae shower earthward as we manoeuvre the ascent, landing in my hair and on uncovered arms. I close my mouth and briefly my eyes, so the grubs won't get in, hands occupied holding the woman steady. The cumbersome retrieval prevents wiping the pests away. Step by step, we progress along the grade, preserving the evidence, and ultimately place the decedent in a body bag. All the while, maggots wiggle and crawl on my bare skin.

Finishing the transfer, I rip off gloves and t-shirt, tossing them onto the road. My torso jumps, a frenzied dance to dislodge insects. My arms flail, hands swiping at extremities to make sure the writhing critters are gone. A spastic rendition of MC Hammer's 'U can't touch this'. The finale is flipping my long hair, to oust anything that might remain. Taking a deep breath, I glance up.

There are a dozen male law enforcement personnel in a semi-circle, motionless. Some scrutinize their shoes, others view the horizon in the distance; a few boldly stare at my pink lace bra. Despite the warm temperature, my chest shivers. Goosebumps and red patches mark unprotected flesh.

A rookie officer, whom I haven't met before, approaches, offering a starched shirt on a hanger. He blushes but continues to look me in the eyes, never wavering with a downward glance at my breasts. I slowly unbutton the uniform and put it on.

Brown
by Meredith Foster

I have my mother's face.

My father shines through, here and there across my features, but it's undeniable after a single glance. I carry her eyes, the tilt of her head, the raucous unchecked laughter.

***

I am ten years old.

It's summer. I'm watching the 1996 Olympic Games, fascinated by the gymnasts, amazed that such fragile bodies can move like that.

My mother is on the phone, crying. I don't know why she's upset.

***

I am sixteen years old.

Less than a month after my life almost ended, my body is still somewhat foreign to me. I wear the scars like war paint, eager to shock and enthral with the story of how I wasn't anesthetized for any of it, how I didn't cry as I watched myself be cut open.

I'm away from home at a convention with my high school theatre group. My mother and stepfather drive an hour south to meet me, and give the news

that my grandfather is dead. Everyone behaves differently when they're drunk. Some people are kind. He was not.

She doesn't cry. I don't, either.

***

I am twenty-eight years old.

July in Indiana is miserable. The humidity clings to my skin and leaves a film of discomfort that never quite dissipates. My mother is anxious. Sometimes our anxiety melds together in a perverted symbiosis of frustration and annoyance, but not today.

She flits from aisle to aisle, as if she's afraid grief will catch up with her if she stands still. I wish I had more than words to offer, but I've never been haunted by my hometown like she is. I know what it's like to carry bad memories. I don't know what it's like to be broken as a child and spend the rest of my life in repair.

I hug her next to the cake mixes. For a moment, she relaxes.

Longing
by Regina Buttner

It was his idea to take the kids on a picnic at the lake.

A breezy blue spring day. She watched him from her blanket as he walked along the pebbled shore, his daughter's tiny hand hidden in his. Her eyes moved to her two-year-old son on his hands and knees a few feet away, digging in the sand with a plastic shovel, then returned to the man and girl.

He was someone else's husband, the only dad in the playgroup.

His little girl stretched her arm toward

something on the ground—a smooth stone, or a wave-washed piece of shell. He squatted and admired it with her, brushed away a bit of sand, smiled.

The other moms chattered to each other—yoga classes, babysitters, recipes. They unwrapped sandwiches, poked straws into juice boxes, called to their children.

Down the beach, his daughter stumbled over a rock and he scooped her into his arms, touched his lips to her wind-blown head.

On the blanket: a catch in her throat, a hollowing out of her heart. *That's what I'm missing. That's what I want.*

Colloquial
by TJS Walter

On the corner stands a circle of clowns, chain smoking and explicating from behind their face paint smiles. Off duty, their makeup becomes lazy and runs from eye creases and smears into hair lines. The words of the clowns are carried away by traffic sounds, but one laughs sharp like a barking horse, and one is smoking a clove, given away by a shifting breeze. The others are serious. Their lips, their real lips, are tight and pressed behind their oily grease smear expressions. I watch them, an absurd little island in a rushing river of business suits and flesh tone faces. None of the fleshies are looking at the clowns. I wonder if I'm the only one who can see them. Traffic stops to let them cross, and I realize I have no idea what clowns talk about amongst themselves.

Interwoven
by Susan
Stamm Evans

EAT CHOCOLATE

WATCH
CHOCOLATE

*Why Women
Crave Chocolate*
by Kari Gunter-Seymour

Tahiti Tropics
by Faisal Warsani

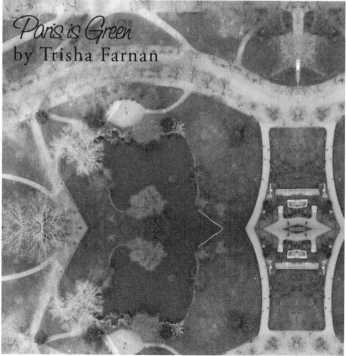

Paris is Green
by Trisha Farnan

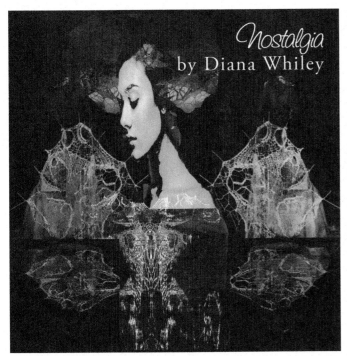

Nostalgia
by Diana Whiley

Nature is Geometry
by Nory Marc Steiger

Yellow Flower
by Taly Oehler

Grass
by Taly Oehler

Purple Roses
by Michelle Webster-Hein

The van was there, in the driveway. Not that he thought it wouldn't be.

The house looked dark in the fading evening light.

No. They were there. Of course they were there. The van said they were there.

He shifted the truck into park and quit the engine, cut the lights. The house was too dark. Something was wrong.

Above the tree line, a dark purple sky. Her face, the bloom around her eye.

Lunch box in one hand, crinkly sheath of flowers in the other. Outside, his boots across the gravel — the only sound. Up the steps, try the door.

Locked.

No.

Drop the lunch box, fumble for the keys. Stop shaking. Kick back the door, call their names.

A trick, maybe. Or a surprise. Their names again, louder.

Check the rooms. Under the beds. Inside the closets. They're hiding. They must be hiding. Of course they're hiding.

The back room, under the heap of coats. The pantry. Behind the couch. Oh, God.

The bathroom, behind the door.

Behind all of the doors.

The attic. Impossible. But still. A screwdriver to pry out the panel. Climb up.

Black, freezing. The light. Nothing.

Outside! Of course! Running. The perimeter of the yard. No.

The field beyond. No.

The stream along the field. No.

No. No, no, no.

Everything dead and flat and cold. The dead stalks cracking. His breath loud and fast.

Gone. Oh, God. They were gone. Oh, God. Gone, gone, gone — the cadence of his running. The same word over and over, not from his mouth but his chest, his lungs heaving up the sound as each boot struck.

Up the back slope, around the side of the house, down the street. Gone, gone, gone, gone. He kept on running until the muscles of his legs began to burn, and still he ran, away from the house, away, away, and then back.

They were there now! He could sense it! When he came into view of their house, warm light shone from all of the windows. A surge of mania, of joy, until he remembered, as he swung back the front door, that he had been the one to leave them on.

Down onto the floor of the entryway, gasping. He twisted sideways and slugged the drywall until it crushed inward and began to crumble. No, no, no. He would change. He would be good. He would be better. She was scaring him straight. She would come back. She would bring the kids. She was too kind to keep them away forever, and too weak.

The flowers lay on the ground where he had dropped them. He kicked at their stems, and they spun to face him, the tips of their rich, red heads already touched with brown. Roses. Did she even like roses?

When he saw her again, he would ask her. He would change in so many ways. He would make a different life, entirely, for all of them. She would see, she would believe. But what if she didn't—she would.

She would, she would, she would.

5-Minute Love Affair
by Monika R. Martyn

Lalit raised his eyes to the clock. He worried; she'd only catch the waving wind of the 8:10 train if she did not hurry. But she was always late. He looked up again, and then, just like that, he made her out; among the bustling, morning crowd. He watched: as she turned her wrist to check the time—as if the blinking, digital clocks, counting time out in heartbeats, could have the minutes wrong. She'd check a second time; disbelieving—hoping they could be. With her slender fingers, she unclasped the belt of her trench coat and paced the length of the granite tiles. Her elegant legs, one at a time, playing hide and seek within the coat; stepping out, but never on the crack.

Stella could feel his velvet eyes bore into her. She wished it were his hands. The rush of running down the steps, pretending to be late, had warmed her. Yet another rush, of longing, burned within her. Sometimes, she lingered close to the kiosk and listened in on the fragile conversations droning on over empty cups of coffee. He was diplomatic, polite; *bite your tongue*, grin and speak of the sexless weather. It was how—she learned his name.

Lalit. She had whispered it a thousand times into the scalding waters of her bathwater. Mouthing into bubbles—drowning with desire. Only in the bath, she was never Stella. She was never a married woman. She was never a mother; nor a professor. She was someone else entirely. This imagined woman lived in a place where Mediterranean waters sparkled and where morning sun warmed clay tile and Lalit's kisses trailed in slow nibbling bites up an arm that looked remarkably like her own. She stole a glance right then, to remember that his skin was truly the colour of liquid honey. She felt a thief, stealing indiscreet snapshots of him over the carafes spewing out hot coffee, over the men and women who dared to stand so close to him.

He longed to know her name. He longed to whisper it in the dreaming wake of making love to her. He would never think of naming her with any other; but her true name. He saw himself reflected in the dove-feather grey of her eyes—on another train. He had sensed a shiver startle her, when her eyes found him so close to her in the crush of the crowd. The stiff gabardine drill of her sleeve had brushed against his hand. He saw her eyes calculate, and when she had done the math, she placed him back, in behind the kiosk. The comfort of keeping him there, eased the furrows of her brow. Despite the invading scents on the carriage train that day, hers, of soap and linen, found him as the sun finds the window in the morning. He longed to let her scent lather over his wet skin, to tangle within his bed sheets and burn his lungs.

The clock blinked on and Stella was

desperate. One more daring dream of reaching for the oiled curl falling over his brow. She longed for *that other woman* to lose her fingers within the pitch black mane. She'd never tame the curls, just finger them. The train, the next one, whistled in the dark tunnel. Soon it would sing *all aboard* and tear her away. The whistle slammed the lid on her desire and folded the pink ballerina away; beneath the lock of the treasure trove. Until tomorrow, until the scalding bathwater and wayward hand.

Oh God! The cursed train is near. Lalit dreaded the whistle of the 8:15. It came too soon; despite being too late. He fumbled with meaningless coins; ground another batch of beans and dared another wilful glance that sent a pleading message only he could hear.

Stella turned. Their eyes met. They forbid each other the need to smile. She shyly turned away. What wife? what mother? what middle-aged woman would dream such foolish dreams? But she understood one thing. If the words were right, if the time were right—she's certain, she would not refuse. The doors—the damn doors—slid closed; the train lurched forward.

Lalit watched as the flash of the fine London trench coat folded into the jostling crowd. It's the last he saw of her. He should not want such a woman; a stranger among the crowd. But he knew if the time ever came—if his mouth found the courage to spill the words—she would not refuse. The doors—the damn doors—slid closed; the train lurched forward.

Lovers
by Steve Prusky

A bullet shattered their window interrupting the spooning lovers sleep. The riot woke many lovers early that humid July night.

The blazing market four floors under their flat lit the bedroom lava red, tinting their nakedness beer bottle amber. Thickened greyish smoke gracefully undulated through the roof vents of the gutted liquor store north. The pilfered gun shop to the south wheezed air starved asthmatic flames.

Maddened human herds wandered the street below like directionless Globules of meandering contagion bred in a petri dish of anger, scrambling to meld, mate, parent a more infectious strain of the temporarily insane. Erratic pistol shots spit choking puffs of Cordite incense into the night air. Klaxon sirens bellowed nearby in every key on the scale chasing elusive howling chaos. Pandemic fire spread from block to block. The lovers resolutely embraced, shivering snug within the mutual sanctity of fear.

Cowering, the lovers pleaded fright, fate, slim chance save them. A plague of roiling smoke prowled up to their floor, hunting, sniffing, clawing every crevice for its next victim's scent. With the obsessive urgency of zealous converts, the lovers chanted redemptive prayers learned rote as children that until that last moment were never meant.

Come Forth And Enter
by Robert Vivian

To come to the gate of the world, to enter it bowing and all adoring, the gate miraculously unlocked and no script to follow for entering, no iron clad rules, to walk through the gate of the world naked and trembling, to hear the gate swinging wide and not rusty per se but almost groaning, yes, a groaning gate at the heart of the world, to gently push open the gate and walk through, to hear my own footsteps treading on the ancient trail, to open the gate of the world and know many have passed before with great joy and great sorrow and pain unimaginable, to come finally to the gate of the world, to say Jesus and Rumi, to say St. Francis and the little engine that could, to pause at the gate of the world and hear birds singing in the dark before dawn, to touch and hold the gate before gently pushing it open, to hold the gate in vast threshold of awareness, to somehow know and intuit on a level beyond reason that the gate is made of love and justice, to know its cross thatched of straw and hoarfrost and early morning poems, to realize that the gate is my friend and my mentor, then to lean into the gate with my shoulder, with my everything and whatnot, to come at last to the gate of the world and hear my heart pounding not in fear but deep inner excitement and the memory of every trembling brook trout in my hands, wet hands, the gospel of brook trout and every worm hole of verse and vermiculations, the walk through the gate at last and know that I am being watched by ancestors who suffered more than I will ever know, to hear even the stones ring with gladness as I walk to the centre and a breeze touches my face, to enter the gate and not look back leaving every pillar of salt behind, to know that I am finally home and one with all there is, to know that death is just like stepping into another room with bright windows and glowing rays of starlight, to bless the gate with my passing and to walk in a sacred manner as Black Elk speaks of, to hear a river flowing in the distance beckoning me to follow and to follow this water even as I hear it coursing through my veins, my body, my beating temples as I say thank you, thank you to the journey and the upright carriage of my new body for after the first death it is only life forever, to love as I have never loved before as my breath turns into prayer, a part of the sky, an offering, the frail mist I was created to give.

Tempus
by Veronica Scharf Garcia

Fish Market
by Kelsey Dean

With every hurried movement, reflected light glints through the shaded tent. The glass tank is filled to the brim with frantic fish; they move like a swollen cloud, always shifting, always changing shape. We point at them and smile at an old woman with a smock and a net. Six palm-sized lives are extinguished in a pan before my eyes, scales blistering like lighting in the steam.

my chopsticks spin
a web of bones

One Night After
by Quinn Ramsay

You wake to an empty pillow, still dented by another body's weight. The smell of perfume lingers. The curtains hang still, framing a pink sunset weighing heavily on the skyline. Nothing moves. Nothing speaks, obeying the solemnity of the moment.

You are exhausted, but you will not sleep tonight. Something is stretching you, pulling you from your bed and into its orbit. You wipe beads from your eyes, smooth down your hair. For whom? You don't know.

The hall is white and unadorned.

Scales
by Quinn Ramsay

It first appeared when I was thirteen, a sharp, knobbed smoothness beneath my child's skin. Alone in my bed, the covers around my chin, I felt myself, pinching, scratching, until a thin fleck peeled away. Under the surface I was not me. I was a hollow shell with some other boy inside, waiting for his moment to hatch.

I did not ask my father. I did not ask my mother. I wore my sleeves long, to hide the green that tinted my milky skin, I wore my hair over

You'd never kept photos in the house—never thought you'd need them. Life was now, and you were young. You donated her clothes, threw out her soaps and brushes. But you find snapshots elsewhere, in the bric-a-brac of shared moments. In your steaming coffee, you smell her morning kiss, recalling damp hair scented with lavender. You find her silhouette in the wine stain she left last Thanksgiving; her champagne laugh, the wild gesticulation that sent the tumbler tumbling.

In the sagging, dimpled couch you see her shadow sitting, dense with things unsaid. Better that way, perhaps. She turns her face to you and already she is hazy at the edges, smudged like a portrait sketched in coal.

my eyes. I feared their notice, and craved it too. They must have seen, but said nothing, so neither did I.

The itching worsened. My skin grew flaky and dry in the winter chill, and though I rubbed moisturizer into it thirteen times a day, it began to slough away. I stood in the mirror and pulled a long thin strip from beneath my eye, a sting like a scab being pulled.

Beneath it I was brilliant, glossy, an emerald tear against the brittle husk of my cheek, and for the first time I felt a rush of excitement when I thought about who I was, and what I would become.

No Postage Necessary
by Kayla Pongrac

When my mailman approached my front door yesterday afternoon to deliver some junk mail swaddled in a newspaper, I kindly inquired if he would care to step inside for a cup of tea. "You're the most interesting person who visits my house yet never comes inside," I said. I watched with glee as he rested his bag full of bills and magazines and tiny boxes on a chair on my front porch. He stepped inside the doorway and I beckoned him toward the kitchen, where my mugs and teapots awaited his company with so much anticipation that I could've sworn I heard their ceramic insides humming. I sat transfixed in my chair as he poured milk and honey into his tea.

I waited and waited for the right moment to ask him to box me. "A large, padded envelope would work just fine, too," I said, but he assured me that he had an extra box in his bag, so I did what I could to cut myself down to size as he finished the contents of his cup. After excusing himself from the kitchen table to retrieve the box in his bag from the front porch, he stood over my contorted body, assembled the box, and then carefully placed me inside. I could hear the tape sealing the lips of the box and then my mailman mumbling to himself—perhaps questioning if he should be the one inside instead, as though he was the one who needed delivered from his sins and his sorrows—but I knew that I was right where I belonged: in a corrugated cardboard box, surrounded by Styrofoam peanuts, soon to be placed on a stranger's front door where I might have an opportunity to be opened and read and replied to as if I had something important to say.

Unwelcome Visitor
by CLS Ferguson

Nostalgia is an acquaintance
I never invited to move in
She presses me against
the rose coloured windows of my memory
beckoning to return
"There's no reverse," I tell her
Her coercion lives in these
scents, songs, scars of yesteryear

She tempts me with the freedom
I never knew I had,
driving as fast as my old car would go
She guilts me with the realization
that my parents really did know
what I was going through,
and I'll never convince
my children of this truth
She manipulates me to dance with her
as she shape shifts into the past lovers
who slipped into their own divergent futures
—the ones I mourn losing, but really don't need
back

She threatens
that if I don't return to fix
all I let go wrong,
my future will never be as I wish

About the time I want to give in to her
my present shows her to the door

Anger
by Jacquelyn Shah

I've developed a taste for it
  savouring even mere scraps
like sweetmeats lodged in the teeth
  licks of cream that linger
I don't dress for the dining
  it's no formal affair
never a breakfast, no fast to break
  my gorging like my breathing's
steadfast   a bevy, my body
  of food vacuoles
a glutton for it, my belly's
  always growling   lucky addict
I have fixes for a lifetime
  grow strains in petri dishes
delirious like a Frankenstein
  I fashion it   patch those saprogenic
memories, monsters, together—
  O sweet Elizabeth, the too dear sister!
In the night I grope for it
  lay with it, my skin crawling with it
like a memory-driven piston
  I'm drilling   drilling
It's holy eucharist!   I sing hosannas
  scarlet letter stuck to my habit
bulimic, I spew fury   molten & common
  as cola   obsidian fact of life—look at me!
a skull & cross-boned bottle
  force no tonic down me   I don't want a cure
besides, it's powerful—my gag reflex

Crepe Myrtle
by K. Irene Rieger

The feeling of release
Is a sprig my grandmother snaps
She, delighted to bestow
A spray of her childhood
I used my fingernails
(cleaned and trimmed by her)
To open each bud
Play God or some spring goddess
Opening the bloom
A moment of force
And then purple sanguine liquid rush
Momentary satiety
Like bursting bubble wrap
—I preferred to puncture one air-filled hemisphere at a time—
You get to the end

But the blooms never looked the same when I unfastened them myself
As they did when the sun opened them, mornings
And forcing the dewy petals back into the bud never works.

Distressed Jeans by Claire Scott

She is wearing her distressed jeans again
my fashionable daughter
skinny jeans intentionally destroyed
acid washed, sand papered
pumice stoned, tumbled in gas
washing machines
faded & ripped at the knee
scraped & shredded at the thigh
priced at a premium by
Calvin Klein, Armani, Levi

really?

I want to wrap her in my arms
& say: *wait*
no need to race to what-comes-next
soon enough pleated skin, nagging knees
soon enough holes in your heart
no designer can repair
no need to leap over yourself
to some frayed future
time will snip & slice soon enough
my daughter, much too soon enough

wait

Perianth
by Veronica Scharf Garcia

Provisions
by Stacey Margaret Jones

We waited, encased
in the gray felt-covered conference room,
drinking industrial coffee with powdered creamer

For our colleague, who entered well stocked
with provisions:
manicured nails, navy suit, leather portfolio, business cards,
stacked heels, nude hose, a colourist's blonde,
executive title,
power she'd had to take
after she had earned it.
She watched the tumultuous sky
over the answering river,
"It's going to be quite a day out there,"
she said, as if it were only out there.

From her chair, she couldn't see the green,
smooth lawn, in the lee
of the building, where a hedgehog brought her
spring babies out onto a miniature pasture.
The trauma of the wind over the river
was this woman's only purview,
because it was all she met, all day long,
in a soft felt world that was
nothing but hard for her.

You Don't Bring Me Flowers
by Jean Gill

from *One Sixth of a Gill*

I burned my hand on your thigh
white-hot the air charged with what
we had not done. You stopped the car.
Went shopping while I sat.
Returned
and placed the daffodils you bought
your wife between us.

Not By Heart
by Janet McCann

She did not know love by heart but
By mind—she studied it in Jane Austen and
The Brontës, then tried a Silhouette but threw it
Away on page five. She tried on the clothing of
Love, silks, cashmeres, tall graceful heels,
But none of it fit.

She wanted to learn love
The way she once learned French,
So that suddenly on a Paris street the scene
And its strange transactions became real,
She would be speaking it, caressing its
Trembling consonants.

She memorized the language of love and its
Past imperfect and future perfect, she tried it out
On mirrors and strangers. She did not know that when it
Came to her at last the world's fabric would
Rip open, she'd be standing there
Naked and wordless.

Shame by David Pratt

She stood at the lectern, very stylish, her dark hair upswept and a silk scarf at her neck. It was Paris, 1968, and Russian tanks had just crushed the Prague Spring. "As many of you know," she said, "I have been a member of the Party since I was eighteen …" She went on for some time, and ended "… torn up my Party card." There were murmurs of commendation, of sympathy. At the back of the room, a small, bald man stood up. "The purge trials of the 1930s," he said, "were before your time, but you must have heard of them. The liquidations under Yagoda and Yezhov. The deliberate starvation of five million Ukrainians, more millions sent to Siberia. The displacement of the Pontic Greeks, the Soviet Finns, the Baltic Germans, the Crimean Tartars. The extermination of the best of the comrades in Eastern Europe. The use of informers, of torture, of extrajudicial murder. The multitudes dying in the arctic camps. The violation of every human right. From Berlin to Archangel, an abhorrent reign of cruelty equalled only by Nazi Germany. All of which you knew about and ignored or discounted or excused. And now, *now*, you want us to *congratulate* you?" Her eyes blazed. Then she burst into tears.

Horses
by Adam Sturtevant

It wasn't you who drove me to drink
you rode me instead
into an unwanted sunset
like the horses you had as a child

I bow my head
the brown of my eyes is no match
for the darkness of yours
lined black with rhetoric and kohl
you laugh with your head thrown back
molars to the sun

My teeth belie my age
sooner pull the rot from my jaw before sepsis
takes me from you
or is it the other way around?
Another round
I may not need them after all—
the middle syllable of your name
requires only a semi-bitten lip

If nostalgia is your north star
then I am, forwards or backwards
a piñata—a cheaper beast of burden
hollow until filled
tethered, centre mass
the ache is higher and left
you are on the green grass
below

The words you wrapped up
candy in cellophane
now scattered and false
you could never be angry
or so you said
your touch, ever softer blunt force
blood and crêpe paper between your legs

To Train a Falcon by Liz Nguyen

Training a falcon requires a certain intimacy; she is your partner, your lieutenant, your wild heart taking flight. There is trade: just as she learns to heed the sound of your whistle, you also learn her kee-chips and chitters, the meaning of raised feathers or a gaping bill. She keeps you sharp, you keep her sated. As the ducks take flight across the silver-blue pond, she leaps from your fist, eager for the hunt.

But even before the taming begins, a certain trial must be undertaken.

You must scour the cliffs for a falcon's nest, a scrape of barren ground upon a ledge. Then you climb, grasping at handholds, the gully below shrinking and expanding all at once. As you near the scrape, the mother will take flight. You must protect your face from her talons, your free hand reaching to pluck a chick from its nest. The one-handed descent is even more precarious, but the danger seems small as you can now feel her heart beating in your palm.

Barbed Sunset
by Trevor O'Sullivan

Dusk
by Ion Corcos

Sticks like snakes
on the pavement

galahs on the grass,
ash grey silence

rain, after none,
slows the dark

white flowers
fold their petals

into night.

Entanglement
by Bruce Louis Dodson

Wires tend to do that
'back of a computer
Shoelaces and string
extension cords
the garden hose so carefully coiled
snarls without provocation
Life.

Cooling
by Lorna Fergusson

Already you cannot feel the heat
Or hear the insistent cicada shimmer.

You sat under the roof of vines at Kalami,
Where once a famous writer lived. Tricky, though:
A bit of a shit, you feel. At least he *wrote*.
('The poet and the dreamer are distinct'—
One does the job, the other plays at it.)
A rose beetle burred past the olives,
Its fat green glitter like a costume jewel.
The speedboat driven by Captain Iakis
Spewed gobbets of pure white foam
And muscular vectors of water-wake,
Passing the dolphins like bodkins, arching
And stitching the blue Ionian.
The full moon rose and spread its shawl
Between Nissaki and Kerkyra.

Your records are digital and written.
Your memory will salvage what it can:
Part reinforcement, part metamorphosis—
Because nothing can be kept, not really.
Your mouth will utter *Do you remember?*
And *Wasn't that lovely?* And *Wasn't it funny
That time?*
The sojourn will sleep on the shelf of years
With all the others. Cullen to Cornwall.
Cannes to Corfu.
But
Already you cannot truly feel that heat.

Maybe Another Time
by Justin Hoo

A coffee cup sits on a table for two, half full and waiting. On one side, he leans forward, eyes trained ahead. On the other, she brings absence. The bitterness of his last sip paces like a wanderer in search of home. It lingers like the gentleman beside him messaging on Facebook, the lady at the sofa perusing a self-help book on the art of conversation, and the croissants set out by the barista whose buttery scent stirs an ache inside his chest.

Up ahead, the girl who jots notes from a social psychology textbook reminds him of her when she was a stranger. A face he wants to know, yet with the crowd ambling along the streets lost in their own worlds, her features become washed away. The ring of a bell echoes, and lights a flame in his eyes the second he turns his head. But it's only a group of students exiting with their drinks. His hopes become smoke. He glances at a clock, relentless and indifferent as if her arriving today is no different than her arriving tomorrow. He checks the message he sent her. No answer.

His fingers wrap around his cup, lukewarm. The girl glances towards him, and for a second he meets her stare—one flicker of connection before she returns her attention to her pages. He lets go, rests his hand on his lap. Everyone here, together and alone, invites the possibility of distraction. Maybe everyone else feels the same—expecting someone to come, but only losing oneself to imaginings of the lives of others as friends, enemies, and lovers. If someone could reach past the screens and pages to touch another person, what could happen? What would they find together?

Jazz piano floats through the air, and then follows with orchestral crescendos which might appear in a vintage film during a triumph or declaration of love. If it were a soundtrack to his life, it'd ring of hollow fantasy. When the door chimes once more, stillness overtakes him. More strangers glued to their phones form a line from the outside like an umbilical cord—chained, but destined to be severed. When the time comes, the patrons vanish like ghosts. When he's the last one, he stands and joins them.

A coffee cup sits on a table for two, half empty and waiting.

Tradition by Cooper Lysek Gomez

Like most people, a paper cup always seeks stability. Like, say, in a travel coaster or on a finely sanded kitchen table. This is mostly due to a tradition among paper cups: they come from a long line of jumpers and are quite known for hopping, and one partic-ular cup surpassed all. This specimen was tired of sitting on his table doing nothing. He was going to become an Olympic Athlete. Despite his mother's warnings he decided to play in the snow. Then, he spotted a plastic cup in the distance. He approached with caution and saw it was a Big Gulp. He hoped It hadn't seen him, but it was too late. It chased him through the forest. It chased him through the parking lot. It chased him through the busy city streets. He ran until he was tuckered and the Big Gulp swallowed him whole.

by Katerina Pravdivaia
From left to right:
Don't Skin Me for a Score
Don't Cut Me for my Curls
Don't Shoot Me for my Spots

Broken by Kendra Liedle

When I shattered, I stared helplessly at particles of myself that no longer made sense.

"You couldn't glue the pieces back together?"

"I wouldn't even know where to begin."

Pack One, Sir?
by Moshe Prigan

Yesterday my TV breathed its last episode.

I go to HARVEY'S ELECTRONICS. As I enter, I'm welcomed by the song WHAT A WONDERFUL WORLD. I close my eyes to absorb the beauty of the melody, wishing it would never end. The song repeats and I open my eyes.

Children waving Kalashnikov guns surround me. Dozens of dozens militarized screens.

I see trees of green, red roses, too

Next to them ten to twelve-year-old girls, in white muslins, hold men's hands wearing tuxedoes. 'Just married,' I read.

the bright blessed day

To my left an elegantly dressed Mine Manager – as his tag says – is being interviewed while police force away dirty clothed kids trying to approach the cameraman.

I see them bloom, for me and you …

Two kids in military uniform draw my eyes. They are slaying a dog. He is battling. Dozens of screens, voice muted, are shining with red colour.

I see skies of blue, and clouds of white,

The kids smile proudly at the camera. Dozens of screens smile at me.

What a wonderful world

I almost barfed.

A young mother, looking straight forward with cool sunglasses on, is pushing the stroller of her child along the fifty yard wall of hung TV screens.

And I think to myself

I am glad I'm alone, and that my granddaughter is in school.

I change direction. The scene hits my face. Grandfather and his granddaughter are lying down on their bellies on an asphalt road, chins resting on hands. A red-lettered uppercase caption: 'ROCKET SIREN' runs below.

What a wonderful world.

I hear my heart drumming. It's about a year since some cameraman took pictures of us while being on street, rocketed. It was holiday and we were on our way to watch a children's play when the rockets started falling. On that day my nine-year-old granddaughter, with her classmates, had a shelter practice in school to see how quick they could run, so she told me to lie flat. As if I have never been in war.

I want to go home.

The TV shop seller walks up to me. "Don't fret, Sir. All my screens are sharp, bright and clear. Pack one, Sir?"

What a wonderful wooooorld.

Goodnight Irene
by Irene Hoge Smith

"I'll have a Grande skim latte, please."

The barista has a broad grin, close-cropped dark hair, and a wisp of goatee. He's not as old as my youngest child.

"Can I have a name for the order?"

"Irene," I say, as someone turns on the espresso machine.

"Eileen?"

"No, Irene, with an R." I suppose I could just let it be "Eileen," I think, not for the first time.

He marks the cup, still smiling.

"Tell me," I ask him. "If I had said 'Irene, like the song,' would that mean anything to you?"

"I'm afraid not." Apologetic, he looks down at the cash drawer.

"How about if I said 'like the hurricane?'"

"Oh, yeah," he laughs.

A few summers back, that hurricane was bad enough that the name has been retired. No more Katrina, no more Sandy, no more Irene.

Goodnight Irene, goodnight Irene
I'll see you in my dreams

I was two the year the Weavers' hit single topped the charts for six months, and as far back as I can remember adults would start singing to me when they heard my name. I didn't know why they thought it was so funny, or how they could always think they were the first ones to make the connection. As much as I craved attention, I was painfully self-conscious. I took to saying "I hate that song!"

The song made me special, for a while and to some people, and I'm wistful now that it's mostly forgotten. But it was always complicated.

My mother named me not for the popular and sweet Weaver's version, but for the original, a dark and hopeless ballad by the blues singer Lead Belly. The melody is lovely, but the words tell a story of anger and despair. It was the first song I ever heard, and sometimes I can almost remember the crib, a dim room and my mother singing.

Sometimes I take a great notion
to jump in the river and drown

She had a pretty voice, but didn't care for pretty songs. Of all the ballads in The Fireside Book of Folksongs she was drawn most to those with themes of dissolution and destruction. She thought I should know not just the words, but what they meant. Lily Marlene, underneath the lamppost, was a prostitute. Willie the Weeper was addicted to cocaine. Foggy, foggy dew means whiskey, and Joe Hill was framed. She sang all the verses of "Irene."

I wish to the Lord I never seen your face,
I'm sorry you ever was born.

Her father, the brilliant young Grandpa I never knew, might have been the last person she really loved. She told us how he left Harvard to join the Navy in World

War I, met Grandma in Hawaii, came back to New England to build the first transatlantic radio transmitter. But then he got a strep throat, she said, and it was before antibiotics. The infection went to his lungs, and he went to the hospital, when he was barely thirty and she was just six. For two years she was told her daddy was going to get well and come home, but she never saw him again, never got over it, and never forgave her mother for lying to her. Those bitter songs seemed to give voice to how she'd always felt.

I love Irene, God knows I do
I love her till the sea runs dry.
And if Irene turns her back on me
I'm gonna take morphine and die.

I couldn't see any of it—why she was still so sad about her father and so mad at her mother, couldn't be happy now that she had her own family. But it's all there, looking back. She expected good things to go bad, and they did. People you love are going to hurt you, and the more you need them the more likely they are to leave.

One back was turned after another. Her father died, her mother didn't really love her, her husband wouldn't stay faithful.

Now me and my wife are parted
Gonna take another stroll downtown.

She didn't warn me, probably because it wasn't really a plan, just the thing that had to happen. She left when I was fourteen, and I didn't see it coming any more than she'd believed her father would really die.

The very last words I ever heard her say,
was, please sing me one more song.

GOODNIGHT, IRENE

Words and Music by Huddie Ledbetter and John A. Lomax
TRO-© Copyright 1936 (Renewed) 1950 (Renewed) Ludlow Music, Inc., New York, NY. Used by Permission.

Nickel
by Nicholas Finch

There was something that felt like a bone dead in the flat of my hand. It was a tooth. Sam was on the ground, crying. I put his tooth in my pocket. Mom came out onto the lawn yelling. Sam stood up. He looked at me in a way I hadn't seen before. I felt like the bigger one. Sam ran home holding his hand up to where I had socked him. Mom started wailing on me where I was already red.

I told her what happened. Sam was showing off a nickel that he had gotten in exchange for a tooth. He'd started listing off all the things he was going to do with that nickel and how there were more nickels to come. I got sick of it and told him to stop. Sam persisted. I shoved him. He kept putting out his hand with the nickel in it but when I reached for it he'd slap me. Then he tried pelting me with the nickel but missed and hit my step-dad's truck. For that, I hit him across the mouth. And then there it was, his tooth in the dirt. Panicking, I picked it up and hid it away in my pocket.

I told all this to mom but later she made me explain it again to my step-dad. He asked me if I knew why it was wrong to do what I did. I shook my head no. I thought he was about to start on me like mom did but he didn't. He walked out the room.

***

I was in the mirror comparing his tooth to my own. I found the corresponding one and began to work at it. It was a canine tooth. Pinched between my thumb and index finger I tugged away.

I wiggled it slightly, which made me wince. The tooth's root scratched and cut at my gum. I could only think of my step-dad jacking up the truck and the way he worked at it. Once jacked up, he'd prop the truck up on bits of wood, but he didn't do that anymore. He told me that his dad taught him to put it up on wood because it's reliable. It was his dad's truck before it was my step-dad's. He had taken care of it the same way as his dad did, but one day the wood either slipped or broke and the truck fell hard on its belly, messing up its insides. He jacks up the truck differently now.

The tooth snapped out of my mouth with a squirt of blood that sprayed the mirror. I cleaned my tooth off and compared it to Sam's. I think mine looked a little different.

No one spoke at dinner but I made sure to show off the gap where my tooth was missing. Neither my mom nor step-dad said anything about it. I hardly ate, instead I dabbed at the hole in my mouth with a tissue. I'd put down the bloodied napkin next to my plate full of food, but still, they said nothing, both of them just went on eating.

That night I put both teeth beneath my pillow.

When I woke up in the morning the teeth were still there.

A Lot to Say by Trisha Farnan

The Gutter
by Elizabeth Bruce

One dollar. One whole dollar. Her life savings. Gone. Fallen out of her pocket into the gutter below. The girl tried to look into the opening but her head was too big and the darkness down there scared her. Daddy says there's rats down there, don't go sticking your hands down into that gunk, baby girl, he says. You need a dollar, your daddy will give you a dollar. New and shiny as that diamond ring your mama's always talking about. Don't you never go getting yourself into some dark hole just for a lousy dollar, pumpkin. Not for one dollar, not for ten, not for all the dollars in the world, you hear me now, baby doll? You listen to your papa, now and keep your hands outta the gutter and sparkling clean. "Dear dollar," the girl whispered into the depth. "Remember me. PS: Be careful down there, dollar, my daddy says it's dangerous down there."

Sunday Sweetness
by Irene Blair Honeycutt

I used to think if I were lost on a deserted island—no books to read, no watch on wrist, no calendar in my back pocket—I'd know when Sunday rolled in with the waves because a certain calm would settle

Paper Cup
by Claire Scott

They give me pills each night: two blue, three pink
Carefully placed in a crinkled cup passed out by
Margie, Carl or Sam who smile at me like a submissive child
They don't see I spit them in my sleeve as I fake-shuffle down the hall

Fake-shamble to the room I share with Sundowning Sue
Revved up for a night of cantankerous confusion
They think they have done their duty, drive home to cosy houses
Sleep easily with Leonard or Steven or Liz

They don't know I toss all night tormented by what never happened
no uncle, never, ever, whispered in my bed
What never could have happened
no uncle never, ever, lifted my nightgown

I spit out the two round and three oval pills
To remember and remember
What never, ever, should have happened
so it can't happen again

They will never suspect as they pass out
Their paper cups of pills
to remain innocent some
secrets can never be spoken
never, ever

Dickinson
by Olivia Pellegrini

Emily Dickinson never fell in love
She consumes time
like small,
            incidental
                        tea leaves, between
            floorboards of gum and enamel

                        that creak and sigh.

Her feet, they please her
For if she had not tiny hands,
She would know how a heart expands
            and moans

to greet her own.

---

inside me. There'd be that lump in the throat Frost spoke of or the day might begin with a Dickinson slant of light. This morning I think my dogs must sense it's Sunday. They've been outside shifting from sun to shade for hours without a bark, without a pawing at the door. Such sweetness lies in their quietness—silent as river stones. Bluebirds inspect the new house nailed to the fence, as do the Carolina wrens. Not one makes a claim. I'm rooting for Blue, but I'll not make a fuss if Wren moves in and sings for its mate. The concrete garden rabbit looks happy next to the pansies. Jarrell liked greeting them at his front door. Said their studied faces reminded him of his students. Sunday. For a while the world feels at rest even though it isn't. When the wind rushes through the attic, we must count our blessings.

Tiger's Eye
by Mori Glaser

He gave me a ring for my left fourth
a tawny tigers eye proud in silver.
I had to ask but he said yes.
He wanted to give me cubs
striped generations of apex predators
that open their eyes
grow teeth and claws
and leave an empty lair.
Tigers to love but not to hold.
I buried the ring under a full moon
before it gnawed my finger.

Venelle
by Diana Whiley

Now
by Phill Provance

In a bar, staring
at the bister liquids
martially arrayed in stiff-necked
bottles, my glasses and cap are off
in an attempt to look younger
when the truth is
I'm just some
non-descript
stranger,
some old creep
shooting for hip,
and it occurs I've wasted
my best words on one
who didn't deserve
a pronoun.
Of course, I tried.
Bought us a house,
mid-American Taj Mahal,
decked to the rafters in leather furniture,
carpet with pile so high you'd swear you'd drown.
A brand-new dishwasher, Keurig, flat screen—
steel-tone linings, everything black and gray,
with which I prayed to corral my loss.
Still I dutifully continue to pay
the mortgage, have learned
a woman to start with
must be mad
to want a poet
for a man.
So now I wake
mornings to cruel quiet
drink the last stale backwash
and stare at my toiletries
in their tiny phalanx.
And tomorrow
or someday
after you
will find
a lump
at the end of the bar:
that'll be me—
too young
to think
too old
to live
on fables

My Mother's Breasts
by Melissa K. Downes

A stranger asks me to help her
buy a bra. She keeps undoing
buttons on her cotton blouse.
She pushes aside crisp white
and teal stripes; she snaps, pulls
the old bra beneath. She offers
her breasts up—offers her opened
shirt and the wings of her hands.
The gap reveals white, ruched flesh,
blue veins, a sternum still nested
smoothly in the cleft between
shrunken, gently pendulous breasts.

She is not as old as my mother
was when she died: still, she shows
the focus of a woman alone,
planning long journeys with forged
papers, unrecorded meetings
forgotten before they happen.

Her daughter has let her out to buy
underwear. The mother smiles, dentures
pretty as porcelain dolls: she wants
something sexy for her second husband,
something clean and new, with no sag
or pinch, no wrinkle nor unravelled
seam, but she cannot remember
the size or shape of her own breasts
or what woman's flesh means
in numbers, in letters: 36, 40, B, C, D.

I remember my mother's breasts:
I will not say no to this woman
who makes me her personal shopper,
saleslady, rented daughter.
She asks me if she should pay me,
fumbles for her dollars, like her blouse,
I size her up, judging her body
by my mother's body; the cup
of her breasts by my mother's breasts.
I bring her something with no wires,
something that whispers spring
beginning, The bra fits
like Cinderella's shoe on the tiny,
callused foot of the right girl.

Sick
by Penny Dearmin

Sick is hundreds of white shredded ID bracelets from the Children's Hospital hidden under car seats and stuck to the bottom of shoes. Sick is children in red wagons, laying in blanket nests, regurgitated food hung in a bag from the pole, dripping down a tube. Sick is walking the labyrinth in the chapel on the first floor, pausing in each inlaid square to pray for a family to bring their healed child home; and then sitting in twenty chairs to cry for those that were taken to be buried instead. Sick is the jolt of the helicopter landing on the hospital roof, waking me from a dead sleep.

Sick is buying a Children's Hospital Colorado ornament for my Christmas tree. Sick is sending Christmas cards to as many doctors and nurses as family and friends. Sick is sewing a red quilt with a winter scene for the doctor who saved my child's life. Sick is bringing cupcakes to the hospital for the nurses and patients for my son's birthday year after year. Sick is the red, yellow, orange, and blue courage beads given to mark each milestone of treatment: first surgery, MRI, spinal tap.

Sick is invisible and secretive. Sick is a medi-port hidden under his pale translucent skin where a butterfly needle pierces his chest. Sick is a chocolate-kiss-sized glob of numbing cream dolloped under clear press-n-seal wrap to mask the pain of the needle. Sick is a tube left in his port, stopping him from swimming with his friends. Sick is an entire kitchen cabinet with bottles, creams, and pills that keep the symptoms tucked away from prying eyes. Sick is healthy sisters farmed out to friends while pretending no one is sick. Sick is putrid yellow plastic basins meant for catching sick so that it doesn't spill out everywhere, found in every room of the house.

Sick is proselytizing to the universe that his eight-year-old life holds more promise than mine. Sick is watching my child scream and vomit from the pain that no one is able to stop. Sick is wanting only one needle poke instead of four while pinning my son to his gurney. Sick is seeing my child misplace his memory like a set of keys and search my eyes for all that is lost. Sick is giving anything to not be sick.

Sick is a communal experience. Sick is always sharing a room with other sick children. Sick is a roommate spurting blood out of her port from across the room onto my son's red wagon filled with Lego sets and lunch box. Sick is knowing there is no five-second-rule for blood contamination. Sick is not being able to explain to my son why he will lose more than his logos.

Sick is parents leaving their children alone in our shared room who cry to no one for help to go to the bathroom. Sick is judging the parents of the other sick children. Sick is calling the nurse for a change of clothes because the child wet the bed when no one helped the child in time. Sick is the belief that my actions can lead to suffering, and thus healing. Sick is blame.

Sick is a five-year-old boy with a genetic disease that requires infusions once a week. Sick is praying his infant sister won't inherit the same disease. Sick is trading names of physical therapists and advocates for your kids. Sick is hoping his parents get insurance coverage so they can have the third child they desperately want; to choose embryos without the genetic makeup to utilize the amino acid responsible for his crooked fingers and beaming smile.

Sick is celebrating the health of others while my child is still not healthy. Sick is seeing Patrick, who once played ball with my son, have his feeding tube taken out, colour return to his skin, and hair appear on his head. Sick is eating his cake and laughing at his stories of starting high school.

Sick is starting to believe that a future can happen, but that sometimes it doesn't. Sick is learning to accept what is given and what is taken. Sick is my son coming to the hospital every twenty-one days, for two consecutive days, year after year, for a chance at a life worth living.

Salvage
by R.M. Cooper

There's nothing to eat in her trash bin. The insides are all credit card receipts and old medical bills and bank statements and a letter from her sister in Tucson. Check around back. There's a big plastic cylinder that smells like chicken bones and soiled milk, but inside everything's turned to dirt. Beside the cylinder are brown bags filled with similar-smelling dirt, each labelled in black permanent marker: For Garden. There are eight bags beside the cylinder. The yard is filled with wood chips which stick to your bare feet and require no watering in the dry mountain summers. Try the front door, the back door. A light comes on when you try the window. Flop face-down in the wood chips. Take shallow breaths for twenty minutes until the light winks out. Return to the trash bin and stuff whatever papers you can manage inside your coat. Leave.

Fold down the corners of papers with account numbers. Set aside an out-of-state receipt. Call and dispute the receipt with the bank: $15.95 at a nail salon. Make threats regarding the closure of your account. Ask to speak with a manager. Make Ted, the manager, stutter. Ted is only filling in. He usually doesn't work weekends. Play stupid. Play belligerent. Keep playing until Ted relents. Find the folded paper with an address. With a home phone number. With the last four digits of the debit card. Write down the account number Ted surrenders.

Rent an efficiency apartment. Apply for a third-party credit card. Pay rent. Buy groceries. Afford new clothes. Get an interview at a movie theatre. Get a second interview at a convenience store. Get a third interview at a day care. Say you're happy to work for cash. Off the books is fine. Employee health insurance, yes—Obamacare. Agree: It's killing small businesses. Say you're only interested in the children. Bike to work, even during winter. Say it's for the exercise. Say it's for the environment. Avoid libraries and post offices. Pay your bills on time.

Three years pass before the husband arrives. When you answer the door he looks surprised. He tries to look around you inside your apartment. He asks if you know Laura Peters. Touch your collarbone along the seam of your robe. Say that's your name. Let him laugh when he tells you about the estate papers listing the apartment as a second address. Pretend not to notice the word estate. His eyes are bloodshot. His chin is unshaved. He says he thought his wife was having an affair. He tries to look past you again. Laugh. Touch his shoulder. Say you grew up with a Laura Peters too. Ask if there was a pop star with that name in the

seventies? An actress? Ask if she went to your high school. Ask if he and Other Laura (you've called her this twice by now) would like to join you for dinner. Talk about death on his terms: passed. Offer condolences: cancer is terrible, the body turning on itself, the radiation sickness, the burden on the family. Give him a minute. Give him another. Try not to look impatient when he doesn't leave your door. You'll want to comfort him. You'll want to send him away. Instead, step forward. Lean into the doorjamb and let your fingers drift inside the seam of your robe. Ask if there's anything you can do. Say you're sure he's been strained, felt alone for a long time. His brow will furrow. His jaw will tighten. When he tries to look around you again, move to meet his eyes. Make sure he knows there's nobody inside but you.

The Unmade Bed
by Janet Buck

I sit beside an unmade bed,
but won't crawl in.
Sheets lack fairytales I need.
My bony elbows sore
from armchairs with the padding split.
My PCP mutters in a dreamy voice,
"Here, just take this little pill."
I trash the script the second
he exits the room.

White sheets are ghosts.
Grey sheets are ghosts.
Blue sheets are ghosts.
They're closing drapes.
Diving in means this—
I quit, I failed. Supine is death.
Rest, complete anathema.
A pillow is a stone
I hit my head against & bleed.

Little Pissers and Blank Walls
by Deborah Guzzi

hidden in charcoal
below the street's overpass
a wild child spray paints
can in hand—drugged fumes rise
filling the dank midnight air

light from a street lamp
fluoresces from puce green
to vampiric red
grandiose dreams of Hoosan
flash past his fluttering lash

the restaurant barge
with its partygoer cargo
slithers by below
hoots of jammed laughter tickle
waves lap, he waters the floor

some tag and some paint
reaching as high as he can
blue runs down his arm
he's no spot jockey, he'll rise
his art has killa merit

really up, he was
there'd be no buff job on this
the outline is crisp
the tips of his fingers black
his stiff jeans won't recover

it's all about art
he thinks groovin' through ear buds
Picasso tin canned
beyond the plum purple haze
soon he'd have a legal wall

Chai in Delhi
by Laura Brinson

Delicious milky spiced masala chai. Traditionally served in tall narrow glasses – like a creamy sweet shot. Each chai wallah has a unique blend which changes according to the time of day. In the mornings it is often gingery, and later in the day a dash of pepper is added to the cardamom, cinnamon and cloves. I sit on the concrete step, a folded India Times under my backside, and watch as the morning blend evolves. With a tin cup the tea and spices are carefully measured out. Dark spidery leaves and earthy red spices go into the bubbling water and milk mixture. On the corner of his workbench is a slab of stone and with a practiced thump a lump of ginger is mashed to a fibrous pulp with an improvised pestle, the piquant smell released as it's scraped up and added to the saucepan. His hand reaches down to a bag of sugar and six times he deftly fans white crystals into the pot. Now the wait while the brew bubbles along. It can't be hurried. Local men gather round the stall. He draws a ladle out and tips it back from a height, testing the viscosity, smelling the aroma, and finally his tin cup goes under the steam for the taste test. It's ready.

What We Collect
After Lunch Poems
by Robyn Groth

It's the Monday after Thanksgiving and even though
we have leftover turkey and leftover rolls we eat
fresh chicken salad on fresh croissants
and leave the leftovers a while longer.

I shoo the kids and dog out the door
and open my laptop to e-books on sale
for Cyber Monday, but as I click between
The Name of the Rose and *King Dork*,

I can't commit without feeling the weight,
and seeing the white space, the font size.
Pages thick, deckle edge and textured
or onion-skin thin and gilded?

Then the kids and dog crash in
and collide with the bookshelf
and *The Sound Patterns of English* falls flat
on the floor, but its dust takes flight.

And I'm on tiptoes now
numbly fingering books, top shelf university library,
their spines warm and frayed, mine cold but young
as I choose between a grammar on Quechua and one on Quiche—
and South America is just down the street.

We Are All Dealers In Used Furniture
by Howard Winn

Do we really want the very latest
from *Crate and Barrel* or *Ikea*?
Do we slaver over the styles of *Sonoma Williams*
and the clean lines of *Pier One Imports*,
becoming the straight arrow
into the heart of *Target*?
We do and we do not.
We also crave antiques.
The glow of old wood
and the patina of time
entreats our souls
(or what passes for them)
and we haunt shops,
attend auctions,
hoping to outwit those
who do not recognize
quality, time, the hand
of the craftsman as we wish to do.
The coated paper catalogues
grab our attention;
four colour printing and models
worthy of *Victoria's Secret* passion
that will turn our spaces into Today.
The choices irritate us,
like the thorn in the Lion's paw,
or the hangnail of the present.
Our DNA says the past is in our flesh
and we remember it
whether we wish to or not.

Dingbat Closet
by Lynne Potts

I am *in* a moth ball. I *am* a moth ball, so to speak,
speech being about what we thought we'd be when
we grew up and now look; so we wander around
with a lantern and sometimes they're drawn to it
and sometimes they stay closeted and eat our clothes.

Dirty Dice
by Janet Buck

I dial 1-800-die-ties.
"Al's Body Shop, please hold."
I hold because there's nothing left to do.
This year, your birthday cake arrived
in guises of a morphine drip—
courtesy of hospice care.

Fate threw dirty dice at you.
I wasn't there to hold your hand.
Last I heard, the tumour in your liver shrunk.
"The chemo makes me sick as hell,
but it's working, it's a miracle."
A month or two—no calls, no texts.

Last night I called again.
Your cell phone rang & rang—
dinner bells without a scrap of food,
just empty chairs. Finally, the message cue:
"This is Susy—leave a message"—
uttered in your chirpy voice.

I left an epic, ending with *Call me,
call me, call me, I'm getting worried—
hoping you're busy working at that
light molasses tan I'm jealous of.*
Your husband phones me back.
"Susy died. Four days ago—
You're the one she could not call—
I want her to remember 'us,'

Dark Square With Russet
by Dick Evans

*sitting on a park bench in the rain—
if I hear my best friend's voice,
I'll crack and talk. We never used umbrellas
when it poured. That's what she said and I repeat."*

I beg to put my heart on ice,
let salt mines liquefy, turn to ink—
cease the sobbing long enough to type.
That's how my knee knows how to bend
beside the holes where coffins go.
I wanna choke the animal that threw the dirty dice.

At the Bus Stop
by Trisha Farnan

The Stray
by Michelle McMillan-Holifield

First published in *A Quiet Courage*

Parkside Drive
by Linda Lowe

1975

New home, new marriage, new children. Step children, both his and hers, like monogrammed towels in the fancy master bath. The fancy house, custom built, sits across the street from the second tee of the country club golf course. The new husband has his own swanky business, which means he doesn't go into the office until noon. Which means he stays up late drinking his J.B. on the rocks with a twist and plays Neil Diamond or the Bee Gees or whoever he wants. When he fires up the Jacuzzi in the back yard, the motor whines, the music blares, the laughter is loud and raucous from too many of his old friends. The neighbours, what could they do? The cops would come, the cops would go. Upper class noise is a small thing in a town where in other neighbourhoods people are shot for their Nikes or their boom boxes or even pocket change. So for the neighbours there's only one thing to do, and that is to blackball him from the country club, which does hurt his feelings. If one could call them feelings.

The dog's pregnant again. The stray beauty who sleeps on the porch: gray concrete cool against her flamed cheek. So swollen, she whines to me. Seeks help extracting a thorn: the play

gone from her eyes, her paw arrayed lifeless for a moment. I've prayed for a child. Outlook may be bleak. The dog's pregnant.

What does she wish for, a display of sympathy for her pain? May—be she senses mine, wants to speak a kindred call: damaged, sweet, weak cry. Desperate. My heart gives way. The dog's pregnant.

Having Driven Over to Swedesboro by John Repp

alone just to drive the back roads on a sunny,
bleak November afternoon to where it gets hilly
near the river, I realized not for the first time
I was alone, but this time the snapshots I took

of the leafless peach orchard would rest
beneath the counter at Forcinito's for me
to pay for & cradle in my spidery hands
in the parking lot before driving to Newfield

or Malaga or the Methodist camp where Ida
the egg-candler lived. I knew the precise culvert
near Gouldtown where the whole family would dip
for shiners just a few legendary years before

& where the eels grew fat in the brackish creeks
near Fortescue. Everyone had shrunk or gone,
but to breathe the damp cold & hear the crunch
of dead cornstalks & not have anyone to tell

filled me with joy. We buried our best dog
around here somewhere, so heavy & stiff
he lay in the wheelbarrow, the wind
riffling his fur as we trundled along.

Snowchild by C. Wade Bentley

Watch a kid—nine years old, maybe—rolling
a snowman in the front yard, trying to get the head on
before dark and dinner, a carrot from mom in her pocket
with an old scarf, watch as something about the light
changes or the snow begins to bloom like jellyfish
or she catches a glimpse of her family through
the window, preserved in the amber light. It's almost
as if she has caught the scent, coming from the woods
behind the house, perhaps for the first time, of just
the leading edge of a sadness that will one day wash
over her. As if the powerlines overhead begin to feel
the new and growing weight of snow, something
in the world flickers briefly out, so that even as she holds
the two rocks for eyes, one in each hand, she pauses
long enough to notice the cold that had always
been there, before shaking herself free again, screwing
the hard, sightless eyes into the snowman's face.

Selective Memory
by Erica Travers

This is how I want to remember you:
curly blond hair falling lightly over
laughing eyes that don't remember
your casual violence and the hurting
words your mouth emits—a
missed connection or mental
block, misplaced without intent.

Your beard that grows so
effortlessly and innocently white
around the corners of your lips
carelessly dangling a perfectly
rolled cigarette.

Your arms as they wrap around me
tight and barricade me in against the cold
while I fall asleep wondering
where to go from here.

Evening, 1984
by Robert Crisp

I looked down
and saw your body,
a question mark in the water——

beautiful, as always,
even from that distance,
as I counted the rain drops,
too few to summon fear in you,
but the other swimmers scampered
out like children suddenly summoned.

You lounged in silver light,
turning softly over the waves
that I knew one day would carry you,
born aloft like a goddess, away from me.

A Life Not Lost was inspired by this painting. Artist Unknown.

A Life Not Lost
by Liza Perrat

The trucks careen into the village, tyres shrieking as the vehicles stop at the refuge. Across the road, through a crack in our shutters, we watch the men stride inside and drag the sleepy children from their baguette and hot chocolate breakfast. My heartbeat quickens as they bundle the little ones, like sacks of corn, into the open-ended trucks.

'Wherever do they take those poor children?' my wife says, her finger-nails cutting into my forearm. 'Where do they take all our people?'

'To camps in the east,' I say, averting my eyes from the jumble of cries, thin limbs and yellow stars disappearing down the road as the trucks zoom off. 'Or somewhere .'

We keep watching until the faces of the little ones are pinpricks, and all that remains are whiffs of ersatz petrol and puffs of exhaust fumes.

I clamp my hands on my wife's shoulders, stare into her eyes. 'It'll be us next time. No one can escape them. You should go now, Sabine. Go, and take our children to safety.'

'Come with us,' she says, though I hear the defeat in her voice. She's given up on me. 'Please, Leo.'

'No!' I shake my head, angry with myself for shouting at her.

'They won't chase me from my home … the home that has belonged to our family for how many generations?'

Sabine keeps her gaze low. 'I don't know … I don't know anything, anymore.'

***

Sabine and the children have been gone a week and still I sit at my window, painting with the urgency forced upon me.

Le Garon—our river—glistens silver-grey through early mist, my brush sweeping a nimbus of gold across the water, for the sun afloat. In the foreground, oak trunks shelter within cloaks of ivy, and branches are brown tangles bearing the green buds of leaves I'll never see or touch.

For our stone well, I curve an arch of beige above an oval, a rust-red dab for the flour mill, dark strokes squaring fields of sunflowers with mud-brown eyes. And the hills beyond—where hidden men whisper in code and blow up trains laden with enemy arms—are moss green, with yellow dandelion dots.

My brush trembles over our courtyard cobblestones, wavers on the concrete steps rickety with the footsteps of an untroubled past. I choose strong colours to echo my heart that still pulses strong for all they have condemned: rich brown for the oak door, deep green for the shutters to frame the windows. My sky is a patch of vivid blue, with dark specks of sparrows gliding on a freedom not governed by race, politics, or religion.

My arm aches but I don't stop; can't stop. I'm hungry but there is no time to eat. I smile at the irony, for what need is there now to nourish this body? None. Of that, I am certain—as certain as the scarlet red of summer's cherries, the bleached white of winter snow, the muted pinks and golds of autumn leaves. As certain as one man's folly.

I scrawl Leo Weiner, '43 in the bottom right-hand corner of this, my final tableau, then I rinse my brushes and fold my easel. I clamber upstairs to the attic, store it behind the panel with all the other paintings.

I am ready.

I don't have to wait long.

It's not an open-ended truck that comes for me, but a black Citroën, gliding into the courtyard as if it belongs. Knee-high boots gleam, click on cobblestones, stomp up concrete steps. Impatient fists thump on the door until the oak splinters, cracks and collapses towards me. They spill through the doorway.

Black breeches boast terror, grey-green helmets speak indifference, skull insignias and red swastika armbands stink of power. The dark muzzle of a pistol spells the end.

They hustle me outside, down the rickety steps and across the old cobblestones. I smile to myself, thinking how many times I have cursed these uneven cobbles, tripping me up. Wishing my step could falter, just once more.

As they bundle me into the Citroën, I think about when this madness will be over, and someone will find a secret panel in an attic. I picture that person pushing back the panel and discovering my paintings. Wiping off the dust, the mouse droppings, the dampness. Their gaze follows my loving strokes; the harmony of colours that blends a river, a well, a house. A home.

A life not lost.

Redemption
by Chumki Sharma

Where you cleared the forest
off the summit, flattened
the hill with bulldozers,
laid shiny culverts,
a sleek road going nowhere
for miles of uncut grass,
built the exact same house
row after row.

Yes, that place,
beyond the builder's insolvency
and the realtor's tin shingles
lies a slope at the end of which
after every rain children float
paper boats and fill the air
with jubilant cries.

If redemption had a voice,
would it sound like this?

White of endless cotton
sway in the breeze,
Blood on the hawk's talons.

The Poem Is
by Phill Provance

Because at five I caught
my dad, his neck craned
in the dust-smothered,
olive-curtained, spare
room of our trailer,
scribbling and crying on
a near-exhausted legal
pad as my Uncle Don
helped shove his clothes
in a Rubbermaid bin.
Because, after dad left,
there was a warm divot
in my parents' comforter
where me and my brother
would lay like two blind
puppies stretched below
a window, before we'd
lash our arms around our
mother as she opened
Danny the Dinosaur
to our favourite page.
Because I first fell into
myself in second grade,
the day Mrs. Mann had
us write poems, and when
my eyes turned to the playground
they suddenly divided
the sky from the rain.
It is because all this has
recurred in swells and waves:
The tear-soaked paper.
The empty bed. My son
asking for the peace
The Giving Tree gives. Now
and then, again and again—
when nothing's left,
the poem remains.

Ostrich Dreams
by Vakseen

Vakseen

15

Today's the Day I Realized
by Vakseen

Quadrillions
by G. M. Monks

Four in the morning, 6000 feet up,
100 miles from a town. Summer's
night is black as ever. Can't see my
cold hands, let alone my feet.

Moon's nowhere.

Who glitter bombed the sky?
Stars, stars, stars thicker
than all city lights.
The Milky Way stretches east to
west.

I can't touch them, smell them, hear
them. They're light years away.
Trillions of miles. Quadrillions.

Just me and them.

Necessity
by Jim Gustafson

Today I read solitude is necessity,
it didn't say what for. I am relieved to know
time alone is vital like water, which I'm told
is disappearing, even as it lifts itself
to drown the oldest shores. There is no scarcity
of fire. Matches strike no thought for conservation.
Smoke curls curse the air with chemistry. Scent travels
back to the never seen. By night, light is thrown
out of unknown places, not worthy of a search.
The isolated bulb speaks in tongues and shadows.
Horizons pitch illuminant from poles, casting
illusions of security, as if evil
can take place without darkness. We all know better.
Our darkest days come to us in the best of light.

Dingbat 1 by Lynne Potts

Climb this way, they said. *Put your foot here*, and then
they pulled me up onto the cloud. But guess what?
After a while I realized the cloud had a hole in it
so of course, I had to go down, because in circum-
stances like this I'm always wondering how deep it is.

Dingbat 4 by Lynne Potts

You hang a curtain and you think it will hang there
for years and years, but later it fades into mountains
where you are asleep in a goose down sleeping bag
and you can't find the zipper but you have to get out
and remember where you put the hooks for the rod.

Making Space
by CLS Ferguson

The horizon is full of colours I can't describe
I'm looking into a future with hopes I shouldn't pile on you
Dare me to tell you how long I've dreamed of you
We're a love story written in Sanskrit and Aramaic

Making space, making space, making space

You won't be conceived in my womb
It will remain empty while I make space for you
You were/are/will be conceived in another's womb
She loved/loves/will love you so much, she will pick me

Making space, making space, making space

I don't know you yet, but I yearn for you to love me
Not in my body, but in my heart and soul I'm making space
I've ignored those who tell me I shouldn't love you
Still ignoring my fear you'll one day shout, "You're not my real mom!"

Making space, making space, making space

Just as my mother made space for me

Beach Rocks
by Bee Williamson

The Mist from Myanmar
by Deborah Guzzi

The blades of winter grind into ice flirting with
the rosy cheeks of puppy love. Crusted mittens cling
like chapped skin on bitten lips, scarfs twirl as we spin.

Steam rises from the cup, reminiscent of the first kiss,
across swamp-grass hummocks, rotten ice, lace tripping,
the rosy cheeks of puppy love. Crusted mittens cling.

Black hair, fair skin, dark-eyed, he cajoles a grin.
In the steam, not the leaves, she remembers him
across swamp-grass hummocks, rotten ice, lace tripping;

they spin. Assam seeps in porcelain, another cup
she pours. In an empty nest, the china clinks saucer;
in the steam, not the leaves, she remembers him.

From sunrise through the fall of snow, she sees a mist,
falling flakes through chinks of memory.
She pours. In an empty nest, the china clinks saucer.

The recollection of youthful laughter trembles
across the crackled surfaces of her mind's walls
falling flakes through chinks of memory.

Random squeaks in the oaken floors recall returns,
these missed images swirl from tea to family
across the crackled surfaces of her mind's walls.

A long lost cat meanders through the shrouded scene
in peace the images rest beneath tapping fingertips;
these missed images swirl from tea to family.

Every loved and loving one returns mist-born
within a porcelain cup of tea from Myanmar,
in peace the images rest beneath tapping fingertips.

Estate Sale
by Kelsey Dean

Bedspreads folded up and piled onto tables, along with tea towels, candleholders, sheet music, butter dishes. A set of ceramic salt and pepper shakers shaped like ears of corn. A bird whistle. A book about seashells, lovingly dog-eared, in the corner by the red lamp. A Russian nesting doll. A hundred leftover pieces of a person stacked in stale air that smells like mothballs and lavender.

The line moves slowly, paper bags rustling, nickels and dimes tinkling like the music box behind the glassware.

with fluttering hands
magpies collect
abandoned treasures

Antoinette by Veronica Scharf Garcia

Jaymi Creates the Platinum Raven's Code

Excerpted from *The Beasts of Electra Drive* by Rohan Quine

by Rohan Quine

So here comes the code of this in-game Beast who personifies transcendence in a white-blonde flavour, but treacle-black and blood-orange inside herself.

She will allow Jaymi to lob one tiny Easter egg of unique sweetness from the shadows here where he stands, into the empty circle of spotlight awaiting her there on her creation floor, before he must get down to uncompromising business with her transcendence. OK then, so there goes the little chocolate egg, curving up in slow motion through the air in his study, twirling end-on-end as it levels off in mid-arc, gliding in through the spotlight-cone's soft perimeter and landing in the white-lit circle on the floor of the darkness, where it spins to a foil-wrapped halt … the egg-foil opens busily, as if in speeded-up footage, and out hatches a flash-forward memory of a lost time in the Platinum Raven's notional childhood, hidden there recessively in her otherwise blank history, when her five-year-old self is standing beside Jaymi's five-year-old self in an elementary-school playground. They hardly know each other and will never get around to speaking with each other again, as it happens. But just for this one moment, they share something that he at least will never forget: both standing on tiptoes to peer through the frosted window of a locked shed in the corner of the playground, they agree in loud whispers that the face they think they can see in the darkness of the shed's cluttered interior is the face of a secret monkey living inside, which nobody else knows about!… The two of them giggle together at this, shushing each other in gleeful surprise at this shared monkey secret. Then they skip away across the playground in opposite directions, into separate lives, smiling still, never to exchange a single further word.

The cone of spotlight flicks off and slams away, sucked into blackness and silence. There—that's all the Platinum Raven will allow Jaymi, in the chocolate egg department.

Now: the business of transcendence please. From his insides, to hers…

Her charisma will derive from emotional self-containment and unpredictability, as charisma tends to, but also come from an intelligence that's primal, defeating analysis. The question "Has the Platinum Raven got it?" will be answered "Yes." It—that quality that'll make her stand out from the sphere of other Beasts around her.

She'll be isolated in the middle of things, but will contrive to make it feel an honour for another Beast to know her. Such other Beast will know the Platinum Raven could bite them worse than they could bite her, while believing correctly that she won't bite, unprompted. The trust they'll place in her will feel all the more rewarded for their having contemplated the danger of its being broken.

Her power to make others love her will rest upon an essential innocence on her part, in being fascinated by herself as a character rather than as a set of interests to be furthered—a self-celebration with nothing heavy or solipsistic in it. Simple though this will feel from her viewpoint, nonetheless for others it will tend to cause everything about her to be a denial of expectations that everything else about her has already raised.

Further down, there'll be an element or two of the dictator or murderer, somewhere in her. Those twin shadows will be there, in the sense that fantasy will sometimes clamour to become reality, cool and ferocious; yet luckily those spectres will loom small enough, within her landscape, to be sublimated.

And so it will be, when inspiration strikes her, that she'll plant a platinum kiss upon the game-skin of her universe…

Then without warning he reaches into this cold theoretical code of hers and unleashes an extravagant death-wish at the heart of her: hot and red inside, where she lounges on the driver's seat, her foot upon the pedal as the car flashes scarlet under headlands of rock around Pacific Coast Highway curves at ninety miles an hour, with the crackle of the cables in the sweaty air of night above, ecstatic to be leaving life any second now, beneath the stars, with the bottle in her hand and her unseen lover-boy sitting right beside her…

Jaymi hits the Enter key before her car can crash, sealing up within the coolness of her code a red-hot death-by-the-ocean whose voltage will strain against the inside of her ribcage, never to be earthed.

He sinks back, exhaling aloud in exertion, as the driver's seat melts back into his seat upon the terrace behind the house on Zeus Drive. He saves his work, and backs it up.

The code of a brand-new Beast now exists!

Power stations of the mind
by Roz Morris

I'd spent too many hours at the wheel, racing the December dusk to get to our destination before darkness fell. Too many hours scrutinising every junction, traffic lane and sign, of passing through new places and barely seeing them. Now, at last, we were here. While Dave unpacked the car, I stood in the chilly twilight and finally looked at where I was.

An ornamental folly built in the 1740s; our home for the week. It resembled a miniature chateau, with tall windows, classical pediments and a roof like the lid of a square teapot. Behind was the darkening hulk of a wood. And just beyond, which I didn't expect at all, an enormous power station, softening into the fog. A boiler chimney stitched with a line of twinkling red lights. A row of cooling towers blooming steam into the sunset. It was so close, it dwarfed the house. Yet it was completely soundless.

Dave pulled me into the house. 'Come on. Let's get in. We can look at that tomorrow.'

Tomorrow came. I bounded out of bed, eager to see our new world in daylight. And to check this spellbinding structure that hung outside in perfect silence.

I opened the shutters and saw the thickest cotton-wool mist. As if something had breathed hard on all the windows. A skinny winter tree managed to make itself seen, but beyond that there was nothing but white. There was no trace of the power station, not even its twinkling lights.

The mist receded hour by hour. It revealed a rolling sweep of meadow, sloping steeply down to a river. The power station was far away on a bend. It wasn't close at all. The previous night it had seemed huge, like a galleon berthed right behind us in the woods. I was convinced we were mere yards from the foot of the cooling towers. But now the fog had cleared, it was several miles down the river and would barely dwarf my thumb.

We established a routine. Out early for exploring, walking and shopping, then return mid-afternoon for tea on the lawn as dusk fell, watching the power station do its thing in the distance. One day we came back to find it was dormant. Usually smoke and steam rose steadily from all its openings. But at three on a sunny Sunday afternoon, it was dozing. Just a faint puff from the main chimney and hardly a wisp from the cooling towers. We made a cup of tea and continued to watch. As we did, the smoke from the main stack began to thicken. Two of the cooling towers began to mist. We were witnessing it fire up as the world came home and put the kettle on. Sitting outside our 1740s chateau like time travellers, watching the rhythms of the 21st century.

Still, I puzzled about that first looming glimpse. Especially returning from the bathroom in the middle of the night, half in a dream. The bathroom was downstairs and we left a lamp on so we didn't grope and crash around. Coming back up the stairs, a trick of the light meant you'd see your shadow growing gigantic on the bedroom door. Was that it? Had I read somewhere about fog having a mysterious magnifying quality? If so, where had I read it? Was it in a sensible work of fact or the Hound of the Baskervilles?

Or did my brain play tricks in those first moments of arrival, unplugging from the hypervigilance of driving, the luxury of finally being able to stop and look? Wow – there's the house. Wow – there's a power station. Every day I checked for it, never quite believing it would not be giant again.

Roman Agora
by Ion Corcos

A single bell chimes
short like a stone
struck on a pebbled path.

A man wanders
among the marble ruins
of an old Roman market.

Chamomile blossoms,
some words spoken in Greek,
relics lost
in the long grass,
a robin on a tree.

Pillars stand
without a roof,
no stalls,
no goods.

The man sits
in the heat,
alone on a block
of worn marble
watches bees
hover in flowers,
sparrows flit.

Frog Rider by Jessica Gawinski

III

How stars gnaw at the clouds
spring onion grass sharpens
metal lawn chairs shiver

how tulip spears pierce the ground
just as broken glass works its way
through flesh and out into the world.

IV

In the cistern, rainwater swells with darkness.
The night echoes with skunk, with maple leaves,
with the thin cry of the snake. In the cistern, secrets;
frogs drowning in words that cannot be spoken aloud.

V

On the front porch, metal lawn chairs
overturned against the storm crackle
as maple leaves turn silver in the wind.

In the morning sun, a termite swarm,
the house alive with wings.

VI

The way ants tend a peony bud
a million tiny touches, a push

against shiny skin, drinking
the dew that collects at dawn

how I tend the farm

the dark crops of memory
the rising fogs, the maples

what passes through the air
or falls into the cistern of night.

The Poet Farm
by Patti White

I

On summer nights the corn rustles
like insect wings scraping the dark
or rodents skittering, a pebble
turned over, a bit of leaf mould
disturbed. The horse breathes
softly, an angel waiting for dawn

II

A house burns on the horizon. The river
rises, or sends fog to smother the blaze,
those sleeping never see, the smoke
never reaching the bedrooms, the fog
thickening over the lawn, a blanket
of cool damp air or a careful sponge.

My Father's Funeral Home
by Amanda Chiado

In the basement my father is a man of anatomy.
In the kitchen I bang the pots.
My mother has the ears of a musician.
She sings to alleviate the sound
of bodies being embalmed.
Sometimes, you can hear my father
join the song from the basement.
My father likes to count the freckles
of the dead or guess the colour
of the dead debutante's toe nail polish.
My mother makes him shower before dinner.
My mother mashes the potatoes.
My mother hates him working overtime,
eating–while downstairs a body grows
like a blue hyacinth waiting in winter months.
My mother says that somehow the stories
of those dead bodies seep through the vents
and turn her dreams into untold histories.
My father places his clean tools into neat rows,
life lines, patterns of prayer and silver hunger.
The body's stillness is a stained glass
from which my father sees the warped world,
but released, more periwinkle. My mother thanks
god for my cooing which balances the house of the dead.

Rapsody by Diana Whiley

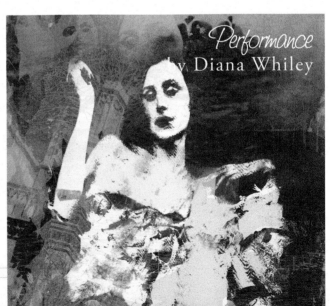

Performance by Diana Whiley

Under the Arbutus
by David Pratt

A breeze ripples the lily pads. The sun in the water is no longer a disk but a blinding column across the lake. Lying on my back I see the leaves of the arbutus tree lit from underneath, translucent green. We watch the bees. A dog swims for sticks.

I'd just broken up with Alan, you are saying, and it was February and I'd been overworking. I said to Barbara, just take me to a beach. So we went to a resort in Acapulco. That was where I met Miguel. His firm was doing business there. We enjoyed each other's company, and after that we were together for a year. We'd meet twice a month; either he'd come to San Francisco or I'd fly down to Guadalajara. He was married and had two daughters, whom I was never allowed to see. One day, when we were at the apartment he kept for us, he said, Well, maybe when we're old we'll be together. And I started crying and couldn't stop. I shut myself in the bathroom and I cried and cried, but it couldn't contain my crying, so I went out in the garden. I wouldn't let Miguel near me, he was completely at a loss. I just sobbed and sobbed; it was all the grief of all my life, and will no one ever just be with me? He took me to the airport and I never saw him again.

Your hair, still wet from swimming, lies on my shoulder. The pines on the opposite shore are a black ragged palisade, the mountains a horizon of torn paper. An ant runs over the back of my hand.

Barcelona Rogueros
by Nory Marc Steiger

Why Waste Money
by Taly Oehler

Gun by Randall Droll

He sat all morning on the city bench
Tattered, he wore a windbreaker
Perhaps he sought to spite July's sun
I saw him rise, he came into our store
Everyone ducked into the rear
I was left to serve the small, strange man
"I see that you sell paint; I don't need that."
"Paint and supplies, that's mainly what we sell."
I tried to keep my voice from breaking.
"I'd like cash, open up the till,"
He said and reached inside his jacket
"I don't have a key." I choked in fear
"Wrong answer, in my pocket I have a gun.
It's pointed straight at you, now get me cash."
"I can't, I don't have a key, honest."
 "Don't be stupid, you're close to being shot."
I froze, did nothing, "I don't have a key."
"Get one; don't you think I have a gun?"
In all my life, I did what was most stupid
"No, I don't think you have a gun."
He shrank, pulled his empty hand from
his jacket. "You're a good young man."
He began talking about the war
Said he hoped I never would be in one.
"But you're a good boy, you probably will be.
I'd best be on my way, but first advice.
Never say 'I don't think you have a gun.'"
And I never have.

If I Believed in God and the Inherent Joy of Violence by Marie Marandola

No one answers their phones,
even though the news is good

so I walk down to the neighbourhood park.
There's no birthday party tonight,

no pick-up soccer game, just one guy
at a picnic bench, bicycle propped

beside him. I sit on a swing, bare feet
trailing through playground grit,

and tuck and reach my legs until I swing
so high the chains jerk taut, sear red braids

into my palms. Until my pointed toes
slice into heaven, kick an angel in the face—

his screams ring out like harp chords. I swing
until I'm nauseous, gargling my heart,

gulping the sky. I swing until I don't
feel happy anymore.

189

Incomplete
by CLS Ferguson

Foundation laid, skeleton of wood waiting for metal or drywall
There's a crack in the concrete
But we've come this far
If I patch it, you may notice, if I don't, you'll fall through
The windows were meant for the walls, not the floor
Just another thing to swallow you whole
The moving truck is coming with all the baggage we couldn't bear to let go

We'll put it in storage until

      until

            until

                  until

So many untils we'll never get anything done

We'll forget to punish ourselves for all our wrongs
We'll squeeze too tightly to our broken mirrors
You were struggling to clean the dishes in this house I built for you
No running water, no counter space, no walls, no roof
Just the kitchen sink filled with dirty dishes
The crack in the foundation is spreading
But we've hung the pictures and made the bed
If anyone comes for dinner, do you suppose they'll mind the cracks in their plates?
If we don't mend these cracks the lawn may grow through the floor
Perhaps no one will notice the crumbling foundation
I've bought a new area rug

The Morning After
by William C. Crawford

Detective Work by Cooper Lysek Gomez

I ease open the truck door and step onto the sunbaked pavement. I lug myself across the barren patch of yard to the crime scene. It seems like the usual day: just do a quick check-up and get it over with. But then I see the first body, sprawled like a slinky across the dirt. I walk over to inspect it, ignoring the reek of death. A strange murder, the victim wearing scratches like a coat of medals. Too thin to be human. I call my mother over, confirm I'm not losing my mind. While she takes samples, I take in the rest of the scene: blood on the trees, feathers in the flowerbed, six other bodies just like the first. We lost eleven good chickens that day.

Dog's First Spring
by Grant Clauser

When every scent is new
like birdsong strung
on tree branches
when the way soft ground
that was hard yesterday
is something that needs
to be thought about
like a sunrise needs
to be thought about
like a rabbit needs
to be chased
because it is a rabbit.

Down the Hatch
by Maryanne Hannan

Your cup fills up with whatever you put in it, predicts Meta-Mama. My real mother mostly ran from cabinet to cabinet, lamenting broken crockery. Her teacup held a big old cheesy meatball, not bad for an Irish girl. Fifty years ago, my best friend took me to her Lebanese family reunion, so I gravitate to minty torpedo-shaped kibbeh. But these days, you need more than meatballs in your cup. My husband, perfectly calibrated to some metric of temperature and exertion, fills his cup with the sweet sweat of his brow. His clothes, sluicing the headwaters, only amplify our latest laundry product. When dry, fine lines of salt undulate across them. A couple glasses of water, Gatorade, and he's back to normal, a tidy sum acquired for his mug. With my idiopathic internal heat and cooling system, I adapt poorly to low altitudes and regular hours. I like body surfing. All that unencumbered beauty, sloshing in and out of my tumbler. When I raise it high, I don't know what to toast. *But I to you of a white goat*, wrote Sappho. That might work.

Isabel del Mar
by Veronica Scharf Garcia

senryu
by Charles Leggett

summer evening air
sweeter than sex ... i wrote that?
yes with misgivings

Bosbefok
by Lee Nash

We said ja for yes,
takkies for trainers,
just now when we meant later on.
We'd tell a dog to voetsek.
Cry eina for ow.

We binged on koeksisters,
gnawed on biltong,
hitched rides to the koppies
in the backs of bakkies.

We ate sarmies and naartjies,
crunched our packets
of snoek-flavored chips
in the bioscope.

We bought smokes
not cigarettes,
said stompies for butts,
sat on the stoep and skinnered.

We drank dumpies;
put meat on the braai.
We were often in a dwaal.

We said border
whichever border it was
where our guys
were sent to war.

We waited for them
and when they came back
said yes when they wanted to graunch.

We shimmied close
as they opened their albums
and said, "These are the men
that we killed."

We looked at those bodies
and shivered
as if we had eaten
a vrot avocado
or stepped on a shongololo.
We said nothing at all.

Colour Enhanced Mannequin
by William C. Crawford

Hepatitis
by Cameron Mount

I have never considered
being an alcoholic,
not that it's usually a choice,
until the day they told me
to never drink again
Hepatitis, they said, causes
cirrhosis
alone
Don't escalate the damage
by drinking
My mouth went dry
the way alcoholics
claim
A drink, something
I hadn't had in more than a week
and hadn't really missed,
suddenly became compulsory
unavoidable
craving
It ached too much to ignore
parched
And I poured
a shot
I celebrated my diagnosis
with a whisky
a dram
and another
and another
alone

Metanoia
by Annie Blake

Metanoia is when I wake up
from being delirious and hot and black and white and realise
I am in a 3D movie, where the roads and the sky
and the houses look flat but the leaves of the trees
and the lipstick colour of the fire
hydrant jump out to me.

The brown leaves are made from new crafty
paper created by healthy
children and no matter
how long they rattle in the wind they will not
fall. As I walk down the path, the flowers are breathing
out their bright trippy smoke. You give me your hands, your fingers—

And I promise I will never kill you.

Fast Break
Previously published in Carolyn Martin, Finding Compass (Portland, *OR: Queen of Wands Press, 2011)*
by Carolyn Martin

I snatched his scarf, dug in my skates,
    and dashed fast breaks around the ice.
        Taunting him to ditch the other kids
           and catch my breeze, I wanted
                to be caught. I willed him

to surprise me from behind, grab
    balance in the bitter wind, enfold
        me in his scarf, share breath, a tease,
           a kiss on Woodbridge pond, sixth grade,
                that brazen New Year's Eve.

But truth's a risky skate around a rutty pond
    where *want* outraces *is* for just so long.
        I'll resurrect that day again, again—
           the break, the pain. An ankle, mine.
              The scarf he flung around his neck.
                The laughs that skated on.

Cloud
by Joshua B Huitz

The Glass Slipper Snail
by Rachel Linn

Not just once upon a time, but all the time, the common slipper snail looks for partners—a stack of them. Slipper snails don't have a problem finding a shoe that fits. Left-spiralled and right-spiralled snails cannot make larva together, but very few are born sinistral, limiting love-lessness to a very small handful of loners. Furthermore, all slipper snails are shoe-shaped, and though some of their shells are more arched than others, like feet, that is of no consequence. Neither is size. Inside their shells, they are all spineless and sponge-like. They can make it work.

If you are a slipper snail, all you have to do is find an older, larger female to clamber on top of—perhaps even your own stepmother, unless she is already above you on the stack between you and your father—and, if you don't quite fit, you need not cut off your heels and toes, which you do not possess anyway—you can simply become a boy. If you are smaller than the other snails in your stack, you will transform spontaneously.

The largest snails are firmly female. You have to be determined about gender consistency, as it requires feeding constantly—or else barely at all.

***

Not all of us can be slipper snails. Potential partners often refuse to let me lie on top of them, even when I am smaller and less threatening than they are, which I usually am. I try to explain that I find their forms comforting, like a therapist's couch—except with a spiral of tightly curled hair at their tops instead of a roll of fabric—this causes offense. Romantics

prefer a long chase to a chaise longue.

They also become suspicious when I bring along a smaller man to make myself seem larger. This is not an attractive tactic, I've been told, and it makes people less likely to shack up or stack up, as the case may be. They shut their opercula and act like I'm not even a man at all, which I might not be, since proximity to a smaller male makes me more considerate and nurturing.

If the other man is small enough, I begin to taste the salt tears of others through my skin, even when they're not crying. When that happens, I am happy to be at the very bottom of the snail stack even if everyone else has suddenly taken on a plush, velveteen shine, ankles narrowing to wooden points and feet dwindling into decorative claws, and I desperately want to rest on their cushions while having my dreams analyzed.

Then, I will only eat things that do not have eyes; never potatoes, even if they are peeled and mashed, their eyes striped and discarded. I will be too sensitive.

***

Members of Gastropoda, like the slipper snail, are only a stomach on foot, if you trust their name. I often wish that my desires were so simple. Their neritiform shells seem merely rounded pebbles from above, blending into the real rocks on the beach. You can't tell by looking that they're polyamorous and hermaphroditic, or even alive.

People can't tell by looking at me either. My cloche of woven coralline gives me the appearance of a woman if I wear it one way and a man if I wear it another. In one position, which I've only found perfectly once, it makes me look like a

man and a woman. You can't tell which I am becoming, only that I am sliding between the two. Or, you might wonder if there should be any number at all. For slipper snails, there is no perfect amount in a stack and gender is only a matter of how much algae and decaying plankton you were able to scrape off rocks during the last high tide.

***

Marine scientists have commissioned see-through blown glass hermit crab shells in order to more easily observe their secret motions. No one does this with slipper snails because they are glued to their shells and you would have to rip off skin to move them into a new container.

In my case, however, a glass shell would be a useful means through which prospective partners could observe me. I often do things in reverse order and don't like to be judged for this sinister chirality. For example, people are often nice at first and then years later you find out that they see you as merely a comfortable piece of furniture, a barcalounger that only reclines or an ottoman the cat has clawed the stuffing out of. I notice your humanity more slowly, at my own snail pace, not at first sight, but then I will not forget, even if seabirds have smashed my glass shell open and pecked out my eyes.

First Kiss, Last Kiss
by Robert Hambling Davis

Darling, here we sit, you and I, on a boardwalk bench by the sea, having met for the first time an hour ago. As the spring tide comes in, our lips join in a kiss that deepens this moment, the only time when we can live. Arms around each other, we share the taste of our mouths, our tongues tentative at first, darting and retreating, and then lingering boldly together in the twilight.

"Ralph, how many times must I tell you the dishwasher's busted and it's your turn to wash the dishes. Just look at them piled up in the sink."

"Please, not now, Alice. I'm writing."

"You've been writing all day, drinking wine too. Now wash the fucking dishes."

"I will when I finish this."

"I should've listened to my mother and married a plumber. Now we can't even afford one because you quit your job to write and haven't sold a goddamn thing. Why'd I ever marry you?"

"It was love at first sight, Alice. You told me that. Remember?"

"Well, it's not love in hindsight. Now get off your ass and wash the dishes."

"I will in a while. Give me some space, Alice."

Darling, how many lives have we been together? What else explains love at first sight? We met in our present forms, strolling opposite ways on the boardwalk, and slowing and stopping five feet apart, knowing if we missed this chance we'd probably have to wait till our next coinciding incarnations to find each other again.

"I'm going out, Ralph. I can't stand being with you another second."

"I'll wash the dishes, Alice."

"Too late for that."

"It's past midnight. You can't go out now."

"Don't wait up or you'll miss lots of sleep and go crazy. But you're crazy already."

Darling, our kiss tells the tale that has no beginning or end, the tale of here and now. Our love is a mystery to savour, not solve. What better way to remember to wake up and live?

"Maybe when I'm gone, Ralph, you'll

sell stories that'll double the divorce rate."

"Don't go, Alice. Please don't leave me. I'll wash the dishes and get a job."

"Bye, Ralph."

Darling, the moon is up, the tide is in, and we're no longer who we were before we met.

"Get back in the house, Ralph."

"Why are you doing this, Alice? Why, why?"

"Let go of me. You've been drinking and you're making a scene."

"It's what I want to make."

"Go in before the neighbours call the cops. And don't try to follow me."

"No."

"Give me your car keys."

"No."

"Give them to me, Ralph, or I'll call the cops."

"Okay, okay. But give me one last kiss before you go."

"No."

"Please, just one, Alice. And I promise to leave you alone, forever."

Diagnosis
by Brad Garber

The biopsy was positive
as if bad news can be,
words falling like leaves.
I was a rotting plant,
fungal tendrils spreading,
first to roots, then flowers.
Walking across the lot
to the safety car,
I floated on soiled water.
And, on the silent seat
I wept deep within me,
both eyes dry as death.

A Large White Fly
by Dah Helmer

Near the soggy edges
of a stream
thumb-sized toads are trolls
under large green leaves
They fade out with each hop

Between summer and autumn
earth's damp pungent odour
Big white clover scatters
like scented snow
A blindworm's topical escape

I see a pair of toy eyes
on a small face with whiskers
a black coat neatly pressed
little cautious field mouse
A large white fly buzzes

In the alleys of fern
a teeny rustling of imagination
overloads my logic
I am sitting on a toadstool
Perhaps myself, perhaps not

A mole of Thumbelina delight
stirs and trembles
barely beneath the surface
of brown mulch
A swallow zigzags happily

Spellbound by the rolling sky
the sun staggers to keep up
I ogle an orange mushroom
the size of a teensy umbrella
The cloudbanks are paunchy

I move to where darkness begins
slightly before nothing
There's an unexpected rejoicing breeze
with the motion of a body
blowing over tiny footprints

Southern Comfort
by Jackie Braje

A bull tore through
the gate while the man on
its back wavered, flimsy
plexiglass, one arm to the heavens,
one gripping the reigns. Back
snapping like a bundle of

twigs. Grandma, with her
ten redcoat soldiers, clutched
a bag of Twizzlers and patted
jet black tresses unmoved
since '73, hollering at the new

40 inch big screen

"get 'em, get 'em." Candy
bag crinkled down and
clamped by paperclip. Dog
days of Florida, broken AC,
my gangly homunculus

sprawled on cool living room
tile. Dressed down in navel—
high silk underwear and cotton
shirt, she stepped over me with
hobbled heel and varicose veins,
battalion of vines around each

calf, liver spots like oil drops;
a body soft in its waning.
Grandpa's in the next room
piecing an old Springfield, nimble—
fingered under yellow fluorescence,

a jaundiced sadness like a
veil. Dust particles floated into
ether, ether glinted off bullet
cases, gunpowder smelled
like orange juice and alphabet
soup on a sick day. TV commercial
showed a grandfather

with a voice like embrace and
hounds-tooth vest. Grandpa hollered
from the garage like a shove.
Grandma, a real anatomical
picture of a heart with all its
chambers and veins, drooped

her black tresses down,
empty bullet cases
falling from a barrel.

Vista Grande
by Dick Evans

The Empty Rabbit
by William C. Crawford

Night Poetry
by Jennifer Jones

Darkness hovers along the upper edge of the sky.
Heavy, brown boots kick piles of oak's spent fertility.
Winter's impending chill swirls, a halo of breath, as
I remember the fireflies from July-past.
Movement accompanied verse as they danced at twilight.
Frogs' throaty, rich voices—of earth and timelessness—
Provided melody.
The stars gazed down on this night poetry;
Their glowing smiles twinkled approval as the velvet sky
Radiated with showered applause.

***

The frogs have long since quieted their nocturnal musings.
Fireflies lie in deep slumber, dreaming of that starry dance.
Shadows settle, blanket-like, over the leaf littered soil, as
One lone porch light winks in the distance and
A curl of chimney smoke beckons hearth and home.
Even the stars burrow under cloud quilts—to ward off the chill.
Yet, into night air heavy with dusk and autumn's perfume,
Stillness
Whispers night poetry of its own
For anyone willing to hear.

Talking at Once
by Fiona Pitt-Kethley

Talking at once, a very Spanish thing.
It's easy to despair and get no grasp,
until you see it as an orchestra.
It's necessary to know some people there.
X is intelligent with lots to give,
Y frequently just spouts a load of shit.
Watch carefully, select a voice to hear …
Pick out the melody, block out the rest.
Move from the flute and try a violin,
on to bassoons, but leave the timpani.

Atalanta
by Veronica Scharf Garcia

"Why doesn't he run away?" Alun pointed at the dog lying on a stripy blanket in the shoe-shop doorway. The brown mongrel and its owner looked back at him. Neither seemed too willing to waste energy on answering the question. Behind the man and his dog, Alun could see his own reflection shimmering like a ghost among the pairs of shoes, which were stacked in pyramids like a fairground game. If he had a stone with him and chucked it with a bit of spin at the black lace-ups bottom left, he could probably knock the red sandals smack into the bum of the shopper bending to pick up some trainers. Alun's image put its arm back down by his side and his thoughts returned to the question. If nobody answered him at home, he just kept on asking.

"Why doesn't he run away?" he asked again. The man's legs were stretched out in front of him, open, bent at the knees. His arms rested easily on them and he lifted his right hand now and then to take a slow drag. When he lifted his arm, Alun could see a hole in his trouser leg and the frayed ends of a woolly grey sleeve. Some kind of hat lay on the stripy blanket, with a few coins in it, but the man didn't seem to be making much effort to get attention from the passersby. The dog was lying down, its head resting on crossed front legs. Its eyes guarded the hat and followed the passing shoppers, returning to Alun without much interest.

The Big Issue

Story and photograph by Jean Gill

A second pair of deep brown eyes focused on Alun and the man spoke. "He's a good dog."

"Why don't you sell *The Big Issue*?" was Alun's next question.

"Why don't you?" asked the man, in that same slow drawl as if speaking were just another pointless effort. This answer was not nearly as satisfying as the first one and Alun had just opened his mouth to explain why the man should sell *The Big Issue* whereas Alun obviously had no need to, when the man spoke first.

"I gotta go somewhere. Will you look after the dog?"

Alun imagined sitting on the stripy blanket by the dog while the man went shopping. It would be just the same as waiting for his mother, who was taking so long that the man would probably be back before she came. He hoped none of his friends were in town but it would be worth it to talk to the dog. He could say it was a sponsored something. You could get away with anything if it was sponsored.

"All right." Before Alun could sit down on the blanket, the man had stood, the dog following his movements with its head cocked, fully alert, and the blanket had been folded up. The man took a length of string out of a pocket, tied it round the dog's neck and gave the other end to Alun. The dog listened to the man, whispering something in the dog's ears, which drooped immediately.

"I'll be here again next Thursday," he told Alun, and disappeared. The dog stood by Alun, waiting for something to happen and Alun stood by the dog, the string clutched tightly. The usual drift of couples, families, and kids passed, chattering, but there was no trace of the man. Just as Alun thought his heart would burst from panicked beating, he saw a familiar face—not the man but his mother. This was as bad as it could be.

***

The argument was still going on in the kitchen and Alun could hear his mother's voice, shrill and angry, "You just encourage him" and then the lower, more dangerous tones of his father, "He's only eleven, Anne. If you want, we'll take the mutt straight to the vet and finish it off. It's half-starved anyway and there's no pain … just one injection and that's it."

There was a silence as deep as a dog's brown eyes. Alun sat on the cold patio stone because he thought the dog would feel more at home with someone sitting beside him. The dog gave no sign of feeling anything. It lay beside him in the same pose it had kept on the blanket. If Alun had been braver he would have sneaked a blanket out of the airing cupboard, but one memory of his mother's face when he had tried to explain to her what had happened and he knew the dog would have to lie on the cold stone, at least for now. The silence lasted longer than he could hold his breath, which was a bad sign and very unlucky. He had told himself that if someone spoke before he breathed again then everything would be all right. The next words were spoken too quietly for him to hear but it was his mother's voice. Alun smoothed the dog's short fur, noticing how silky the forehead and ears were compared with the thickness of its back. He wondered how the dog's weatherproofing worked and considered how it would be to have a friend like this, who just sat beside you and thought doggy thoughts.

It was his mother who came out into the garden. Alun was reminded of those films where you saw two characters locked in mortal combat, then you couldn't see them anymore and it was only when the victor emerged that you knew who had won. Except that with his parents there wasn't a goody and a baddy, and it depended what you wanted as to who you wanted to win. And it was always his mother who told him the verdict, whoever had won, so that meant nothing.

"I'm disappointed in you Alun." This was nothing new. "You're old enough to have a sense of responsibility. I can't believe you talked to a stranger at all, never mind bringing home a stray."

"He's not a stray." A glare from his mother shut him up.

"And we've said no to a dog often enough. "But," she sighed deeply, "your Dad thinks it's a chance for you to show whether you can look after a pet. We'll try to take him back next week but if you ask me, this con-man just wanted rid of the poor thing, and you'll have had enough so we'll take it to the dog's home then and they'll do what's best."

***

It was only three days since the dog had moved in but Alun could not imagine life without it. He didn't have to look down to know that the dog was at his side, following his every move, listening to his every word. *[cont. on pg 200]*

The string had been abandoned straight away when it became clear that the dog was not going to run away. Quite the opposite: the dog wouldn't run on its own at all. It sat, lay, walked beside Alun, slept where it was told to, and it would even run beside Alun, if he ran. It was not something he could say to his parents but Alun knew there was something wrong; the dog was just too good.

Day four was Sunday, one of those autumn days when the sun gave a last burst of heat and the garden flickered gold. Alun's Dad stopped digging, groaned and stretched to ease his back. He idly threw a stick for the dog, shouting, "Fetch," and Alun watched as the dog's eyes followed the stick, while its body stayed rock-still, in its usual working pose.

Dad shook his head and frowned. "We can't have that on a weekend. Anne?" he called Alun's Mum and went off into the house, emerging minutes later. "Come on, we're off to the beach. Bring the string, just in case." Alun, his mother, and the dog did as they were told, the back of the car being just another shop doorway as far as the dog was concerned. It didn't wince as Alun's Dad sang along with the car radio, not even when his Mum joined in.

You could always smell the sea, before it appeared as a glint behind a field, hiding with the twists of the lanes and totally invisible from the car park. Alun cricked his neck round to watch the dog. Perhaps this was its first time. Alun sniffed as if it was his first time; if you covered wet clothes in mud and salt, you still wouldn't come close to the freshness of the wet tang, with a hint of metal and machine from the

small railway line which hugged the coast. Had he imagined it? Alun kept watching and sure enough, the dog's nostrils were flickering, twitching with interest, and the fine, straight hairs on the back of its neck were standing up, as if in a breeze which only the dog could feel.

The walk started sensibly, feet and paws moving as in a perfect fire drill, all straight lines and regular pace. Then Dad started zigzagging and walking backwards, making Mum laugh until she skipped into pigeon steps and wrote his name in huge letters in the sand. Alun veered off his parents' course towards the low breakers, starting to run, his movements shadowed by the dog. They ran into the waves, Alun stopping as the waves lapped the calves of his wellies but the dog continuing to splash in deeper until it was forced to swim. "You're out of your depth," Alun told it. The dog carried on swimming. "Dad!" Alun yelled, suddenly afraid, and his father, holding a stick, was suddenly at his side.

"Fetch!" The stick was thrown just in front of the dog's nose and retrieved without hesitation. The dog doubling its clumsy paddles to turn around and bring the stick back. When it reached the shallows, it dropped the stick in front of Alun, wagged its tail and gave a sharp bark. He was slow to understand and the dog nudged the stick with its nose, wagged its tail, and barked again.

"Go on, throw it," his Dad told Alun, and the games began in earnest. In its excitement, the dog turned somersaults in the incoming waves. Even when the dog rushed out of the sea to shower Alun's mother with seawater as it shook

itself right beside her, even then there was just shrieking and laughter, as his father encouraged the dog to chase his mother. It had been a long time since Alun had seen his parents playing.

"We'll call him Sandy," said his mother on the way home and Alun started to hope that they might keep the dog.

But the man was there the next Thursday, just as he had said.

"Where did you go?" asked Alun, despite his mother nudging him. The man just shrugged. "Were you ill? Are you better now?"

The man looked at him steadily, ignoring his mother, who hovered anxiously beside Alun, not sure of the social rules. "I wanted the dog to have a holiday. He's too young to understand this life."

"You've got to give Sandy back, Alun." His mother was impatient to get it over with but no longer because it was what she wanted.

Alun smoothed the dog's head and sent it back to the blanket with unspoken love. Man and dog greeted each other with a touch, a lick, a tail wag, and a smile. "If you sell *The Big Issue*, my Mum would buy one, wouldn't you Mum?"

"Maybe," she said.

"So you will sell it then," Alun persevered.

"Maybe," said the man, and he turned his attention to the dog, dismissing Alun and his mother even before they turned to go.

Before dawn,
in mirrored light but no sun,
       she saw the birds leaving.
       Going south. Row upon row
       in strict cuneal formation.
Or raucous, in cluttered disarray.
Flying low, fading high
up in the sky.
Heading out.

Later, running past the cove
in mittens and hat,
she heard them cry far in the distance:
a nameless feeling of affection and regret.

Only the loons remained,
Old friends.
Their time would come, too.

The time of long shadows.

mice and red teeth
       the gardens mourning
the muffled ships
       like unpaired socks
a shoe in a novel
       hair tied in plaid ribbon

silver and cold words
       like a blurred memory
the gates fraying like mornings
       the alarms trembling
the candles flinching
       a studio on a cold evening

seas and fragile desires
       a rose in a dream
the distant rain
       cheeks and wild opinions
just enough light to see
       a hotel with red doors

Long Shadows
by Michael Campagnoli

Foreign
by Lisha Ruan

Red Ukelele
by Kari Gunter-Seymour

Dawn
by Diana Whiley

Firefly Hour
by Shannon Magee

What do you do with your dreams?
I pour them out,
Cold tea on a dampened lawn
So the herbs infused in the once-hot water
Scent the air, sink deep into the soil,
Wrapping round the thick, knotted, gnarled roots—

We used to play in them, when we were younger,
Crawling under the knobby knees they curved skyward,
Jumping over them to avoid being ensnared by the unknown.
We didn't mind that they were cold and rough,
Grooved dirty, knotted knuckled bones reaching
To live above the soil they were condemned to.
Silently, they taught us to rise against—

Now we trip over our beloved roots as we feel our way home in the dark,
Stumbling to lie on the night-drenched grass,
The heavy scent of dreams in the air.

Tahiti
by Faisal Warsani

Visit With An Old Boss
by Charles Leggett

Tashi at home enduring birthday gifts,
mortally bemused; dining in Edmonds
later –"That's the plan," he sighs—at Tom's;
displeased with a daughter's smell. "Pooped," Gompbo sniffs.
Now "Yangdhi chews me off" for busy dart guns
purchased earlier today. "I didn't
buy them." With a wink, says "Gompbo did."

Allied Safe and Lock—am I still temping
there?—and we discuss our livings made.
Parts Room, handling zip-locked, dust-caked, frayed
bags of spindles, door contacts. How Tsering
Dorjee, Tashi's latest clerk, complained
again about his "money situation"—
puts none aside and spends what need might shun,

in the aggregate, on prostitutes.
Insists (meanwhile he's purchased Tashi's Mazda;
he's thinking now of fishing in Alaska)
that "*not one minute*" of it he regrets.
On Tsering Dorjee's odds of lasting on a
fishing trawler, Northern Lights at bay—
an even smirk from Tashi: "Not one day."

Mitigation Plan
by Chris Tannlund

The vendor has not offered a solution,
the email read, adding that *We need*
to discuss a mitigation plan … I'm counting

no fewer than eighty-seven names
on the distribution list, pretty much
the whole freaking office. And I'm wondering

just whose stroke of genius plan it was
to point the eyes of every Chicken Little
to the sky at once? What I see falling now

is less the firmament than hope this day
could possibly end well. But then a memory
of you when I brought coffee to the bed,

pulling me beside you, and your kiss
that whispered *stay…* And suddenly I'm listening
for any opportunity to slip

past Henny, Ducky, and all their trembling crowd
of acorn-dodgers. All the mitigation
my plan needs is lessening the space

between me and the parking lot, and you
at home, my earth to fall upon, my sky
to open wide my arms to, lift my face,

invite your rain to dance upon my tongue,
to taste with fearless confidence solutions
the likes of Goosey Loosey never dreamed.

New Friend
by Nancy Devine

He arrived whole,
like a rare baby.
Instantly in the yard next door
he stood near the raspberry patch,
one hand tickling the small fruit with the bees,
the other the wind, whatever came his way.

For a long time,
no one approached him;
they must've been inside watching the final episode
of the earth on flat screens
strapped to their backs.

Finally, the old crag who shouldn't be driving anymore
brought him a dish tucked in a dish.
They began to feast there, together,
all their fingers flirting like thieves.

Study in Pink by Nory Marc Steiger

Vera Jewel
by Michelle McMillan-Holifield
first published in *Confidante*.

My grandmother ruffles through a box of material
that smells of mothballs. 4x4 squares
of old curtains, denims, dresses, ties, scarves.
Anything that could be cut and saved to make quilts
packs so tightly into a yellowed box
the colour on the fabric had no room to fade.
She searches for a newspaper article.
I've been through the box twice. It is not there.
But she is so sure, so serene
as if by memory alone she can will it there.

Her fingers lull through the fabric
loosening the earth of her past.
Each square, a sermon, a kiss, a new dish.
Hands still immersed, she recites the article.
It is of my father's early promotion in the Army.
I know how she must have studied it, line by line,
until the words became his uniform,
his boots, his medals, his tags.

She does not find it but smiles. She offers me
the fabric to make quilts, pillowcases,
anything that can be sewn together into a memory.
I take it, though I have already memorized her.
The smell of mothballs on her hands,
the rows of vegetables she nurtured
wearing the flowered dress that lies in pieces in the box.
I see her in my sleep. Words on a page.
I recite her.

The Rocking Horse Loser
by Janet Buck

The hospice nurse sitting on a wicker chaise creaks advice, admonishment:
"Why won't you rest?" *There isn't time.* The clock whirls like a Cuisinart.

The limp I used to hate I love, because it's out of reach. *Push. Push. Push.*
I'm screaming, *Get the last word in!* Light the joss stick—learn to pray.

This year's crop of daffodils, quickened promissory notes of spring,
will outlive platters of my bones curled sideways in a chair.

Shifting weight, one red radish ulcer to another, I wince & ride
the rocking horse. No saddles left where disks should be.

My ancient dresser squawks in seagull choirs. The nurse pulls out a single sock.
An absent leg should not feel cold, except it does. It itches too.

The drawer makes noises of a coffin's lid in ready mode.
Living is a flagrant wish—yet stasis is impossible.

"Hurry, *please*, just put the photos on the bed," I say.
Sit & wait, sit & wait—I blend with pictures on the walls.

Busy clicking knitting needles, chewing on a garlic bagel,
both sides spread with thick cream cheese, she's not even listening.

She's a lily camouflaged by grass—she's safe. I grab the box,
rusted scissors, cut my body out of every photo sprawled across the bed.

Leave my chin, or part of it, which used to wear a half-moon smile,
not work the loom of languishing until no hands survive.

A sylvan gloss is on the ferns. I watch it through the open blinds.
Please make my death a sutra scroll of Spartan grace.

The hospice nurse falls sound asleep—a cooing bird, a puppy snore.
She's not afraid to wake a hermit living in oblivion.

Cancelled
by Claire Scott

sometimes I sense her in the cancelled light
      sometimes I hear her sigh
see her nautilus shape curled tightly
      cut off from the slipstream of life

destroyed by the callous blade of
      no love dislove love not
I cannot lift you from your death
      you who never became

my shrivelled heart too full of fear
      sometimes I sense you see you
your tiny fists drenched in tears
      sometimes I close my eyes

the earth spins and spins with no relief
      clocks click a widening gap
I am losing you my little one

      sometimes my soul so heavy heavy
      like stone like shame like sorrow

Indicted
by Alaine Dibenedetto

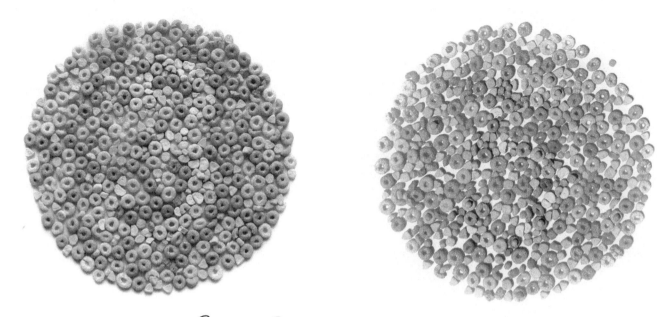

Number Series by Monika Malewska

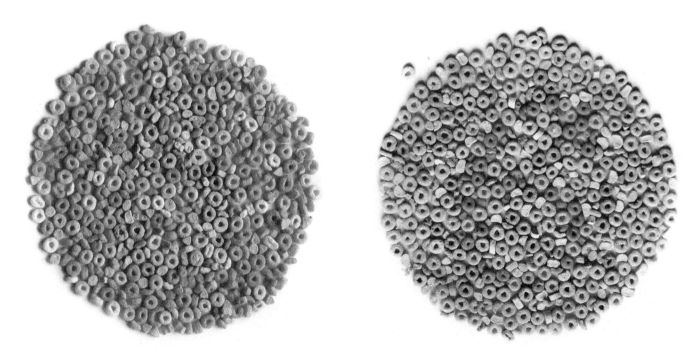

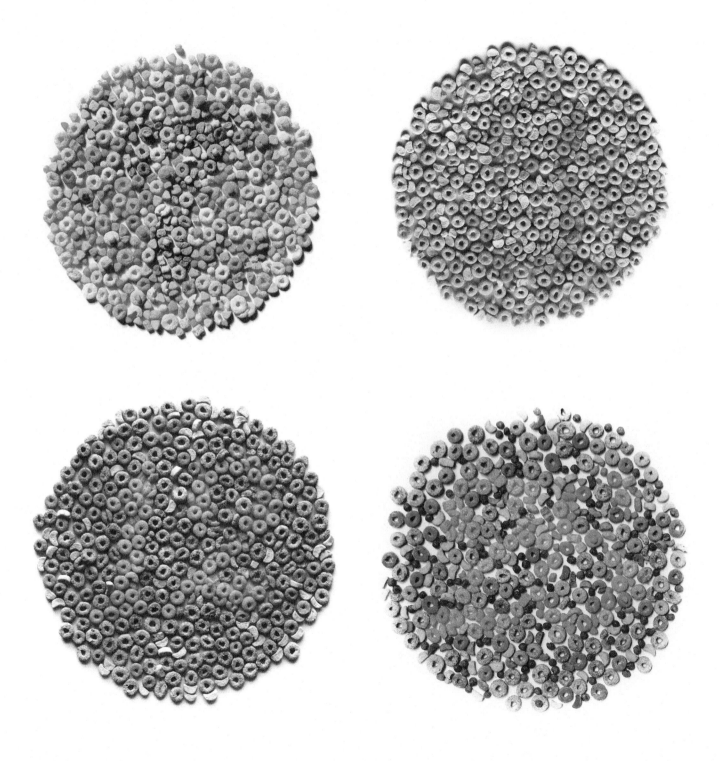

The Other Side
by Roy Dorman

Rocky Raccoon and Merlin Muskrat were chatting while peering through the fence, watching the occasional car whiz past on the interstate.

"I'm goin' across," said Rocky. "I can see cornfields for food and a small woods to live in. I just gotta go over."

"Rocky, look behind you," said Merlin. "There are cornfields as far as you can see and a little woods up on the hill. You don't need to go over there; you've got everything right here on this side of the highway."

Rocky looked back at the field they had just crossed. "Yeah, but I've been here all my life; I've gotta see for myself if there's more than this."

Changing tack, Merlin said, "Why do you think they put this fence down low to the ground? It's so we don't go runnin' across the highway and maybe gettin' ourselves squashed, that's why."

"The Man put this fence here so his cars can drive seventy miles an hour and not have to risk havin' an accident tryin' to miss one of us," scoffed Rocky. "The Man doesn't care about us; he's just tryin' to keep us in our place."

"Sammy's scampered over and back a bunch of times," said Merlin. "He says it's no different over there than over here. He just goes because he likes the thrill of dodging the cars. He's a little whacko if ya ask me."

Rocky continued to stare at the opposite side of the highway. It was early morning, just before sunrise, and traffic was at its lightest.

"I'm gonna go," said Rocky. "Tell everybody 'bye' for me, will ya?"

Merlin couldn't say anything. He had a lump in his throat as he watched Rocky squeeze under the fence and waddle down to the shoulder of the highway. It was so dark, the only time Merlin could see him was when the lights of a passing car on this set of lanes briefly lit up the vicinity.

"Bye, Merlin," Rocky called out of the blackness.

"Bye, Rocky," Merlin called back.

There were only a few more cars now and Merlin hoped that Rocky was making his way across the two lanes on this side, would have time to make it across the grassy median strip, and then across the final two lanes on the other side.

He waited a bit and then called, "Rocky, did you make it? Rocky? Rocky, answer me, please. Are you all right? Rocky!!!"

The sky was now turning a pale shade of pink in the east and traffic seemed to have picked up a bit. Merlin squinted to see if he could see across to the second set of lanes. "Damn, I guess I'm gonna have to go down there," he grumbled to himself. "He might be hurt."

As he made it to the shoulder of the first set of lanes, Merlin saw Rocky lying in the centre of the second set. He saw him struggle to raise his head to the sky.

"I made it, Merlin," called Rocky. "But you don't need to come over; you've got everything you need on that side of the highway."

After waiting to make sure no cars were coming, Merlin started across the first set of lanes.

Untitled
by Saffron Wilson

The old man's lips say more without opening, than his mind can recall or try to say.

The cracks in his lips look like the mirror in his bathroom or the gaps in his history he can't remember. He glosses them with a long swipe of his tongue but it's only ever temporary. They crack again, getting worse and worse, red blisters under pink skin under white dead cells.

The dry flakes of skin sit patiently on top, looking like a milk droplet on a kitchen counter left to congeal and be scraped up by a knife. The small circles sit along the bottom lip and in the middle of the top. Pushing them with his tongue it feels like an imperfection, a minor imperfection that can be overlooked. He can lick his lips and the white fades for a few seconds, but they always reappear first before the cracks begin to show.

The wrinkles surround the lips are like the sun rays he drew as a child. A permanent reminder of all the times he puckered his lips for his mother, his girlfriend, his wife, his kids and his cigarette. The lines all point to the same destination, looking like a map all leading to the same place, as if they wanted to share their story. They all point to the part that's meant to speak, to recall tales and information and keep his history alive. But now, his lips say more. His tongue is dormant and doesn't twist around letters and sounds like it did.

When he parts his lips to expel sound they quiver. Constantly unbalanced and missing their other half. When his mouth his open an eclipse happens. A black orb surrounded by unrelaxing fire, forever jolting and bustling around the circle.

The orb is full of so much potential but the lips are accustomed to the chorus of "Oh, I forget."

The "oh" is torture, the two halves of the lips try to kiss each other before being pulled apart again, forming a circle around a wind tunnel that dries them out further. They wait for a droplet of moisture to be expelled by the mouth, always by accident but the hand or the sleeve that used to wipe it away never visits. The spit just stays clotted on the once vibrant pink, slowly getting absorbed.

The teeth rip into the bottom lip on the 'f' of "forget." Not just once or twice but as many times as it takes until the rest of the word awkwardly follows. The bites are like a wallpaper scraper, bearing down on the damaged skin, pulling teeth backwards trying to form the letter. As it scrapes the skin folds into itself, giving up under the pressure. It becomes comes from the pink flesh and changes. White and thin, it's structure collapsed behind the teeth before the mind catches up, and the 'or' sound brings relief. The breath's warm but cold breeze against the stripped skin more prominent without its extra layer.

The 'g' stretches them out in the same way a smile should. The cracks on the lips pull themselves apart further and weep bright red at the memory of a smile, before they recoil back and let the tongue finish the work of the sentence. They stand idly by as the 't' gets pushed up to the teeth and expel the sound between the lips again.

The quivering slows at the end of the word. The lips pair themselves together and are nourished for just a few moments by the swipe of saliva again. So relaxed after the ordeal they look as though they can never be parted again. The cracks rivet the skin, they don't look they were ever soft enough to touch someone else's, but maybe that's because they kept the memories that his mind could no longer hold.

He lips say more than he can now.

Cyan Eyes
by Steve Prusky

Now, too old too young, once a fluttering nymphet on parade, her flaxen hair, long, thin, cascaded in gold rivulets past her shoulder blades as if she were Debussy's Girl With The Flaxen Hair. Smooth glassy waves brightly glistened in her gaze the depths of clear blue tropic seas. Thin, fair skinned, she was a post-pubescent blossom bursting vital, driven, bound to thrive. Each quake of laughter shook her alive.

Her vision refused to wane each time a lover left. Her vigour briefly ebbed like tides recede then rise to wash away small footprints on a sandy shore.

No longer lean, hair worried dull, dirty blond; all past wrongs pale next to the constant solace in her cyan eyes.

Suburban Tyranny
by Monica Rico

Can an unkempt lawn look any other, then unkempt? Disarrayed foliage of the ugliest sort, riddled with thorns, no dandelion to be seen. So hideous are the weeds, that in death they turn a wretched black, like oil, like sludge, more forgotten than abandoned, this yard, dense weave of ragged leaves, a barrier even to the most curious of cats. I have heard of a thirty year conspiracy, one where the walnut trees obliterate the visible landscape, leaving squirrels the size of dinosaurs as heirs to the neighbourhood.

Earth at Midnight
by Christopher Suda

over, beneath, between
all stars heaven's body,

building the rest of our lives
blooming like pistols burying

those too soon to be born

again fragments deep against
noiseless soil, oceans.

I trudge ahead,
down sinks the rock.

Blood Poem
by Brenda Yates

The campfire burns a circle of light, opens darkness to flickering edges where shadows take form. I've come here, into wilderness for just this reason. And so, I beckon, and unbuttoning my skin, clutch it quickly, softly, to my chest, the way a Spartan might have hidden a stolen fox under his cloak. In the lit up world's white silence, its fur and gills and feathered claws are familiar. Blue-black ink spreads like mysterious bruises.

Grievances
by Lisa Mae DeMasi

I'm standing at the stove, frying a couple of eggs, sunny-side up, in the enormous kitchen of our rented apartment in a two-family Victorian in Norwood, Massachusetts on a wintry morning. It's 1989 and the place is drafty. Wind whistles through the upper and lower sashes of the windows, brittle brown leaves whirl and bat against the glass. The appliances are mismatched and awkwardly placed about—stove (harvest gold), refrigerator (avocado green), dishwasher (wood tone). Wallpaper and linoleum are curling up in places; trim is scuffed up. A classic first residence for a young engaged couple that with the snap of Martha Stewart's fingers could be transformed to modern utility. Keith says for me to forget about Martha and learn to like it, improvements mean the rent goes up. I tug the tie around my robe tighter.

We never discuss our mistake, the what-ifs, had we had the baby. Made the sacrifices. We don't know yet that our marriage will end in divorce in five years' time because he wants to procreate, on purpose, when he's established in his career and we've bought a cute little Cape from a sweet elderly couple with the type of kitchen décor that reminds us of our first apartment. We're innocent to knowing passion will never truly ignite between us and I cannot build a baby in my compromised insides that will bring complications and nine months on bed rest with a man-child who shares no spirited resemblance to my first love Michael, or respectively, I will become a cheater, an adulterer, swooned by a man my mother's age. All I know is what's in front of me: the delicate orange orb that's intended to nourish a pullet's developing embryo.

My impulsiveness, a guise for guilt, a sense of claustrophobia and the headiness I crave in independence, will simmer away beneath the layers of my flesh—I'm twenty-five, twenty-seven, twenty-nine. Midway through my thirtieth year, the angst will spout like a geyser and I'll find myself behind the wheel of a large automobile gunning it for the California coastline. Untethered, unleashed. The road will open its arms to me, invite me on the journey, provide the opportunity to roam for a home. Behind me I'll leave loved ones hurt, worried, confused. Apt time will be floundered. In lieu of mining the solitude for nuggets of gold in self-understanding, I will try on a number of people and places and come to dwell in the barrenness of the desert, miles and miles from home, barren inside.

Still ahead for Keith and me, wrapped like the wedding champagne flutes in tissue paper, wait our grown up, sometimes fragile and complicated lives: my episodes of illness, surgeries and procedures, get-togethers with our in-laws, my mother's assertive opinion, stripping the avocado-coloured wallpaper from every room in the house, graduate school, uninspired sex, our unhappiness and tenuous connection with one another. There's no hint in our expressions on the mantle, Keith wearing a tux and me in my mother's wedding gown, that suggests anything will go awry. At twenty-three and twenty-five we are perfectly naïve.

UnAlone

by Salena Casha

There are days when you wake up sweating him out your pores. You sit there on the lonely sheets and feel him spill from your body and you think this time, maybe, you'll burn him out completely like a spiked fever.

But your mom had been there then with cool washcloths and ibuprofen and now it's just you and him even though you haven't felt his hand in years.

You force yourself out of the bed, out of the room, because it's in everything now like the cigarette smoke that used to condition your grandmother's knotted hair. You shower four times, trying not to wake your roommates, scrubbing, pulsing, pushing until you're red and raw and the scent of cucumber soap is so strong it makes you bend over the toilet, naked, and vomit.

It's become a ritual up to this point, a sick and twisted form of religion because you know exactly how the rest of your day will go. You know that the hair on the back of your neck will stay puckered and that there will be an ache, that painful relief of where part of him has fled you. But he is never gone and that makes you even more ill and you excuse yourself from an auditors' meeting and stand in the communal restroom staring at yourself in the mirror so hard you swear the glass breaks for a moment.

At the sink, someone says excuse me, can I get by you to the soap, and it takes all of your willpower to force yourself back into motion because you don't remember feeling this dehydrated before.

So you go back into your office and shut the frosted glass door and pretend you're on the phone when really you're just staring into space trying to get the scent of his citrus-tinged cologne out of you. You just stay as still as you possibly can, bringing even your breathing down to a minimum because, maybe if you do that, you won't have to accuse your skin of being a traitor. Maybe, if some part of you asphyxiates it'll be the part he inhabits.

You go home and stay sleepless. Rinse. Repeat. You go out and you meet other people and you bring them back with you to your small apartment and your small blue bed and you start sleeping again and you think you've stifled him finally. The sweat that pours out of you smells and tastes like your own and you think, finally, yes, you've won, because you haven't thought about him in more days than you remember.

But he's still there and he comes back when you least expect it, right when you're looking into someone's black-brown eyes and you feel tears streaming, unchecked, down your face for no reason. Those black-brown eyes look at you in alarm, ask if you're all right. But the tears are noiseless and you know they'll pass even though your next day is planned out. That, even if you wake up with someone else, you'll smell like him.

And you know he isn't the first one. He's one of a few which might be one too many. He's the hand around your throat and the thing around your neck and the body pressed up against yours so hot that it brands and sears your back until you beg yourself for mercy.

Sadly, even though he's not there, it all makes you feel less alone.

Contributor Biographies

A. J. Varden received her Bachelor's degree in English from the University of Montevallo. She now lives in Hawaii with her husband and spends her days writing and exploring. Her short fiction has been published in Sigma Tau Delta's *The Rectangle*, and in the University of Montevallo's *The Tower*.

Adam Huening grew up in a small town in the American Midwest. He earned degrees in English and Journalism from Indiana University and currently resides around Bloomington, Indiana. His work has been published in *Soliloquies Anthology*, Burningword, *A Lonely Riot*, *Crab Fat*, and *Gravel*, among others.

Aditi Sengupta is a secondary student with profound interest in literature. She has always been a perfectionist with correct vocabulary, and has read about great Australian women and their contributions. Her goal is to remain in the minds of children with disability and write about them in the near future.

Alaine DiBenedetto's publishing credits include; *Louisiana Literature*, *The Rose & Thorn Journal*, *The New York Quarterly*, blah, blah, blah. DiBenedetto, known as the "silent poet," writes and paints from a dimly lit cave far away from snakes, dentists, and liars. Coffee and bacon are her faithful companions.

Alan Catlin has been publishing for five decades. His latest book is *Walking Among Tombstones in the Fog* from Presa Press.

Alex Garcia Topete is a writer, filmmaker, and entrepreneur from Tampico, Mexico, but based in Dallas, Texas. His works of fiction and nonfiction have been published in different publications in Mexico and the United States.

Alexis Henderson is a college student and writing tutor. Her work has been featured in *Helios Quarterly*, the *Literary Hatchet*, and other literary magazines. When she's not writing she likes to paint landscapes, wander used bookstores, and take long nature walks along the Lowcountry salt marsh.

Alice Tarbuck is a writer based in Edinburgh. Her work is forthcoming from *Antiphon*, *Zarf* and others. She was shortlisted for the Jupiter Artland Poetry Prize, and is working toward a first collection.

Allie Long is an economics and English double-major at the University of Virginia. Her poetry appears in *Ground Fresh Thursday*, *Words Dance*, *Bird's Thumb*, as well as others. Read more of her work at: alliesanxietydiaries. wordpress.com.

Alyssa Cooper is a Canadian author, poet, and artist currently living in Kingston, Ontario with her partner, two cats, and a Boston Terrier. She is an active spoken word performer, and has authored three novels, a short story collection, and a poetry collection since her first publication in 2008.

Alyssa D. Ross was born in Guntersville, AL, but spent over a decade living in Northern Virginia. After abandoning art school in Richmond, she went on to pursue writing. She now holds an MFA from George Mason University and a PhD from Auburn University where she teaches courses on writing and literature. Select readings are available at www.alyssaross-writes.com

Amanda Chiado is the author of *Vitiligod: The Ascension of Michael Jackson* (Dancing Girl Press, 2016). Her poetry and fiction is forthcoming or appears in *Paper Darts*, *Cheap Pop*, *Jersey Devil Press*, *Arcana: The Tarot Poetry Anthology*, *All We Can Hold: A Collection of Poetry on Motherhood* and many others. Her poem 'The Devil Has Taken His Dress Off' won the Molotov Cocktail Shadow Poetry Award. Amanda is writer, credentialed teacher and arts advocate. She is the Program Manager for the San Benito County Arts Council and is an active California Poet in the Schools. She holds degrees from the University of New Mexico and California College of the Arts. She edits for *Weave Magazine* and *Jersey Devil Press*. Get weird at amandachiado.com.

A M Morton, author of the acclaimed Roma Nova thriller series is a 'Roman nut' with six years military service, a masters' in history and a lifelong love of adventure and thriller fiction. A 'what if' explorer and wine drinker, she lives in France with her husband of 30 years. Find out more: alison-morton.com

Andrea Farber De Zubiria works as a physical therapist, specializing in chronic pain treatment. Her poems have appeared in *Hoot*, *Cargo*, *Smokey Blue*, *Mothers Always Write*, *Foliate Oak* and others.

Anirban is a 20-something Finance post-graduate. Apart from crunching numbers and listening to music, he thrives on guilt-free sarcasm and gluten-free poetry. His works have appeared or are forthcoming in publications like The Meadow, Kitaab, *In-flight Literary Magazine*, *Wizards in Space Literary Magazine: Issue 001*. His physical form was last sighted at Bombay, India.

Anna Graziosi is an artist and poet living in upstate New York. She focuses on illustration and photography, paired with carefully chosen words often conjured in quiet moments when her pen meets paper and the world falls away. In her work she looks to convey moments of sorrow, discomfort, and disassociation.

Annalisa Crawford writes dark contemporary stories, and has been winning competitions and publishing short stories in small press journals for many years. She's the author of four books, and won 3rd prize in the Costa Short Story Award, 2015. Find out more on her website: annalisacrawford.com.

Annie Blake is an Australian writer who resides in Melbourne. Her poem 'These Grey Streets' was nominated for the 2017 Pushcart Prize by Vine Leaves Literary Journal. You can visit her on Facebook, Pinterest, Goodreads and annieblakethegatherer.blogspot.com.

Ariel Dawn lives in Victoria, British Columbia. Her poems appear in places such as *Vine Leaves* issues 8 and 16, *Queen Mob's Tea House*, *Elbow Room*, *Tales from the Forest*, *canthius*, *(parenthetical)*, and are forthcoming in *A Furious Hope* anthology. She is studying Tarot and finishing her first collection of poems.

Ashlie McDiarmid graduated from the University of Northern Colorado in 2011. She has been published in *Snake~ Nation~ Review*, *The Crucible*, and *Vine Leaves Literary Journal*. She lives, writes, and pets cats in Aurora, Colorado.

Bee Williamson is a poet, designer and artist. She has been part of 25 exhibitions; published in books and journals, including *PCP's Reflecting on Melbourne*; and self-published 10 books of poetry, novella, memoir and playscript. Her latest book *Torment & Soul* is available at independent bookshops in Melbourne, hive.id.au, beesboutiquebooks.biz.

Benjamin Wheeler is an artist and scientist from St. Louis, Missouri. In his work he strives to find ways in which science enables art, and art inspires science. The beauty of the mundane is something he hopes to illuminate in all he does. He aspires to get a cat soon.

Brad G. Garber lives, writes and runs around naked in the Great Northwest. He fills his home with art, music, photography, plants, rocks, bones, books, good cookin' and love. He has published poetry, art, photos, essays and articles in many quality publications. 2013 Pushcart Prize nominee.

Brandon Hansen is an English-Writing/Environmental Studies student at Northern Michigan University in Marquette, Michigan. He scratches for truth in everything and finds it exhausting and weird a lot of the time. He is currently a Writing Center tutor and is applying for MFA programs. Website: Brandon Hansen Raving @ Wordpress.com

Brenda Yates is the award-winning author of *Bodily Knowledge* (Tebot Bach 2015) whose publications include *Mississippi Review*, *The American Journal of Poetry*, *Tor House News*, *City of the Big Shoulders: An Anthology of Chicago Poetry* (University of Iowa Press) and *The Southern Poetry Anthology, Volume VI: Tennessee* (Texas Review Press).

Bruce Louis Dodson is an American expat living in Borlänge, Sweden. Some of his recent work has appeared in, Writers Abroad Anthology (Foreign & Far Away), *Trip of a Lifetime Anthology* (Sleeping Cat Books), *Pirene's Fountain*, *Tic Toc* and *Storm Cycle* Anthologies, *Cordite Poetry Review*, *Buffalo Almanac* and more.

C. Wade Bentley teaches and writes in Salt Lake City. His poems have been published or are forthcoming in journals such as Cimarron Review, Best New Poets, Rattle, *Chicago Quarterly Review*, Pembroke Magazine, and Poetry Northwest. A full-length collection of his poems, *What Is Mine*, was published by Aldrich Press in January of 2015. Visit wadebentley. weebly.com for complete information about his publications and awards.

Cameron Filas writes short, usually dark, fiction. He's been published at Yellow Mama, *365 tomorrows*, and *Five 2 One Magazine*, among others. He lives in sun-baked Mesa, Arizona, with his fiancée.

Cameron Mount served as a US Navy officer from 2001 to 2007 before leaving for a career in writing and teaching. His work has appeared in *Wilderness House Literary Review*, *Scintilla*, *Mead*, and *Frogpond*. He had also published a chapbook, *Evening Watch*, in 2009. His most recent work is the self-published *Nostalgia and Ruin*.

Carmen Kern is a Canadian writer/photographer living in Phoenix, Arizona. Carmen spends her days making things up and writing them down and loves that she doesn't have to shovel snow 8 months of the year. You can find her at carmenkern.com or on her photography site, decent-xposure.com.

Carol Cooper is a British author, journalist, and doctor. Her latest novel, *Hampstead Fever*, is a contemporary tale of London life. She is now working on a novel set in Alexandria, where she and her family used to live. *Egypt, 1954* is part of that story. Visit her website: drcarolcooper.com.

Carol Middleton is a Melbourne journalist, writer and storyteller. She is a critic for *Australian Book Review* and *Australian Stage*, and has published work in *The Age* and *Canberra Times*. Her story *The Devil's Music* came second in The Age competition 2010 and is published in Melbourne Subjective (2014). Visit her website: carolmiddleton.com.au.

Carolyn Martin is blissfully retired in Clackamas, Oregon, where she gardens, writes, and plays. Her poems and book reviews have appeared in journals throughout the US and UK, and her second collection, *The Way a Woman Knows*, was released in 2015.

Carrie Mumford is a fiction writer living in Calgary, Alberta. Her short fiction has appeared in journals such as *Full of Crow Fiction*, *Bella Online Literary Review*, and *WCDR's Whispered Words* anthology. Carrie is currently revising a novel while practising yoga and wrangling many animals.

Cath Barton is an English writer and photographer who lives in Wales. She is active in the online flash fiction community and recent publication credits include *The Tea-Time Visitors in Story Shack* and *Buttercups in Sixteen*. She is also a regular contributor to *Wales Arts Review*.

Chad W. Lutz was born in 1986 and has been terrorizing the world ever since. Running, writing, living, loving. Those are the axis of their divinity. If Chad isn't writing, he's clocking sub-2:40 marathons or picking up trash in local communities. He identifies as non-gender-conforming. Everybody love everybody.

Charles Leggett is a professional actor based in Seattle, WA, USA. Recent publications include *Claudius Speaks*, *ConSTs* and *Scarlet Leaf Review* (Toronto, Canada). His work previously appeared in Vine Leaves Literary Journal Issue #12.

Charley Karchin is a writer with work appearing both online and in print, a mead-maker, an employee working for a non-profit, and a girl that would prefer to sip a beer than to drink anything out of a coconut.

Chelsey Clammer is the author of *BodyHome*, and won the 2015 Red Hen Press Nonfiction Manuscript Award for her essay collection, *Circadian*. Her work has appeared in *The Rumpus*, *Essay Daily*, *McSweeney's*, and *Black Warrior Review*, among many others. She's the Essays Editor for *The Nervous Breakdown*. Visit her website: chelseyclammer.com.

Chris Tannlund lives and writes in the heart of the rolling prairie of Southwest Missouri. His recent poems have appeared in *Fickle Muses* and *Eclectica Magazine*.

Christie Wilson lives in Illinois with her husband and daughter. She is currently writing a collection of poems and a novel. For links to her published work, please visit her website: *christiewilson.net*.

Christina Dalcher is a writer from Virginia with over fifty worldwide credits. Recognitions include Bath Flash Award's Shortlist, nominations for Best of the Net and Best Small Fictions, and second place in Bartleby Snopes' Dialogue-Only Contest. Laura Bradford represents Christina's novels. Read additional work at *christinadalcher.com*.

Christopher Owen Nelson thrives in the vast landscape of the American West. He studied fine arts at Rocky Mountain College of Art where he learned classical methods. Mr. Nelson focused on alternative materials; sculpting with used carpet, found objects and glass. He pursued a career in construction, gaining valuable knowledge in concrete, steel and woodworking that would lay substructure for a new, innovative artistic approach.

Christopher Suda is a poet and musician from Birmingham, Alabama. He studied Creative Writing at The University of Alabama at Birmingham. He has been published in many literary journals and is currently working on a new chapbook.

Chumki Sharma is a poet from Calcutta, India. Everything passes. Only words stay, words that wound, words that heal.

Claire Scott is an award winning poet who has been nominated twice for the Pushcart Prize. Her work has been accepted by the *Atlanta Review*, *Bellevue Literary Review*, and *Healing Muse* among others. Her first book of poetry, *Waiting to be Called*, was published in 2015.

Clare Flynn writes historical fiction with a strong sense of time and place. Her books often deal with characters who are displaced—forced out of familiar surroundings and comfortable lives. She is a graduate of Manchester University where she studied English Language and Literature. Visit her website: *clareflynn.co.uk*.

CLS Ferguson, PhD speaks, signs, acts, publishes, sings, performs, writes, paints, teaches and rarely relaxes. She and her husband, Rich, are raising their daughter, Evelyn and their Bernese Mountain Border Collie Mutt, Sadie in Alhambra, CA. Visit her website: *clsferguson.wix.com/clsferguson*

Cooper Hepburn is a multimedia artist living and working in Missoula, Montana, USA. He studied creative writing at University of Montana. Recently, his work has been published in *The Cadaverine* and their art showed at Fathom Space Gallery in March 2016. Visit his website: *cooperhepburn.biz*.

Early on **Cooper Lysek-Gomez** learned the power that words have to create magical worlds and far off places limited only by imagination. Twelve-year-old Cooper lives in Harding, New Jersey. He lives with his parents and his two dogs. He owns eleven chickens and five fluffy rabbits.

D.W. Schmidt lives with his wife in Hughson, California, on a spread called the Belly Acre, where he does his chores every morning. He teaches English at Modesto Junior College.

Dah Helmer's fourth book is *The Translator* (Transcendent Zero Press, 2015). His first three books are published by Stillpoint Books. Dah's poetry has been published by editors from the US, the UK, Ireland, Canada, China, Philippines, Spain, Australia, and India. Dah lives in Berkeley, California, where he is working on the manuscripts for his fifth and sixth books. Visit his websites: *dahlusion.wordpress.com* and *dahlusion.blogspot.com*.

Damien Titchener is an enthusiastic nerd. As a part-time writer he produces short fiction which can be found on his blog *The Emergence Initiative* (*teid-titchener@blogspot.com.au*). Birthday is his first published work. He can be contacted on Facebook as *Damien Titchener* and on Twitter *@dtitchRav*.

Daniel DeLeón is a writer and musician from Chicago. While his work appears in numerous web publications, this is his first time appearing in print. For further reading, visit *deleoncreation.com*.

Dave Barrett teaches writing at the University of Montana in Missoula. His fiction has appeared most recently in the Potomac Review, Midwestern Gothic, Prole,Worker's Writel, Scarlett Leaf Review and Gravel.He is at work on a new novel.

David Anthony Sam lives in Virginia, has three collections, and was the featured poet in *The Hurricane Review and Light: A Journal of Photography & Poetry*. His poetry has appeared in over 60 publications. His chapbook *Finite to Fail* was the 2016 Grand Prize winner of GFT Press Chapbook Contest, and his collection *All Night over Bones* received Honorable Mention for the 2016 Homebound Poetry Prize.

David Pratt is a writer living in Kingston, Ontario, Canada. He has published one book of poetry and eight books of nonfiction. He writes in order to defy the Second Law of Thermodynamics.

Elizabeth Bruce's debut novel, *And Silent Left the Place*, won Washington Writers' Publishing House Award. Distinctions: Texas Institute of Letters, *ForeWord Magazine*. Publications: *Gargoyle64*, *FireWords Quarterly*, *Inklette*, *Lines&Stars*, *'Merica Magazine*, *Pure Slush*, *Olive Press*, *Remembered Arts*, *Washington Post*, *Weasel Press*. Grants: DCCAH, Poets&Writers, McCarthey-Dressman Education Foundation. Visit the following URL for more information: *washingtonwriters.org/wordpress/portfolio-item/elizabeth-bruce*.

Deborah Guzzi, author of *The Hurricane*, writes full time. *The Hurricane* is available at *aleezadelta@aol.com* and through Prolific Press. Her poetry appears in journals and literary reviews in the UK, Canada, Australia, Hong Kong, Singapore, New Zealand, Greece, Spain, France, India, and dozens of others in the USA.

Dell Kaniper has worked as a book editor, a writing professor, and a waitress. She received her MFA from The New School in New York City and now focuses on completing her first novel, *Deep Down are the Cinders*. Her writing can also be seen in *Narrative Magazine* and *Make*_____.

Diana Whiley's inspiration comes from nature. She considers its impact on our body and psyche as it transforms. Interested in customs and ritual, she likes to explore the forms they take as they have been expressed in music, in our costume, and dance.

Dick Altman moved from New York's branding world to the high desert plains of New Mexico, in 2007. His work has run in the Santa Fe Literary Review, *The American Journal of Poetry* and elsewhere. He won first prize for poetry in the Santa Fe New Mexican's 2015 writing competition.

Dick Evans was born in the "Land of Enchantment," New Mexico. Having grown up in a rural farming community in the Texas panhandle, he had no exposure to art until he started college. Fortunately, he was required to take drawing and design as he started his major of architecture. He soon realized architecture was not right for him, but also that he loved ART.

Donna-Claire is an author living in New Jersey. She interns as a creative writing teacher in the spring time. Her work appears in *Emrys Journal*, *Crosswinds Poetry Journal*, and *Centum Press*. She spends her free time drinking black tea and reading to her parrot Ernest Chirpingway.

Dr. Alyssa D. Ross is a native of Guntersville, Alabama, though she studied art and literature in Northern Virginia for many years. She holds an MFA in Creative Writing from George Mason University and a PhD from Auburn University where she teaches Composition, Literature, and Technical Writing. Her writing has appeared in *Meat for Tea*, *The Foliate Oak*, and *Hawaii Pacific Review*, among others.

Dresden de Vera believes in the principles of writing, meeting, and throwing snakes. Keep an eye out for his novel. You may find more of his work here: *dresdenwrites.blogspot.com*.

Eileen Herbert-Goodall has had many pieces of non-fiction and fiction published, including a novella titled *The Sherbrooke Brothers*. She holds a Doctorate of Creative Arts that she earned at the University of the Sunshine Coast (USC), Queensland, Australia. She is Director of the online writing organisation, Field of Words, which is dedicated to helping writers improve upon their craft.

Elena Petricone's work has appeared in *Slice Magazine*, *The Writer's Chronicle*, Mused, and *Apocrypha and Abstractions*, among others. She holds an MFA from Lesley University and lives in Massachusetts. Elena's scrappy, ungrateful cat tweets *@NikeTheCat*. Visit *elenapetricone.com*.

Elena Rielinger is currently a high school senior residing in a suburb near Cleveland, Ohio. In addition to the *Vine Leaves Literary Journal*, her poetry has also been published in *The Noisy Island* and *Sprout Magazine*.

Eliza McGowen draws her inspiration for writing from the plethora of places she has lived in—Massachusetts, Wyoming, Colorado, and beyond. Currently she works as a remote freelancer—check out more work at *elizamcgowen.wixsite.com/mysite*.

Elizabeth Lovatt is a proud graduate of the Write Like a Grrrl programme run by For Book's Sake, the website that champions women writers. Her flash fiction and short stories have featured in *Popshot Magazine*, *Halo Literary Magazine* and *Severine Literary Journal*. Elizabeth lives in London and works for Tate.

Elyse Hauser is a Seattle-based writer and editor with a Master's in Writing Studies from Saint Joseph's University. When she's not writing, she's exploring her loves for dance, fashion, yoga, travel, and history. You can find more of her work at *elysehauser.com*.

Erica Travers is a writer with a passion for music and travel. Her poems are found more often in underground zines and underneath highway bridges than in literary magazines.

Erin Conway is an experienced educator and non-profit trainer who has worked both locally and abroad. Erin's writing is an intersection of family histories across the years and miles. She currently lives on her family farm in Wisconsin. Her author website and blog can be found at *erinconway.com*.

Faisal Warsani is an architecture student at the University of Texas at Austin. When he is not building models, he enjoys painting tropical landscapes. His work has become a cohesive body of work representative of literal paradise. See more at *faisalwarsani.com*.

Fiona Pitt-Kethley is the author of more than 20 books of poetry or prose. She lives in Spain with her family and an adopted colony of feral cats.

Frances Saunders has been published in the anthology *Steeped in the World of Tea*, and in the journals *Reflections*, *Marco Polo Arts Magazine*, *One in Four*, and *Lifelines*, among other journals and presses. She lives and writes in Cambridge, MA.

Francesca Grazioli is a high school freshman in Charlottesville, Virginia. She loves travelling, volunteering, playing piano, foreign languages, and art (especially photography).

G. M. Monks lives in California with her husband. Her work has been published in *The RavensPerch*, *Embodied Effigies*, *GFT Press*, and elsewhere. She was the runner-up in Big Wonderful Press' poetry contest and received an honourable mention in the New Millennium Writings competition. She was a semi-finalist in the 2015 Tucson Festival of Books Literary Awards, and in the 2014 Horatio Nelson Fiction Prize. She is working on her first novel and a collection of short stories. If you would like to read more about her, please visit *gmmonks.wordpress.com*.

Gabrielle Rowe is completing postgraduate study at Sydney University, and loves compassion and humour. Her poetry has been published in the ACU 2015 Prize for Poetry chapbook: *Peace, Tolerance & Understanding*, *HERMES 2015*, *Poetry & Place Anthology 2015* (Close-Up Books).

Gail Factor was committed to the painting process for more than five decades. An obvious artistic aptitude emerged early on leading her to Chicago Art Institute at the age of five. Factor pursued ongoing academic achievements with the same enthusiasm, culminating in: a BFA from the University of Southern California magna cum laude and a fellowship in Fine Arts from Yale University.

Gerard Sarnat authored *Homeless Chronicles*, *Abraham to Burning Man*, *Disputes* and *17s*. *Melting The Ice King* (2016) poems were accepted by seventy magazines including *Gargoyle* and *Lowestoft*. For *Huffington Post* review, reading dates, visit *Gerard Sarnat.com*. Gerry's staffed clinics for the jailed/marginalized, been a healthcare CEO and Stanford Medical School professor.

Gleah Powers is a classically trained visual artist and the author of the novel, *Edna & Luna* (Vine Leaves Press, 2016). Widely published in print and online, she has worked professionally as a painter, actor, and dancer in New York, Los Angeles and Mexico City. Visit her website: *gleahpowers.com*.

Grant Clauser is the author of the books *Necessary Myths* and *The Trouble with Rivers*. Poems have appeared in *The American Poetry Review*, *Cortland Review*, *Painted Bride Quarterly*, *Southern Poetry Review* and others. By day he writes about electronics and sometimes fishes. He blogs occasionally at *unlambic.com*. Twitter: *@uniambic*.

Gregory Piko was joint winner of the WB Yeats Poetry Prize for Australia. His poetry has appeared in *Verity La, Poetry d'Amour, The Best Australian Poems, the Australian Poetry Anthology* and *Haiku in English: The First Hundred Years*. Gregory lives in Yass, New South Wales.

Gregory Stapp received his BA from the University of Oklahoma and his MFA from Queens University of Charlotte. His poems have appeared in *Lime Hawk Journal, Forage, The Cortland Review* and *The Sierra Nevada Review*, among others. He recently served as the Poetry Editor for *Qu: A Literary Magazine*.

Halli Lilburn has works published in *Tesseracts 18* by Edge Science Fiction and Fantasy, *Spirited* by Leap Books, *Carte Blanche* and many other publications. She designed and produced a colouring book in 2017 called *Collections and Curiosities* available through Chapters. She is a librarian for the Lethbridge School District and art teacher at CASA. You can find her at *hallililburn.blogspot.com*.

Hayley Davis is an Atlanta, Georgia, native. She currently lives in Buckhead with her husband of two years and has taught in Atlanta-area schools for four years. Hayley attended the Visiting Student Program at Oxford University and this is her second publication with Vine Leaves Press.

Hedia Anvar lives in Los Angeles where she's working on a novel. She suffers from "chronic dichotomy" and writes about it at *gunmetalgeisha.com*

Heidi Seaborn lives in Seattle. Her poetry has or will appear in *Into the Void, Carbon Culture, Gold Man Review, Flying South 2016 Anthology, 3Elements Review, Windfall, Fredericksburg Literary and Art Review, Ekphrastic Review, the Voices Project, Ice Dream Anthology* and at *medium.com/@heidis*.

Former BBC journalist, **Helena Halme** has published five novels. *The Good Officer* is the fourth book in a series, which follows the tumultuous love affair between the Finnish Kaisa and British Navy officer, Peter. To receive a free book, join Helena's Readers' Group at *helenahalme.com*.

Honor Clement-Hayes has been writing poetry since she was 11 years old. She's now an advertising copywriter, but takes some solace in creative writing on the side. You can find more of her work at *hellopoetry.com/honor-clement-hayes*.

Howard Winn's poetry and fiction has been published in such journals as *Dalhousie Review, Galway Review, Descant, Antigonish Review, Southern Humanities Review, Chaffin Review, Evansville Review,* and *Blueline*. He has been nominated three times for a Pushcart prize. He is Professor of English at State University of New York.

Huye & DiBenedetto are studio-mates who work individually and collaboratively on painting & poetry series. Oil, words, smoke, caffeine. Magic mojo.

Brigita Orel has published short stories and poems in various magazines. Her work was nominated for the Pushcart Prize and other awards. She is currently studying Creative writing at Swansea University, with her research focused on writing in a foreign language. Visit her website: *brigitaorel.com*.

Ion Corcos has been published in *Every Writer, Grey Sparrow Journal, Plum Tree Tavern, Rose Red Review* and other journals. He is a Pushcart Prize nominee. The themes of his work centre on life, nature and spirit. He is currently travelling indefinitely with his partner, Lisa. Ion's website is *ioncorcos.wordpress.com*.

Irene Blair Honeycutt has published four books of poetry, the latest released in 2017, *Beneath the Bamboo Sky* (Main Street Rag Publishing). Her work has appeared in numerous journals and anthologies, including *Nimrod, Southern Poetry Review, Southern Poetry Anthology - Vol. VII*, and *Virginia Quarterly Review*. She lives in Indian Trail, NC.

Irene Hoge Smith lives, writes and practices psychotherapy near Washington D.C. She is completing a memoir about her lost-and-found mother, the poet francEyE (also known, in the early 1960s, as Charles Bukowski's mistress and muse). Her essays have appeared in *New Directions Journal, Amsterdam Quarterly* and *Prick of the Spindle*.

Israela Margalit is a critically-acclaimed playwright and television writer, a celebrated concert pianist and recording artist, and recently a published author of short fiction and nonfiction. Her awards include the Gold Medal, New York TV & Film Festival, an Emmy Nomination, and Best CD the British Music Industry Awards.

Writer, journalist, teacher, actor, director and cultural trainer, **JJ Marsh** has lived and worked all over Europe. Author of The Beatrice Stubbs Series, she's also a founder member of Triskele Books, journo for *Words with JAM*, co-editor of *The Woolf*, reviewer for *Bookmuse* and professional blurb writer.

Jackie Braje is a Brooklyn-based freelance writer and poet. Her work can also be found in *The Nottingham Review, Vagabond City Literary Journal, Dark River Review, The Bridge*, and elsewhere.

Jacquelyn Shah, M.F.A., Ph.D.—English literature/creative writing—has taught creative writing and workshops through Writers In The Schools and the University of Houston. Founder of Women Against Violence Everywhere, founding member of the arts organization Voices Breaking Boundaries, she has published poetry in various journals.

Jalil Buechel was an educator for four decades. Now retired, he does whatever he loves. This includes writing a book about children with special needs (and special gifts) aimed at helping others understand them. Jalil has had nonfiction stories published in *The Sun* but can't stop writing poetry, for fun.

James G. Piatt's poems have been nominated for the Pushcart Prize and Best of Web awards, and were published in *The 100 Best Poems of 2016, 2015 & 2014* Anthologies. He has published three collections of poetry, *The Silent Pond* (2012), *Ancient Rhythms* (2014) and *LIFE* (2016), a fourth collection is due soon.

James Wolf is an aspiring teacher from Maryland's eastern shore. He works as an assistant in a Pre-K classroom, using the quiet of naptime as an excuse to write things in the dark. His work has been featured in *GFT Presents: One in Four* and *Sixfold*.

Jamie Donohoe is a teacher, poet and playwright living in Northern California with his wife and big screen TV. He refuses to fold laundry. Explore his latest escapes at *jamiedonohoe.com*.

Jane Jordan was born in England. She lived in the USA for fifteen years, before relocating to Exmoor, in South West England. She began writing in 2004, and has four published novels. Her genre is dark romance. Jane Returned to Florida in 2013, and now lives in Sarasota. Visit her website: *janejordannovelist.com*.

Janet Buck, a seven-time Pushcart Nominee, is the author of *Dirty Laundry: A Memoir in Poems*. Her latest work appears in *The Danforth Review, The Birmingham Arts Journal*, and *Offcourse*. Buck's debut novel, *Samantha Stone: A Novel of Mystery, Memoir & Romance*, was released by Vine Leaves Press in September, 2016.

Janet McCann is an old Texas poet who just retired from Texas A&M after 46 years teaching there. Her latest collection: *The Crone At The Casino*, Lamar University Press, 2014.

Jason Kerzinski is a short story writer who recently published his first collection of stories. His remarkable debut collection, *Ruler of Hearts*, is a work that pulls the reader into the range of emotions one can feel when living in New Orleans. Isolation, jubilation, loneliness, and fragility dance hand in hand through his prose. The single page offerings are reminiscent of the prose poems of Baudelaire while the longer stories serve to evoke a universe that resounds with the bright colours and improbable probabilities of the Crescent City. When he's not writing he's taking pictures around the city. His work can be found at *jasonkerzinski.com*.

Jean Gill is a Welsh author and photographer living in the south of France with scruffy dogs, a Nikon D750 and a man. Her 18 books include poetry, memoir, a cookbook and award-winning historical fiction: TheTroubadours Quartet set in 12th century France. Visit her website: *jeangill.com*.

Jeff De La Rosa is a writer, runner, and swordsman. He lives in Chicago with his cat.

Jennifer Jones is an author, reader, art lover, and accidental coffee snob. She resides with her husband, teenage daughter, and Napoleon-esque dog in the New River Valley of Virginia. Her works have been published in various compilations and literary journals. Want to know more? Please visit Jennifer's website: *wowjenwrites.net*.

Jerusha Rodgers lives and works in Denver, Colorado. Unless she's on a wild misadventure in some far corner of the world. When she isn't writing, she travels the world in search of the perfect beer.

Originally from Michigan, USA, **Jessica Gawinski** received a BFA in Illustration from Kendall College of Art and Design. Her artwork has a home in magazines, galleries, and more. She's eager to apply her skills to the visual development of film and television. Her work can be found at *jessicagawinski.com*.

Jim Gustafson, an award-winning poet and teacher, holds a BA from Florida Southern College and a M.Div. from Garrett Theological Seminary at Northwestern University in his hometown of Evanston, Illinois, and an MFA from the University of Tampa in Florida. He is the author of *Take Fun Seriously*, (Limitless Press) , *Driving Home*, (Aldrich Press), and *Drains and Other Depressions* (Big Table). Jim teaches World Religion at Florida Southwestern State College and creative writing at Florida Gulf Coast University. He is a popular guest instructor at workshops and seminars. He lives in Fort Myers, Florida where he reads, writes, and pulls weeds.

Joanna Brichetto is a naturalist and educator in Nashville, where she writes the urban nature blog Look Around, *brichetto.wordpress.com*. Her essays have appeared in *storySouth, Jewish Literary Journal, Killing the Buddha, November Bees, Dead Housekeeping* and *The Ilanot Review*.

Joanne Jackson Yelenik enjoys writing in her garden and at picnic sites in the neighbouring Judean Hills. Recently her work appeared in *Binah* magazine, *Unbroken* journal, # 10; and *The Moon*. Her debut novel, *Eucalyptus Leaves: Deliciously Asymmetrical in Israel*, is on track for publication in 2017.

Jodi Cleghorn is a Brisbane-based author, poet and artist with a penchant for the dark vein of humanity. The portal into her creative world can be found at *jodicleghorn.com*.

Joe Giordano and his wife, Jane, live in Texas. Joe's stories have appeared in more than ninety magazines. His novel, *Birds of Passage, An Italian Immigrant Coming of Age Story*, was published by Harvard Square Editions 2015. *Appointment with ISIL*, an Anthony Provati Thriller will be published in 2017.

John Repp, a native of the Pine Barrens region of southern New Jersey (USA), is a widely published poet, fiction writer, essayist, and book critic. His latest book is Fat Jersey Blues, published in 2014 by the University of Akron Press.

John Spiegel is an English teacher in Springfield, Ohio where he shares his love for words, beards, and vinyl records. His poetry and essays can be read in *Marco Polo Arts Mag, Indiana Voice Journal, Garbanzo,* and *Birds Piled Loosely*.

Jon Riccio is a PhD candidate at the University of Southern Mississippi's Center for Writers. His work appears in *apt, Booth, Cleaver, CutBank Online, Hawai'i Review, Redivider,* and *Switchback*, among others. He received his MFA from the University of Arizona.

Jonathan Covert earned his BFA from Emerson College. He lives and works in the Chicago area.

Joshua B Huitz is emerging photographer based out of New York, photographing mainly Street Photography, Wildlife and Landscape. Josh's ability to see and capture everyday life and present it in an unique fashion is influenced by Cinema, Film and art. Check out *saatchiart.com/joshhuitz*.

Jude Goodwin is a Canadian poet currently pursuing a degree in Creative Writing with Douglas College, British Columbia. Her poems can be found in various journals, both print and online. You may also read them on her website at *judegoodwin.com*.

Justin Hoo is a writer and graduate student from Seattle, Washington who spends too much time on Goodreads instead of studying. His fiction has appeared in *Every Day Fiction* and *On the Premises*.

K. Irene Rieger is an English professor at Bluefield College in Bluefield, Virginia. She is also a fashion historian and poet whose award-winning work has been published in *Talking Writing, The College English Association Critic, the Journal for the Liberal Arts and Sciences,* and *The Bluestone Review*.

Karen Boissonneault-Gauthier is an internationally published writer, poet and visual artist. She has been a past *Vine Leaves Literary Journal* cover artist and featured in New York's *Calliope Magazine* and *WebSake2k16*, Toronto's *The Scarborough Big Arts Book*, New South Wales' *Long Exposure Magazine* and she designs for San Francisco's VIDA, as a supporter of *Literacy for Life*. See Karen's work on her website *kcbgphoto.com* and follow *@KBG_Tweets*.

Kari Gunter-Seymour's photographs have won multiple awards and been published nationally in *The Sun Magazine, Storm Cellar Quarterly* and *Appalachian Heritage Magazine*. She is the founder/curator of the "Women of Appalachia Project," an arts organization she created to address discrimination directed at women from the Appalachian region. Visit *womenofappalachia.com*.

Kate Bucca is an MFA candidate in poetry and fiction at Vermont College of Fine Arts and the author of a novel, *Companion Plants* (Fomite, 2014). Her writing has appeared in *Limestone, The Nervous Breakdown, DigBoston, Pithead Chapel*, and elsewhere. Find more of her work at *creaturesinminiature.com*.

Kate LaDew is a graduate from the University of North Carolina at Greensboro with a BA in Studio Art. She resides in Graham, North Carolina with her two cats, Janis Joplin and Charlie Chaplin.

Kate Soules teaches Introduction to the Humanities and plays clarinet. She writes poetry and creative nonfiction and has published in journals across the United States and in Europe. She splits her time as evenly as possible between Vermont, Oregon, and Martha's Vineyard.

Katerina Pravdivaia is a Toronto-based visual artist working in mixed media. She is deeply passionate about animal and environmental conservation and creates artwork uniting human and non-human animals as one, to encourage their rights and protection. Website: *katerina-pravdivaia.com*, Instagram: *@katerina.pravdivaia*, Facebook: *facebook.com/katerina.prav.art*.

Katrina Greco is a teacher and writer living in Oakland, CA. Her work can be found in *White Stag, Hot Metal Bridge, Quarterly West, s/tick, Foliate Oak*, and *The Fiddleback*. Originally from Pittsburgh, she enjoys cross-stitching and smashing the patriarchy.

Kayla Pongrac is an avid writer, reader, tea drinker, and record spinner. Her flash fiction chapbook, *The Flexible Truth*, is available for purchase from Anchor and Plume, and her tea-inspired microchapbook, *Kettle Whistles the Blues*, from Robocup Press. To read more of Kayla's work, visit *kaylapongrac.com* or follow her *@KP_the_Promisee*.

Kelsey Dean is an English teacher living in Seoul, where she paints and writes in her free time. Her work can be found in many publications, including *Ember, The Vignette Review, concis*, and others. See more of her work at *kelseypaints.tumblr.com*.

Kendra Liedle's writing has appeared in Chicago Literati, The Gambler Magazine, Dual Coast Magazine, Nebraska Life and The Grief Diaries. She is the author of 'The Best Days Of Mabel Gordon' and 'This Is How We End' (Amazon and Kindle.)She lives in Los Angeles, CA.

Decades ago, autodidact **kerry rawlinson** gravitated from sunny Zambian skies to solid Canadian soil. Fast-forward: she now follows poetry and art's muses, barefoot, winning contests—e.g. *Geist; Mississippi Valley*—and featuring in literary publications—eg. *Main Street Rag; CanLit; Minola Review; 3Elements Review; pioneertown; AdHoc Fiction; Adirondack Review*. Visit *kerryrawlinson.tumblr.com*.

Kerry Wingood is an African/Irish/Australian born in Zambia, who immigrated to Australia as a child. She has studied literature, journalism and publishing and works in publications during the day. She loves writing poems and historical fiction the rest of the time!

Kim Peter Kovac works nationally and internationally in theatre for young audiences and has had 100+ pieces published on line or in print in journals in Australia, India, Dubai (UAE), England, Scotland, South Africa, and the USA. Visit *kimpeterkovac.tumblr.com*.

Laura Brinson has toured with one-act plays, dug for gold in Western Australia, walked the trail to Machu Picchu. She is a funeral celebrant, a costume seamstress, lives in Melbourne and writes prose and poetry. Her work has appeared in *Regime, Social Alternatives, n-Scribe, Mark My Words* and *page seventeen*.

The daughter of European parents, **Lauren Dunne** was born in Wales. Having won an academic scholarship in 2013, she is being educated at Brisbane State High School. Drawing energy from Australia's natural wonders and inspired by its rich history, she began writing.

Laura Eppinger is a Pushcart-nominated writer of fiction, poetry and essay. She's the blog editor at *Newfound Journal*. Her full publications list can be seen here: *lolionthekaap.blogspot.com/p/creative-writing.html*.

Lee Nash lives in France and freelances as an editor and proofreader. Her poems have appeared or are forthcoming in print and online journals including *Angle, Mezzo Cammin, Orbis* and *Poetry Salzburg Review*. You can find a full bio and a selection of Lee's poems on her website *leenashpoetry.com*.

Lee Todd Lacks is a mixed-media artist and clinical counsellor, whose writing has appeared in *Bop Dead City, Tincture, Journal, Oldstyle Tales Press, The Quarterday Review, Crack The Spine*, and elsewhere. His first book of poetry and short fiction, entitled *Underneath*, will be published in the fall of 2016. Visit *fermatapublishing.com*.

Lily Keane is a teacher and writer who loves watching football and tennis, but whose only athletic achievement is walking on the bottoms of her feet. She lives in hope that the *Truth of Silence* will be sought by all.

Linda Lowe received her M.F.A. from the University of California, Irvine. A chapbook of her poems was published by Sarasota Theatre Press. Her work has appeared in *Soundings Review, Gone Lawn, Right Hand Pointing, Outlook Springs, The Linnet's Wings*, and others.

Lindsey Anderson is a Chicago-based writer who covers culture and politics for publications like *ArtSlant, The Clyde Fitch Report*, and *Eater* when she isn't working on short stories or prose poems. Her fiction has appeared in *Chicago Literati* and *Litro*.

Lisa Lindsey resides in Cincinnati, Ohio, USA. Nature and life in a river town are frequent themes in her poetry. Her writing has appeared in The Cincinnati Historical Society Press, Paula Brown Press, The Penwood Review, and Blue Mountain Arts. Lisa works in a parish office as a bulletin editor.

Lisa Mae DeMasi's work has been featured in *Gravel, Slippery Elm, Foliate Oak, East Bay Review, Shark Reef* and her personal blog, *Nurture Is My Nature*. When she's not writing, she practices Reiki specializing in unblocking creatives in all mediums and moving them to the highest vision of themselves as artists.

Lisha Ruan is a Computer Science major and writer at Princeton University. Her poems have appeared or are forthcoming in *The Nottingham Review, By&By Poetry, Jersey Devil Press*, and other publications. In her free time, she enjoys learning languages, reading philosophy, and playing Avalon.

Liza Perrat, an Australian midwife, wrote *The Bone Angel trilogy*—three standalone novels exploring the tragedies and triumphs of a French village family of midwife-healers during the 1348 Black Plague, the French Revolution and WW2 Nazi-occupied France. Her latest, *The Silent Kookaburra*, is a psychological suspense set in 1970s Australia.

Liz Nguyen lives inside of comic books, but frequently emerges from this 2D universe to write short fiction and creative nonfiction. Her work has appeared in *Curve, The Red Wheelbarrow*, and *Defenestration*. She is destined to write a Pulitzer Prize-winning fanfiction.

Lorna Fergusson is an award-winning short story writer and novelist, editor and writing coach. She runs Fictionfire Literary Consultancy (Fictionfire.co.uk) and teaches on various Oxford University writing programmes. The Chase, previously published by Bloomsbury, is available from Fictionfire Press and Amazon. Salt, winner of the Historical Novel Society's London 14 Award, appears in the anthology Distant Echoes, published by Corazon Books.

Lucie Britsch's career peaked too soon when she won a poop scoop slogan contest as a kid. She has since been published in *Barrelhouse, Volume1Brooklyn, Catapult*, and *SplitLip* and won two honourable mentions from *Glimmer Train*.

Lynne Potts portends and pretends so you can never be sure if what you've read is a projection or rejection of falsifications. Nonetheless, she's a poet of a certain note, not notable, living in Boston and New York. And she's been around.

Madeline Sharples is the author of *Leaving the Hall Light On: A Mother's Memoir of Living with Her Son's Bipolar Disorder and Surviving His Suicide* (*madelinesharples.com*). She co-edited *The Great American Poetry Show* and wrote the poetry for *The Emerging Goddess* photography book. She is currently working on a novel.

Maggie Veness lives by the sea in NSW, Australia. Her quirky, contemporary stories have been published across many countries in literary journals and anthologies such as *SLICE, Litro, Gem Street, Adanna, Page Seventeen, Nazar, Bravado, BLE, Maynard*, and *Skive*. She cycles so she can keep enjoying chocolate and red wine.

Marcus Benjamin Ray Bradley grew up in Perryville and now lives in Versailles, KY, with his wife and daughters. Other work can be found in the pages of *Chiron Review* and *Five 2 One* magazine as well as online at the Kentucky Arts Council and *Fifty Word Stories* websites.

Margarita Tenser is a poet and speculative fiction writer from Sydney, Australia. Their other work can be found via their blog at *thepresenttenser.wordpress.com*.

Margo Davis' poetry has appeared in *Wisconsin Review, Midwest Quarterly, Slipstream, Longleaf Pine, Alimentum, Agave Magazine, A Clean, Well-Lighted Place; Louisiana Literature; Untameable City, Goodbye, Mexico*; and numerous Texas Poetry Calendars. A Pushcart nominee, Margo is working on a manuscript influenced by film and photo images.

Maria Garcia Teutsch's collection, *The Revolution Will Have its Sky*, won the 2015 Minerva Rising chapbook competition, judge: Heather McHugh. She is a poet, educator, producer and editor. She has published over 20 journals of poetry as editor-in-chief of two journals, and is the founder and EIC of Ping-Pong Free Press.

Marie Marandola is a badass feminist poet who received her MFA from Sarah Lawrence College. She now lives in San Diego, where she remains in the habit of picking up fallen bits of trees and giving them to people.

Marilyn Flower is a published writer and teacher of writing living in California. Journals in which her work has been published include *Sow's Ear, Poetry Motel, The Southern California Anthology*, and *Van Brock's North of Wakulla: An Anhinga Anthology*.

Mark Brazaitis is the author of seven books, including *The Incurables: Stories*, winner of the 2012 Richard Sullivan Prize and the 2013 Devil's Kitchen Reading Award in Prose. Visit *markbrazaitis.com*.

Mary Jumbelic, MD, an author from Syracuse, NY, has performed thousands of autopsies in her career as a medical examiner. Her stories explore the personal side of the work through the lens of forensic cases. Visit 'Final Words', her blog at *maryjumbelic.com*.

Maryanne Hannan has published prose poems from this series in *minnesota review, Magma (UK), Gargoyle, 1110* (EU), and *Rabbit* (AU). She likes to think it possible that people the world over can laugh together. A former Latin teacher, she lives in upstate New York, USA. Her website is *mhannan.com*.

Mathew Serback's debut book will be available in October of 2017 through ELJ Publications. He has short fiction everywhere in 2016. He's the managing editor of *scissors&spackle*, as well as an assistant editor with *Bartleby Snopes*.

Matt Pucci is a primary school teacher from the UK. He's also been a bar-tender, a snowboard salesman, an English teacher, and a one-time winner of Rant of the Week in *Kerrang!* magazine. His written work has appeared in various locations over the years, now curated on his website, *mattpucci.com*.

Matt Kolbet teaches and writes in Oregon. His second novel, *Lunar Year*, is out now.

Megan E. Freeman's poetry collection, *Lessons on Sleeping Alone*, was published in 2015 by Liquid Light Press. Her poetry has appeared in anthologies and journals, and as commissions by the Los Angeles Master Chorale and Ars Nova Singers. Megan lives and writes near Boulder, Colorado. Visit *meganefreeman.com*.

Melissa K. Downes teaches English at Clarion University of Pennsylvania. Her poems have appeared or are forthcoming in Poet Lore and the Women's Review of Books. She was recently a finalist for Hunger Mountain's Ruth Stone Poetry Prize.

Meredith Foster currently resides in Indianapolis, Indiana. Her work has been featured in numerous literary journals; she writes web content by day and fiction by night. She shares her home with a plush dragon collection and a vampire-fanged rescue cat.

Michael Campagnoli has worked as a waiter, fisherman, journalist, painter, and short-order cook. His poems, stories, and chapbooks have appeared in numerous magazines and anthologies. Most mornings he can be seen running somewhere along the coast of Maine with his mongrel dog, Yogi, and Anthony, his equally mongrel son.

Michael Fontana lives and writes in beautiful Bella Vista, Arkansas, USA.

Michele Harvey's poems have appeared in several literary journals including, Progenitor, Copper Nickel, and The Litchfield Review. Her sonnet, "Dinosaur Ridge," is the focal point for an Art in Public Places display at the Jefferson County Government Center railway station in Golden, Colorado. Poetry is the music of her soul.

Michelle McMillan-Holifield recently completed a writer's residency at Wild Acres in North Carolina. Her recent work can be found in Boxcar Poetry Review, Longridge Review, PIF Magazine, poemmemoirstory, Silver Birch Press's Nancy Drew Anthology, Stirring, and Vine Leaves.

Michelle Webster-Hein has published work in Ruminate Magazine, Upstreet and The Mennonite, among other places. Her work has received a "notable" listing in the Best American series and been nominated three times for a Pushcart Prize. "Purple Roses" is an excerpt from her novel-in-progress.

Monica Rico lives in Michigan and writes at slowdownandeat.com.

Monika Malewska was born in Warsaw, Poland. She received her BFA from the University of Manitoba in Canada and her MFA degree from the University of Texas at San Antonio. She is currently an Associate Professor of Art at Juniata College. Malewska works in several art media, particularly painting, drawing, and photography.

Monika R. Martyn was born in Austria, immigrated to Canada as a teen, and currently resides abroad with her husband of thirty years. She has recently been published in a collection of Canadian Poems and Short Stories and is working on the final stages of her novel.

Mori Glaser grew up in the UK and moved to Israel 30 years ago. She has blogged and written material for non-profits. Her poetry has been published in various journals including Writers Hub, Crack the Spine, A Quiet Courage, Unbroken. Mori's poem Elements Lost and Found won 3rd prize in The Molotov Cocktail's 2017 Shadow Award. Her flash appears in Akashic Books web series Thursdaze, and Arc 24—the journal of the Israel Association of Writers in English.

Murzban F. Shroff has published his fiction with over 60 journals in the U.S. and UK. Six of the stories have won a Pushcart Prize nomination; one has been the recipient of the John Gilgun Fiction Award. His debut short story collection, Breathless In Bombay, was shortlisted for the Commonwealth Writers' Prize in the best debut category from Europe and South Asia. It was rated by the Guardian as among the ten best Mumbai books. His debut novel, Waiting For Jonathan Koshy, was a finalist for the Horatio Nelson Fiction Prize and received high praise from two renowned American authors, one a Pulitzer Prize winner, the other a National Book Award Finalist. Shroff can be contacted at murzbanfshroff@gmail.com.

Nancy Devine teaches high school English in Grand Forks, North Dakota where she lives. Her poetry, short fiction and essays have appeared in online and print journals. She is the author of a chapbook of poems, The Dreamed, published by Finishing Line Press in 2016. Her website is nancydevinewriter.com.

Natalie De Paz is a poet and playwright of Cuban descent who was born and raised in South Florida. Her work has been previously published in Crab Fat Magazine and Tule Review.

Natasha Schapova is a 17-year-old Melbournian who finds solace in writing and has been an avid reader from a young age. She is ecstatic that Vine Leaves Literary Journal, will be the first to officially publish her pieces and hopes that there are many more to come. Her blog can be accessed at: trappedinscript.com.

Nicholas Finch is the former assistant editor of Neon Literary Journal and member of the Center for Writers, University of Southern Mississippi. Finch was raised in England before moving to Florida. Finch has pieces published or forthcoming in Flash: The International Short-Short Story Magazine, Avis Magazine, Fields and elsewhere. Visit finchandcrown.com.

Delaware native **Nina Bennett** is the author of Sound Effects (2013, Broadkill Press Key Poetry Series). Her poetry has appeared in numerous journals and anthologies. Awards include 2014 Northern Liberties Review Poetry Prize and a 2012 Best of the Net nomination.

Noreen Lace is an author living in Los Angeles. Her poetry and fiction have appeared in numerous journals including The Chicago Tribune's Printer's Row and Pilcrow & Dagger among others. Her novellas, West End and Life of Clouds are available. For more information: NoreenLace.com

Nory Marc Steiger is an international artist, having lived and exhibited in California, Manhattan, Barcelona and Sitges. He is the subject of two documentaries, many U.S. and Spanish TV and radio programs, magazine and newspaper articles. Canadian-born, Steiger lives in Montreal, where he has been represented by the Fine Arts Museum. Visit norymarcsteiger.tumblr.com and follow on Twitter @norymarcsteiger.

Olivia Pellegrini is a Massachusetts-born writer and essayist. She attends Sarah Lawrence College in New York, where she enjoys studying the social sciences, as well as writing and music composition.

Poems by **O Mayeux** (web: 4f4d.xyz) have appeared in various journals, most recently Assaracus.

Patricia Behrens is a New York City writer and lawyer and co-editor of Courthouses of the Second Circuit: Their Architecture, History, and Stories (Acanthus Press 2015). Her poems have appeared in American Arts Quarterly, The Same, Perfume River Review, The Main Street Rag, Mom Egg Review and elsewhere.

Patrick Blair is a writer and Celtic guitarist who lives in Anoka, MN. He's had poems previously published in the Summit Avenue Review out of St. Paul, MN.

Patrick Connelly is a scientist and entrepreneur from Harvard, Massachusetts. He received a BA from St. Michaels College, a PhD from the University of Colorado, Boulder, and was a postdoctoral fellow at Yale University. He serves on the Boards of Directors of the Bravehearts and the National Brain Tumor Society.

Patti White is the author of three collections of poems, Tackle Box (2002), Yellow Jackets (2007), and Chain Link Fence (2013), all from Anhinga Press. Her work has appeared in journals including Iowa Review, North American Review, River Styx, Nimrod, DIAGRAM, Forklift Ohio, and New Madrid. She teaches creative writing at the University of Alabama, and was co-founder of Slash Pine Press.

Penny Dearmin is a writer in Middle Georgia, halfway between city and sea. She is an instructor of Composition and Creative Writing, as well as Assistant Creative Nonfiction Editor for Arts & Letters at Georgia College. Her work can be found in Madcap Review.

Phill Provance's work has appeared in The Baltimore Sun, Orbis, Cha and others, has been translated into Vietnamese, and was recently selected by Diane Seuss as one of two finalists for the Crab Creek Review Prize. In 2011, Cy Gist Press published his first poetry chapbook, The Day the Sun Rolled Out of the Sky, whose contents received three Pushcart nominations and one nomination each for the Best of the Web and Best of the Net prizes. Phill is currently completing his MFA at WV Wesleyan College. When not writing and reading, he prefers spending time with the best little guy in the whole world, his son, Ledger.

Phoebe Merten is working toward her MFA in fiction at Chapman University. She has begun to like some things about Southern California, despite herself. Visit phoebemerten.blogspot.com.

Quinn Ramsay is a graduate of the University of Glasgow. His prose and poetry have been published in Paragraphiti, From Glasgow to Saturn, Santa Clara Review, The Magnolia Review, and Gemini. He was recently a co-editor and designer for Williwaw: an Anthology of the Marvellous.

R.M. Cooper's writing has recently appeared in Berkeley Fiction Review (2014 Fiction Award recipient), Cream City Review, Denver Quarterly, Fugue, Passages North, The Pinch, Portland Review, Yemassee, and elsewhere. Cooper lives with his wife in the Colorado Front Range and is the managing editor of Sequestrum. Visit sequestrum.org.

Rachel Linn received an MFA in creative writing from the University of Washington and won the Eugene Van Buren Prize for her thesis project. Her stories are frequently inspired by what she learned while working as a naturalist at a marine sanctuary for four seasons.

Randy Droll is a U.S. citizen and Vietnam era veteran who has lived in Canada since 1980. He has self-published a novel, Human Factors, available on Amazon. He is retired from the Canadian Nuclear Safety Commission and has master's degrees in Physics and Nuclear Engineering.

Rebecca Ciota received degrees in English Literature and Creative Writing from Oberlin College. She has been published in Catfish Creek, the Citron Review, Dirty Chai Magazine, and Words Apart Magazine as well as other venues.

Regina Buttner is a registered nurse who enjoys writing fiction on the side. She lives in western New York State with her teenage son and daughter, and is working on her first novel.

Richard Weaver lives in Baltimore's Inner Harbor. He volunteers at the Maryland Book Bank, and acts as the Archivist-at-large for a Jesuit College founded in 1830. He is also an unofficial snowflake counter. (There are real ones).

Robert Crisp currently hides out in Savannah, Georgia, which he keeps strange hours and even stranger company. Learn more at writingforghosts.com.

Robert Hambling Davis has published in The Sun, Antietam Review, Memoir Journal, Philadelphia Stories, and Santa Monica Review. He's been nominated for two Pushcart Prizes. He was runner-up for the essay in the 2015 William Faulkner Competition, and a finalist for the novel in 2016.

Robert Knox's poetry, fiction, and creative nonfiction have appeared in numerous journals. He is a contributing editor for Verse-Virtual.com, where his poems appear monthly. Suosso's Lane, his novel on the origins of the Sacco-Vanzetti case, is available at web-e-books.com.

Robert Lee Kendrick lives in Clemson, SC. He has previously published, or has work forthcoming, in Tar River Poetry, Xavier Review, Louisiana Literature, South Carolina Review, the James Dickey Review, and a chapbook, Winter Skin (Main Street Rag Publishing, 2016). He can be found online at robertleekendrick.net.

Robin Vigfusson earned an M.A. in Political Science from NYU, but her real love is fiction, especially short stories. Her work has appeared in Coe Review, Windmill, The Blue Hour, Referential Magazine, Caravel Literary Arts Journal, Lunaris Review, Bookends Review, Junto Magazine, Jewish Fiction.net, Fine Flu Journal, Old 67, Feminine Collective and podcast on No Extra Words.

Robyn Groth has an MA in linguistics and writes poetry and short fiction. She lives in the Midwest with her husband, three sons and two cats. Her work has been published in Blue Monday Review and The Tishman Review.

Originally from North Wales, **Roddy Williams** lives and works in London. His poetry has appeared in Magma, The North, The Frogmore Papers, The Rialto, South Bank Poetry and other magazines. He has had two of his plays performed onstage in London and is a keen surrealist photographer and painter.

Rohan Quine is an author of literary fiction with a touch of magical realism and a dusting of horror, celebrating the beauty, darkness and mirth of this predicament called life, where we seem to have been dropped without sufficient consultation ahead of time. Visit rohanquine.com.

Roopa Dudley is an American Chess Painter. She is a huge fan of dark humour, therefore most of her artwork has that incorporated into her paintings in some shape or form. Her goal is to create art that is appealing aesthetically as well as intellectually. She is happily married with two daughters and resides in Maryland, USA. For more insight visit her website: RoopaDudley.com.

Rose van Son is a widely published award-winning Australian writer and poet. In 2015, she was a Guest at the Perth Poetry Festival; her *Three Owls and A Crescent Moon* haiku book with images, is available online. She loves nature, photography, language: its sounds, mysteries, perspectives.

Roy Dorman is retired from the University of Wisconsin-Madison Benefits Office. He is the submissions editor of *Yahara Prairie Lights* and has had poetry and flash fiction published recently on a number of online literary sites.

Roz Morris is the author of *My Memories of a Future Life* and *Lifeform Three*. She was longlisted for an international award alongside Neil Gaiman and is a finalist in the People's Book Prize, teaches masterclasses for The Guardian and is the author of the *Nail Your Novel* series. Visit *RozMorris.wordpress.com*.

Russell Reece has had work published in numerous journals and anthologies including *The Best of Vine Leaves 2012*. He has received fellowships in literature from the Delaware Division of the Arts and the Virginia Center for the Creative Arts. Russ lives near Bethel, Delaware along the beautiful Broad Creek.

S.M. Mack has had stories and poems published in *Fireside Fiction, Vine Leaves Literary Journal*'s "Best of 2015" collection, and *Gone Lawn*, among others. She's a 2012 Clarion graduate and can (always, always) be found on Twitter at @whatsmacksaid.

Saffron Wilson is currently working on a longer piece of prose. For other examples of her work look at the Red Kite publication by Northampton University.

Salena Casha's work has appeared in over 30 publications. Her fiction has been nominated for a Pushcart Prize and featured in the Top 50 Very Short Fictions of 2015. Her first three picture books are housed under the Houghton Mifflin Harcourt umbrella. Visit her website at *salenacasha.com*.

Sally Jeanne Stevens is a singer & lyricist, working in film, tv and sound recordings in LA. Her song "There Is Time" (Music, Burt Bacharach) was recorded by Burt & the Houston Symphony in his album "WOMAN" and "Who Comes This Night?" (Music, Dave Grusin) was recorded by James Taylor in his first Christmas CD 2004. Her photographs have been on exhibit in LA Galleries and at Cite de la Musique, Paris, and her short fiction and poetry have appeared in *Hermeneutic Chaos Literary Journal, Mockingheart Review* and *No Extra Words* podcasts.

Sara Conway has received numerous awards from the Scholastic Art and Writing Awards, including a Gold Key and an Honorable Mention for two of her short stories last year. In 2015, she was awarded a National Silver Medal for her flash fiction piece, "Her Voice," and attended the award ceremony at Carnegie Hall in New York City. Sara is also working towards self-publishing her first anthology, titled *The Storyteller*.

Sarah Brown Weitzman has been published in hundreds of journals and anthologies including *Rosebud, The New Ohio Review, Poet & Critic, The North American Review, Rattle, Mid-American Review, Poet Lore*, etc. Sarah received a Fellowship from the National Endowment for the Arts. Her books are available from Amazon.

Sarah Lyn Rogers is a Pushcart-nominated poet, the Fiction Editor of *The Rumpus*, and the author of *Inevitable What*, a poetry collection about magic and rituals. For more of her work, visit *sarahlynrogers.com*.

Shannon Magee is trying to rediscover magic in the world. She has a degree in English, Creative Writing, and Women's and Gender Studies from Wake Forest University in North Carolina. Her writing has also appeared in *Brilliant Flash Fiction, Foliate Oak Literary Magazine, A Lonely Riot Magazine*, and *Light Journal*.

Shushanik Karapetyan is a psychotherapist by profession and an artist by avocation. She uses writing as an expressive therapeutic tool to foster creativity and introspection in both herself and her clients.

Stacey Margaret Jones is an Arkansas-based poet, fiction and creative nonfiction writer. Her poem "Pale" was recently nominated for a Pushcart Prize, and her poetry has been published throughout the United States and abroad. She's also a market research consultant and a yoga teacher.

Stephanie Thurrott's fiction has been published in *Boston Literary Magazine, decomP, Vine Leaves Literary Journal, MonkeyBicycle, Bartleby Snopes*, and *Blink-Ink*. Her novel in progress is set in Dedham, Mass., where she lives with her family. She studies fiction at Grub Street in Boston.

Stephanie Yu is a working violinist and DJ, currently based in Los Angeles. When she's not practicing, she loves to write. She holds a Bachelor and Master of Music from the Juilliard School. You can find her on Instagram or Facebook @hustlekat.

Steve Prusky is a native of Detroit. Las Vegas has been his adopted home the past thirty years. His work has previously appeared in *Vine Leaves, Southwestern American Literature, Lighthouse* and others.

Sue Jenkins is a fine art photographer, graphic/web designer, and creative director of *Luckychair.com*. The author of several "Dummies" books on Design, she is an award-wining software instructor at *Lynda.com* and teaches full time at small liberal arts university in the USA. For further info, visit *suejenkinsphotography.com* and *Instagram.com/Luckychair*.

Susan Stamm Evans, born in 1952 in Albuquerque, is a third generation New Mexican. While doing her undergraduate studies at the University of New Mexico, she fell in love with sculpting in clay. After she received her BA, she moved to Milwaukee, Wisconsin for her graduate work, receiving her MA in ceramic sculpture. Her first solo exhibition was immediately after graduate school.

Taly Oehler is a photographer and writer. Her work has been exhibited in various group shows throughout the United States, including being awarded the Director's Honorable Mention at the Center for Fine Art Photography, in Fort Collins, Colorado. Her art was published in *LensCulture, Vine Leaves*, and *Buffalo Almanack*. Visit *talyoehler.com*.

Tiffany McDaniel is an Ohio native whose writing is inspired by the rolling hills and buckeye woods of the land she knows. Also a poet and artist, she is the winner of The Guardian's 2016 "Not-the-Booker Prize" and the winner of Ohioana Library Readers' Choice Award for her debut novel, *The Summer that Melted Everything*.

TJS Walter lives in Minnesota with two children and a husband. When she is not writing and attending tea parties, she works odd jobs and almost starts working on her first novel.

Trevor O'Sullivan is an artist and amateur photographer who lives in the Swan Valley wine region of Perth. His interests include sci-fi, sticky date pudding, scrabble and being creatively lazy (or lazily creative). Find his work at *facebook.com/finnmaccsart* & *finnmacc.com*.

Trina Denner lives, loves, and writes in Brisbane. She holds a PhD, which explores Young Adult Fiction, and is a sessional academic and teacher. For fun and inspiration, she likes to run up and down mountains. Okay ... sometimes she walks the up parts.

Trisha Farnan is a Western Australian writer, singer-songwriter, fine artist and traveller. She loves cats and is a rabid music fan.

Tyrean Martinson lives fully in the Pacific Northwest within smelling distance of the salty sea of the Puget Sound. Yet, she writes of distant lands of the imagination. Find her online at: *tyreanswritingspot.blogspot.com* and her books at most online retailers.

Drawing inspiration from women, beauty, fashion & popular culture, **Vakseen**'s collaged-influenced "Vanity Pop" paintings are a visual dialogue about our society's idolization of beauty, the cosmetic enhancements endured to meet the status quo & the potential impact this has on women. To view his #VakseenArt visit *VakseenArt.com*.

Veronica Scharf Garcia was born in Chile and lived overseas. She has exhibited her art extensively and was selected to residencies at the Atlantic Center for the Arts, the Deering Estate, Art Center on Lincoln Rd. & Bakehouse Studios, Florida. Email: *verogoart@gmail.com* and Web site: *veronicascharf.com*.

Victoria Melekian has been published in *Only Light Can Do That-100 Post-Election Poems, Stories, & Essays, Mudfish, Literary Orphans, Atlanta Review, Valparaiso Fiction Review*, and other anthologies. She has twice won a San Diego Book Award. For more, visit *victoriamelekian.com*.

Wanda Morrow Clevenger is a Carlinville, IL native. Over 417 pieces of her work appear in 148 print and electronic publications. Her debut book is called *This Same Small Town in Each of Uspaypal* (edgarallanpoet.com/This_Same_Small_Town.html). Please visit her magazine-type blog updated at her erratic discretion here: wlc- wlcblog.blogspot.com.

Wendy Scott's first book of poems, *Soon I Will Build an Ark*, was published by Main Street Rag. Her poems have appeared in *Painted Bride Quarterly* and *Harpur Palate*, among others. She has an MFA from the University of Pittsburgh and teaches writing from universities to halfway houses.

Whitney C. Hansen is an essayist living in Omaha, Nebraska, as she completes her degree in Secondary Education. This is her second nonfiction publication.

William C. Crawford is a photographer & writer based in Winston-Salem, NC. He developed an emerging photographic technique, Forensic Foraging, with Sydney lensman & poet, Jim Provencher. See *ForensicForaging.com*.

Zvezdana Rashkovich is a Pushcart nominated American writer born in the former Yugoslavia. Currently, she is working on a novel set in the mystical worlds of the Balkans and the Sudan while often journeying to her multiple homelands—East Europe, United States and North Africa.

Acknowledgments

A huge thanks goes out to ...

... all the contributors of this collection for their brilliance and patience during the making of this book.

... all the artists, photographers, writers, and literary magazine enthusiasts, who have supported *Vine Leaves Literary Journal* all these years.

... all my volunteer staff members for their passion and dedication. Thank you for sticking with me despite all the hard work and lack of monetary return.

... Amie McCracken. The brilliant woman who works very much behind the scenes, typesetting and formatting all Vine Leaves Press books. If it wasn't for Amie, this press would not exist. Thank you, from the bottom of my heart. I owe you. Big time.

Enjoyed this book?

Visit **Vine Leaves Press** for more:
vineleavespress.com

CPSIA information can be obtained
at www.ICGtesting.com
Printed in the USA
BVOW05*0013181117
500311BV00009B/23/P

9 781925 417630